REPRESENTATIVE CHORDATES

A Manual of Comparative Anatomy

McGraw-Hill Publications in the Zoological Sciences

E. J. Boell, Consulting Editor

There are also the related series of *McGraw-Hill Publications in the Botanical Sciences,* of which Edmund W. Sinnott is Consulting Editor, and in the Agricultural Sciences, of which R. A. Brink is Consulting Editor.

Representative Chordates

A MANUAL
OF COMPARATIVE ANATOMY

Charles K. Weichert

PROFESSOR OF ZOOLOGY
UNIVERSITY OF CINCINNATI

SECOND EDITION

McGRAW-HILL BOOK COMPANY, INC.

New York   Toronto   London

1961

REPRESENTATIVE CHORDATES

IV
THE MAPLE PRESS COMPANY, YORK, PA.

68984

PREFACE

Courses in comparative anatomy usually consist of lectures, recitations, and laboratory work. In the laboratory the student dissects and studies the anatomy of certain representatives of the phylum Chordata. Ideally it would be desirable to include a cyclostome, cartilaginous fish, bony fish, caudate amphibian, reptile, bird, and mammal in a laboratory course in comparative anatomy. In many colleges, however, only one-semester or single-quarter courses are offered. Therefore, there is not enough time available to study all these forms comprehensively.

In the following pages the anatomy of four representative chordates is described in some detail. The animals selected include the marine lamprey, *Petromyzon marinus;* the spiny dogfish, *Squalus acanthias;* the mud puppy, *Necturus maculosus;* and the cat, *Felis domestica.* A complete study of all these forms in the time allotted may be impracticable. The instructor, therefore, may find it advisable to omit certain portions, selecting those sections for study that best meet conditions peculiar to his own institution.

Copious illustrations of the animals and structures to be studied are included in this volume. This is in keeping with the modern trend in biological laboratory teaching in which drawings by students are not required. The student dissects the specimens which he is studying under direction, finds the various structures with the aid of descriptions and detailed illustrations, and is graded upon the excellence of his dissection and his knowledge of the material.

Information concerning the natural history and the functional role of the organ systems of the representative chordates is included wherever feasible.

The author has been most pleased with the wide adoption of the first edition of this manual. It was originally planned as a companion volume to his "Elements of Chordate Anatomy," also published by the McGraw-Hill Book Company, Inc., a book which treats of the more general aspects of comparative anatomy of vertebrates and which now is in its second edition. "Representative Chordates" may be used together with "Elements of Chordate Anatomy" or quite independently in laboratory courses in comparative anatomy. It has been completely revised, and numerous changes in terminology have been adopted.

The author wishes to acknowledge the help and suggestions given him by former students, several of whom have contributed to the illustrative material. He is most appreciative of the aid given by his wife in the technical aspects of preparing the book for publication.

Charles K. Weichert

CONTENTS

INTRODUCTION

Before actually beginning a study of the representative chordates described in this volume, it is desirable to understand where they fit into the general scheme of classification of members of the phylum *Chordata*.

SELECTED ANIMALS

The lamprey. The marine lamprey, *Petromyzon marinus*, has been selected as a representative of the class *Cyclostomata*. Animals belonging to this class are the most primitive living vertebrates, despite the fact that in some respects they show a high degree of specialization. Among the primitive features to be observed are the absence of jaws, true teeth, and paired appendages—structures missing even in the embryo. The brain and skeleton are poorly developed and the notochord persists throughout life. What little skeleton is present is entirely cartilaginous, bone being lacking. This, however, may be a degenerate rather than a primitive character, since bone is known to have been present in the armor of ostracoderms, the oldest fossil vertebrates of which we have record. The reproductive system in both sexes of the lamprey is also of primitive construction. Although the respiratory system shows a high degree of specialization in some respects, its primitive features are indicated by the large number of gill pouches and the structural arrangement of the gills. Whether the presence of a single median nostril is primitive or specialized is questionable. Most ostracoderms had a single nostril, but in others, paired ventral nostrils were present. Moreover, during development the bilobed nature of the olfactory sac is evident. The larval form of the lamprey, referred to as the *ammocoetes*, is of rather simple structure and in many ways is similar to amphioxus, one of the protochordates.

The spiny dogfish. The most primitive class of living fishes is the class *Chondrichthyes*, the cartilaginous fishes. It is composed of two order, *Selachii* (*Elasmobranchii*) and *Holocephali*. The elasmobranch fishes, as members of the first order are generally called, include those cartilaginous fishes in which the gill slits open separately to the outside.

1

The spiny dogfish, *Squalus acanthias,* is an elasmobranch fish. It has been selected here because of its general availability and because it typifies the structure of vertebrates in general. The animal is relatively easy to dissect, particularly because its cartilaginous skeleton can be readily cut away to expose such delicate structures as the brain, cranial nerves, and blood vessels of the head and gill regions. The elasmobranchs are less highly developed than the bony, or teleost, fishes yet show advances over the cyclostomes in their possession of paired pectoral and pelvic appendages and girdles and in the presence of both upper and lower jaws. Furthermore, the nostrils are paired, and the exposed gill slits have been reduced in number.

The mud puppy. The first vertebrates to assume a terrestrial existence are the amphibians, paired limbs having replaced the paired fins of fishes. A close relationship to the fishes is indicated, however, by the structure of a number of internal organs, so that amphibians are considered to be the most primitive tetrapods. The mud puppy, *Necturus maculosus,* a salamander, is one of the most primitive amphibians and for that reason has been selected for study. Its external features are rather similar to those of ancient amphibians, which are believed to have risen in evolution from primitive fishes. *Necturus* is one of the salamanders which remains aquatic and retains its gills throughout life. The circulatory system in the gill region is usually considered to be in an intermediate stage between that of fishes and truly terrestrial vertebrates. Members of the subclass *Caudata,* including salamanders and newts, are more primitive and generalized than those of the subclass *Salientia,* which embraces the frogs and toads. It is possible, of course, that *Necturus* represents a degenerate type of amphibian which has reverted from terrestrial to aquatic life, but this is rather unlikely, and the animal is more probably a primitive form.

The cat. The cat has been chosen for dissection and study as a representative of the class *Mammalia.* Other mammals, such as rats, rabbits, and fetal pigs, are commonly used for study in zoological laboratories, but the cat is less specialized than these, more nearly approaches man in structural characteristics, and, because of its large size, can be more easily dissected and details of structure clearly observed. Cats are numerous and may be rather easily obtained from supply houses, where they are killed humanely and properly embalmed and injected. Most students who are preparing themselves for the study of medicine are particularly interested in the anatomy of the cat, for it serves as an introduction to human anatomy. From the zoologist's point of view, however, the cat is a rather typical mammal, and study of its anatomy is important in familiarizing himself with the structure of animals belonging to the highest class of vertebrates.

CLASSIFICATION

A brief outline of the main subdivisions of the phylum *Chordata* is given below so that the student may determine at a glance the category into which each of these representative animals fits.

Phylum Chordata
  Group A. Acrania
    Subphylum I. Hemichordata
    Subphylum II. Tunicata
    Subphylum III. Cephalochordata
  Group B. Vertebrata (Craniata)
    Subphylum IV. Agnatha
      Class I. Ostracodermi
      Class II. Cyclostomata
        Order I. Petromyzontia. Lampreys—***Petromyzon marinus***
        Order II. Myxinoidea. Hagfishes
    Subphylum V. Gnathostomata
     Superclass I. Pisces
     Class I. Placodermi
     Class II. Chondrichthyes
       Order I. Selachii (Elasmobranchii)
         Suborder I. Squali. Sharks; dogfishes—***Squalus acanthias***
         Suborder II. Batoidea. Skates and rays
       Order II. Holocephali. Chimaeras
     Class III. Osteichthyes
     Superclass II. Tetrapoda
     Class I. Amphibia
      Subclass I. Stegocephalia. Caecilians
      Subclass II. Caudata (Urodela). Newts; salamanders—***Necturus maculosus***
      Subclass III. Salientia (Anura). Frogs and toads
     Class II. Reptilia
     Class III. Aves
     Class IV. Mammalia
      Subclass I. Prototheria. Monotremes
      Subclass II. Theria
       Infraclass I. Metatheria. Marsupialia
       Infraclass II. Eutheria. Placentalia
       Order IX. Carnivora. Dogs; cats—***Felis domestica***

TECHNICAL TERMS

The understanding of a number of technical terms is essential if one is to follow certain directions when dissecting animals and locating various structures. Since most specimens are dissected with the ventral side up, directions are frequently confusing to the student; for the left side of the animal is to the student's right, and the animal's right to the student's left. In the following pages, unless otherwise stated, *all directions refer to the body of the animal.* For example, if a statement is made that the pyloric end of the stomach passes to the right, it means that it passes toward the right side of the animal, and not to the right of the student who is doing the dissecting.

The following terms are used frequently in this book and should be carefully noted:

Anterior. Toward the head.
Posterior. Away from the head, or toward the tail.
Dorsal. Toward or near the back, or spinal, side.
Ventral. Toward or near the "belly" side.
Median. In the plane dividing the body into right and left halves.
Medial. Nearer the median plane.
Lateral. Toward one side of the median plane.
Longitudinal. In the direction of the long axis of the body or of an organ.
Transverse. At right angles to the longitudinal.
Sagittal section. One made parallel to the plane that divides the body or an organ into right and left halves.
Frontal section. One extending in an anterior-posterior direction but parallel to dorsal and ventral surfaces.
Proximal. Lying toward the base or point of attachment, as in the case of a limb.
Distal. Lying toward the tip or free end.
Peripheral. Lying toward the surface.
Cephalad. Toward the head from. Used even on structures in the head.
Craniad. Toward the head from.
Caudad. Toward the tail from. Used even on structures in the tail.
Dorsad. Toward the dorsal side from.
Ventrad. Toward the ventral side from.
Proximad. Toward the proximal end from.
Mediad. Toward the median line from.
Laterad. Away from the median line from.
Distad. Toward the distal end from.

CHAPTER 1

THE MARINE LAMPREY (*Petromyzon marinus*)

Classification:
Phylum: Chordata
Group: Vertebrata (Craniata)
Subphylum: Agnatha
Class: Cyclostomata
Order: Petromyzontia
Family: Petromyzonidae
Genus: *Petromyzon*
species: *marinus*

NATURAL HISTORY

The lampreys, or lamprey eels, are not to be confused with the true eels, which are bony fishes belonging to the class *Osteichthyes*. There are numerous species of fresh-water lampreys. They are generally smaller than the marine lamprey, *Petromyzon marinus*. Both nonparasitic and parasitic species exist.

Some of the fresh-water forms are *nonparasitic*. Their eggs hatch into larvae, referred to as *ammocoetes*. Anywhere from 3 to 7 years, depending upon the species, are spent in the larval state. During this time the larvae live in tunnels in the sand, emerging to feed on microscopic organisms on the bottom of the stream bed. Water enters the mouth by means of the action of cilia and passes out the gill slits. Food particles are trapped by mucous secretions of an endostyle located on the floor of the pharynx. During the larval period lampreys lack teeth and are blind. Finally they undergo metamorphosis and become adults. At the time of metamorphosis the larvae have reached adult size. In nonparasitic forms no food is taken after this transformation has taken place. Metamorphosis usually occurs in the fall, but spawning does not ensue until the following spring. After the spawning season the adults die.

Parasitic lampreys, of which *Petromyzon marinus* is an example, feed during adult life, preying upon fishes. By means of the round suctorial funnel at the anterior end of the body, they attach themselves to a fish, often at the region just in back of a pectoral fin. The buccal funnel is lined with numerous horny teeth. These, together with the horny teeth on the tongue, are used in rasping a hole in the fish. An anticoagulant is secreted, and the blood which flows from the wound is sucked into the lamprey's mouth. Observations on lampreys kept in an aquarium show that an animal may remain attached to a fish for as long as 3 weeks. Much damage may be done to healthy fishes, which are thus killed or injured. Delicate species, such as brook trout, succumb quickly, but tougher fishes may survive numerous encounters with lampreys. They may be so badly scarred, however, that they have little or no market value.

Petromyzon marinus is anadromous, leaving the sea and going to fresh-water streams to spawn. The sexes are separate in lampreys, although hermaphroditic specimens are occasionally encountered. Before the eggs are laid, a small area, or nest, 6 to 24 in. in diameter, is hollowed out in the gravel and rubble in the river or stream bed. The lamprey does this by fastening its funnel to a stone and then wriggling backward. The process may be aided considerably by the current and may be re-peated many times. Occasionally, stones are pushed out of the hollow by the lamprey, which charges the stone head on. Over 100,000 eggs may be laid by a single female. Fertilization is external. The adult animals die soon after spawning, and their bodies disintegrate rapidly, very little skeletal material being present. It takes from 2 to 3 weeks for the eggs to hatch, depending upon the temperature of the water. The *ammocoetes* larvae live in the sand tunnels for 3 years or more before undergoing metamorphosis. The young lampreys then migrate down-stream and out to sea.

There is a widespread fear of the lamprey. The experience of having a cold, sucking disc attached to one's flesh most certainly cannot be a pleasant sensation. Wood, in his "Natural History," states that he has had as many as six or seven river lampreys attached to his hand at one time without any ill effects.

For centuries a landlocked race of sea lampreys has lived in Lake Ontario, where it is abundant. It also occurs in the Finger Lakes of New York State. The dwarfed, landlocked form, which is full grown at about 15 in., has adapted itself to spending its entire life cycle in fresh water. Here the average length of life of an adult is about 1½ years.

Niagara Falls has been a barrier to the spread of the marine lamprey into the upper Great Lakes. With the construction of the original Welland Canal in 1829 and the new canal which was opened to naviga-tion in 1931, a route became available for the ascent of the sea lamprey into Lake Erie and thence to the other Great Lakes. However, it was not until 1921 that a specimen of the large marine lamprey was first captured in Lake Erie. The animal, for some reason, has never become well established in Lake Erie, although it has reproduced in tremendous numbers in Lakes Huron and Michigan and now is becoming a menace in Lake Superior. It does not seem probable that the dwarfed form, long abundant in Lake Ontario, is the source of the menace. It has been suggested that sea lampreys may have been brought directly from salt water, attached to the hulls of ships that passed through the Welland Canal into Lake Erie and even through the locks at Sault Ste Marie on their way from Lake Huron to Lake Superior. Direct observations of sea lampreys attached to lake boat hulls at Sault Ste Marie have actually been made.

The failure of the sea lamprey to establish itself in Lake Erie may be due to the fact that the possible spawning grounds are poor. The streams where the lamprey breeds must be clean and must have a bottom of sand or gravel without any covering of silt. Most of the streams entering Lake Erie carry great loads of silt or else are contaminated with industrial wastes and other filth.

In recent years lampreys in Lakes Huron and Michigan have multiplied to such an extent that their ravages threaten to destroy the fishing industry of the entire region. The following data, supplied by the Fish and Wildlife Service of the U.S. Department of the Interior, are illuminating. The data refer only to the catch of lake trout in the United States waters of Lake Huron from 1935 through 1949.

Year	Pounds
1935	1,743,000
1936	1,400,000
1937	1,340,000
1938	1,270,000
1939	1,372,000
1940	940,000
1941	892,000
1942	728,000
1943	459,000
1944	363,000
1945	173,000
1946	38,000
1947	12,000
1948	4,000
1949	912

It is, of course, possible that factors other than lamprey attacks may be responsible for the great decrease in the population of lake trout. The Federal government and the various state governments of the areas involved have set up programs for control of the pests. These involve two main lines of effort: (1) prevention of spawning by blocking the streams, and destruction of animals on their way to the spawning grounds;

(2) destruction of newly metamorphosed animals during their passage from stream to lake. These programs must be applied to great numbers of streams and are very expensive since they involve construction, maintenance, and operation of dams, traps, and weirs. The outlook for the ultimate control and eradication of the sea lamprey in the Great Lakes is none too bright.

The *ammocoetes larva*, which in itself is harmless, is of great importance to the comparative anatomist, for it is a very primitive and generalized chordate. Many complicated structures of higher forms can be traced back to its simplified structural organization.

EXTERNAL FEATURES

Obtain a specimen of a marine lamprey, place it in a dissecting pan, and carefully examine its external features.

The body of the animal is long and thin, large specimens attaining a length of about 3 ft. The anterior end is cylindrical, whereas the posterior end is laterally compressed (Fig. 1.1). Numerous small **pores of**

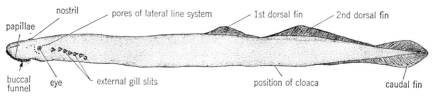

FIG. 1.1.   Lateral view of lamprey.

the lateral-line system can be observed in the head region even though a lateral line proper is absent. A large **buccal funnel** surrounded by a fringe of **papillae** is located at the anterior end. It is beset internally with horny **epidermal teeth** which are definitely arranged (Fig. 1.2). At the apex of the buccal funnel is the **mouth,** through which the **tongue** protrudes slightly. The tongue is a very specialized organ *not* homologous with the tongues of higher vertebrates. In the lamprey it also bears horny teeth. On the dorsal surface of the head is a single, median **nostril** behind which a light area in the skin indicates the position of the **pineal organ.** The paired **eyes** have no eyelids but are covered with a transparent layer of skin. Seven **external gill slits** appear on each side as small apertures arranged in a row, beginning a short distance behind the eyes. On the ventral side at the junction of trunk and tail is a slitlike depression, the **cloacal pit.**[*] A **urogenital papilla,** bearing at its tip a

---

[*] A cloaca is a common chamber into which the intestinal, urinary, and genital ducts discharge. Strictly speaking, a true cloaca is not present in the lamprey since the anus and urogenital papilla have separate openings.

small **urogenital aperture,** protrudes through the cloacal pit. The **anus** lies within the cloacal depression immediately in front of the urogenital papilla (Figs. 1.6 and 1.8). No paired appendages are present. Two unpaired **median dorsal fins,** supported by slender cartilaginous **fin rays,** are located near the posterior end. The **caudal fin** is posterior to the second dorsal fin, the tail being of the **protocercal type.**

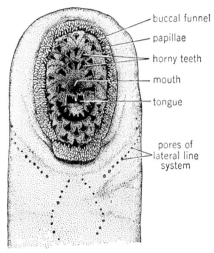

FIG. 1.2. Ventral view of anterior end of lamprey showing buccal funnel and tongue beset with horny, epidermal teeth.

MEDIAN SAGITTAL SECTION

With the aid of the instructor and using a sharp scalpel, make a median sagittal section through the anterior end of the lamprey, making certain that the cut passes through middorsal and midventral lines. It is difficult for a student inexperienced at dissection to do this well without aid. When the cut has been continued posteriorly to approximately the level of the fifth or sixth external gill slit, direct the scalpel laterally, cutting off completely the left half of the anterior end of the lamprey.

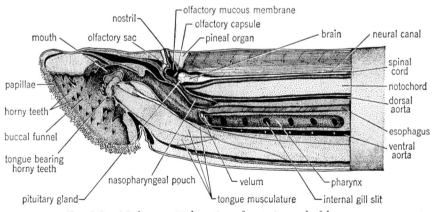

FIG. 1.3. Median sagittal section of anterior end of lamprey.

Set aside the removed portion for future use, and turn your attention to the cut surface of the remainder of the animal. By referring to Fig. 1.3, identify all structures in the median sagittal section of the anterior end.

SKELETAL SYSTEM

The **notochord**, a persistent rodlike structure, forms the greater part of the axial skeleton (Figs. 1.3 and 1.9). It terminates anteriorly just underneath the posterior half of the brain. Small metameric cartilages abut upon the notochord throughout its length. They extend dorsally and partially surround the spinal cord. These incomplete arches represent the rudiments of the **neural arches** seen in the vertebrae of higher forms. Similar cartilages in the tail region extend ventrally to form **hemal arches**. Very slender cartilaginous **fin rays** give support to the median fins.

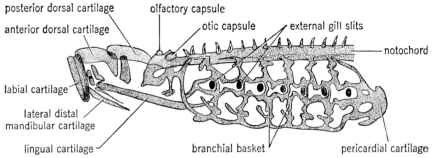

FIG. 1.4. Lateral view of chondrocranium and branchial basket of lamprey, *Petromyzon marinus*. (*After Parker, from Schimkewitsch.*)

The part of the skeleton making up the skull and the branchial basket, which supports the gill region, is more complicated. The **cranium** is rather primitive in structure and consists of cartilaginous plates which protect the floor and lateral sides of the brain. The roof of the cranium, except at one point, is membranous in nature. Foramina for the passage of cranial nerves II, V, and VIII pierce the lateral cartilages. The **olfactory capsule** is an unpaired cartilage surrounding the posterior edge of the **olfactory mucous membrane** (Fig. 1.3). It is pierced by two foramina, through which the **olfactory nerves** pass to the brain. It is united to the cranium only by connective tissue. Other cartilages furnish support for the eyes, tongue, and edge of the buccal funnel.

The "visceral skeleton" is commonly known as the **branchial basket** (Fig. 1.4). The cartilage of which it is composed is continuous. Slender, irregular cartilaginous bars lie *external* to the gill pouches. They support the gill region. There are several reasons for not homologizing these cartilaginous branchial bars with the typical visceral arches or visceral skeletons of higher forms.

The histological structure of the cartilage of the lamprey is somewhat peculiar, there being only a small amount of matrix.   It differs in various regions.

MUSCULAR SYSTEM

Carefully remove the skin from an area about 1½ in. wide on the side of the body of the lamprey and extending from the midventral line to the base of the first dorsal fin.   This will expose the muscles making up the greater part of the body wall in this region.

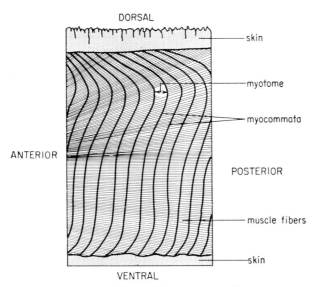

FIG. 1.5.   Lateral view of several parietal myotomes of lamprey in region just anterior to the first dorsal fin.   The skin has been removed to show the muscle fibers beneath.

The muscles of the trunk and tail regions of the lamprey are metameric structures known as **myomeres** or **myotomes** (Fig. 1.5).   They are arranged almost vertically but curve forward slightly on both dorsal and ventral sides and become smaller toward the tail.   Between adjacent myotomes are **myocommata.**   These are tough connective-tissue partitions to which the **muscle fibers** of the myotomes attach and upon which they pull during contraction.   The myomeres are all practically alike in structure.   Since there is no lateral septum in the lamprey, the myomeres are not divided into dorsal and ventral regions as in higher forms.   Only in the region of the head and gills do they become modified as **hypobranchial muscles,** and the superficial metamerism, so easily noted in the trunk and tail regions, loses its identity.

COELOMIC VISCERA

We shall next study the coelomic viscera and identify the various parts of the digestive, excretory, and reproductive systems. In order to expose them, make a longitudinal cut with scissors or sharp scalpel along the midventral line from the gill region to a point about ½ in. in *front* of the cloacal slit, being careful not to injure any internal organs in this process. At each end of the cut make lateral incisions in both directions. Do NOT CUT TOO DEEPLY. Now remove the two long flaps of body wall so formed, being careful to separate them at the anterior end from the outer part of the pericardium, a thick membrane which encloses a large chamber lying just posterior to the gill region. This will expose the viscera for identification.

Since lampreys are usually captured on their way to the spawning grounds, the specimens secured from biological supply houses are sexually mature. In both sexes a single **gonad** extends the length of the body cavity, being suspended from the dorsal body wall by a fold of peritoneum: the **mesorchium** in the male, and the **mesovarium** in the female. In females the greater portion of the body cavity is occupied with the **ovary,** filled with great numbers of eggs which are light brown in color. The **testis** in the male is much smaller than the ovary of the female and is grayish in color.

Remove most of the ovarian or testicular tissue from the body by severing the mesovarium or mesorchium from the dorsal body wall, leaving intact a portion about 1½ in. long near the middle of the body. The long tubular structure, often partly surrounded by the gonad, is the **intestine.** Be careful not to damage it. Make a small longitudinal incision in the posterior end of the intestine. Insert a probe in this cut, directing it posteriorly, and note that it emerges through the **anus,** which lies within the cloacal aperture just anterior to the **urogenital papilla.**

COELOM

The large cavity which has been exposed and in which most of the visceral organs lie is a portion of the coelom called the **pleuroperitoneal cavity.** In adult lampreys the anterior portion of the coelom, containing the heart and called the **pericardial cavity,** is completely separated from the pleuroperitoneal cavity. In hagfishes and elasmobranchs, however, a connection between the two cavities persists in adult life. We shall not at this point expose the pericardial cavity, which is enclosed by the thick, tough **pericardium,** previously observed.

DIGESTIVE SYSTEM

The mouth opening at the apex of the buccal funnel leads into a **buccal,** or **mouth, cavity,** which in turn connects posteriorly with two tubes: an upper **esophagus** and a lower **pharynx** (Fig. 1.3). The pharynx is a blind pouch which bears seven **internal gill slits** on each side. A valve-like structure, the **velum,** guards the opening between the mouth cavity and pharynx. The esophagus continues posteriorly as a straight tube and joins the intestine, which extends directly to the anus (Fig. 1.6). Slight enlargements at either end may be considered to represent the **stomach** and **rectum,** respectively. The single-lobed **liver** surrounds the anterior part of the intestinal, or stomach, region. Its anterior end is concave and partially surrounds the **pericardium,** inside of which the **heart** is located. No gall bladder or bile duct is present in the adult. A few patches of cells buried in the substance of the liver and in the wall of the intestine may possibly represent **endocrine pancreatic tissue.** This is not macroscopically visible.

Continue the longitudinal slit made at the posterior end of the intestine in a forward direction, and examine the lining surface of the intestine.

A conspicuous fold, the **typhlosole,** in the intestinal wall projects into the intestinal lumen. It assumes a slightly spiral course and is sometimes called the **spiral valve.** The typhlosole is believed to increase the digestive and absorptive surface area of the intestine.

The intestine is supported by **mesenteries** only in the region of the

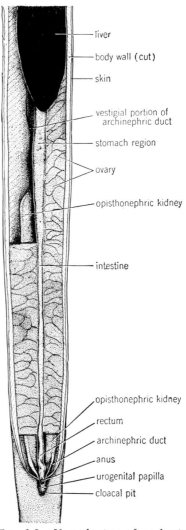

liver

body wall (cut)

skin

vestigial portion of archinephric duct

stomach region

ovary

opisthonephric kidney

intestine

opisthonephric kidney

rectum

archinephric duct

anus

urogenital papilla

cloacal pit

Fig. 1.6. Ventral view of coelomic viscera of female lamprey. Portions of the ovary have been removed to show details of kidney structure.

rectum. These consist of bands of tissue, supporting blood vessels which pass to the intestine from the dorsal body wall (Fig. 1.8). No large continuous membranes, like those of other forms, are present in the lamprey.

When blood, mucus, and tissue fragments, on which the animal feeds, pass into the mouth cavity, they go down the esophagus to the remainder of the digestive tract. The velum at the anterior end of the pharynx prevents the passage of the bloody food into the respiratory system and also prevents dilution of the blood with water which might enter the mouth from the pharynx. When the lamprey is getting ready to feed (T. E. Reynolds, 1931, *Univ. Calif.* (Berkeley) *Publ. Zoöl.,* 37:15), the buccal funnel is first collapsed or flattened, and the water already in it is forced over the tongue into the mouth cavity and **hydrosinus** above. The hydrosinus is an anterodorsal extension of the mouth cavity. Next, the tongue is used to block the passage between the buccal funnel and mouth cavity. The suctorial disc is then arched, or warped, outward, thereby increasing the volume and the degree of suction of the buccal funnel. Water in the hydrosinus and oral cavity is then forced past the velum into the pharynx, the velum serving as a one-way valve which prevents the return of water into the mouth cavity. The tongue, up to this point, is still blocking the passage between the buccal funnel and mouth cavity. The discharge of water from mouth cavity to pharynx creates a low-pressure area extending from the attached disc to the velum. The tongue is now free to move back and forth in rasping. Blood flowing from the wound and tissue fragments pass readily into the mouth cavity and thence to the esophagus and the remainder of the digestive tract. In the meantime the animal is respiring by taking water in and forcing it out of the external gill slits (see below).

RESPIRATORY SYSTEM

The structure of the gill region will next be studied. Prepare a frontal section of the entire portion of the lamprey which was removed at the time the sagittal section was made. This is best done with a scalpel. Be sure that in preparing the section a clean cut is made perpendicular to the sagittal plane through both internal and external gill slits. Refer to Fig. 1.7 in order to identify the parts observed. Frequently coagulated lymph fills the lymph sinuses of the gill region and obscures certain structures. If the sinuses are filled with lymph in your specimen, take it to the sink and knead it gently under running water until most of the lymph has been removed.

The seven **external gill slits** communicate with large, rather spherical spaces, the **gill pouches,** which in turn open into the pharynx by means of the **internal gill slits** previously mentioned. The gill pouches are separated from one another by membranous **interbranchial septa.** On either side of a gill pouch is a series of vascular **gill lamellae** arranged in a semicircular manner but forming a **hemibranch, or half gill.** Each hemibranch is separated from the interbranchial septum by a **lymphatic space,** across which extend small **connective-tissue strands** which support the hemibranch. Two hemibranchs enclosing between them an interbranchial septum are termed a **gill, or holobranch.** Thus there are 14 hemibranchs on each side but only 6 holobranchs, since the first and last hemibranchs do not form parts of a holobranch (Fig. 1.7).

During respiration the lamprey normally takes water in and out the gill clefts through the external gill slits. Thus the gill lamellae are bathed by a constantly replenished supply of water. This method of respiration is quite in contrast to that employed by the true fishes, in which water enters the mouth and passes over the gills on its way to the outside through external gill openings. The method utilized by the lamprey is necessary because when the animal is attached to some object or engaged in feeding, the mouth opening is blocked. It is, of course, possible that when the animal is free, water may pass through the buccal funnel into the mouth cavity and to the outside via pharynx, internal gill slits, gill

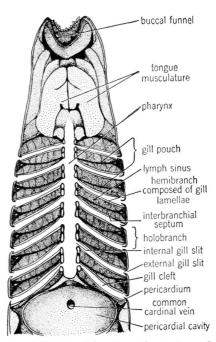

Fig. 1.7. Frontal section of anterior end of lamprey, showing arrangement of the gills as seen from below.

pouches, and external gill slits. It is doubtful, however, whether this method is employed, at least to any appreciable extent.

UROGENITAL SYSTEM

The kidneys of *Petromyzon marinus* (Figs. 1.6 and 1.9) are of the opisthonephric type. They are long, strap-shaped structures which lie on either side of the middorsal line from which they are suspended by mesenterylike membranes. Running along the free edge of each kidney is an **archinephric duct.** Vestiges of the old embryonic pronephric ducts can be seen anterior to the functional part of the **opisthonephros.** At the posterior end of the body the archinephric ducts open into the **urogenital sinus,** which is the cavity within the **urogenital**

papilla. This opens by means of a **urogenital aperture** to the outside. A **genital pore** on each side connects the urogenital sinus with the coelom (Fig. 1.8).

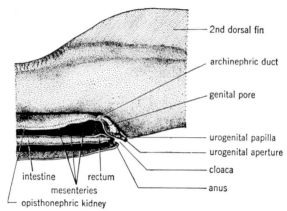

Fig. 1.8. Position and arrangement of left genital pore of lamprey. It is through the genital pores that the reproductive elements leave the coelom to enter the urogenital sinus.

Cut a small nick in one of the archinephric ducts about an inch in front of the cloacal slit. Insert a probe into the duct and direct it

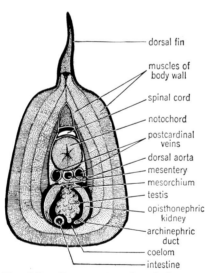

posteriorly. Note that the tip of the probe emerges through the urogenital aperture. Next locate the genital pore on one side by removing carefully any remaining portion of the body wall at the posterior end. Consult Fig. 1.8. Insert a probe into the genital pore and direct it posteriorly. Note that it emerges through the urogenital aperture.

In both sexes, when the reproductive elements (eggs or spermatozoa) are ripe, they break out of the gonad into the body cavity and find their way through the genital pores to the outside. No reproductive ducts are present and *fertilization is external.* When

Fig. 1.9. Cross section of male lamprey at level of first dorsal fin.

spawning takes place, the male wraps the posterior part of his body about the female and sheds spermatozoa over the eggs as they emerge.

ENDOCRINE SYSTEM

Most of the structures belonging to the endocrine system in the lamprey are extremely small or diffuse and do not lend themselves readily to gross dissection. Among them, however, are the following:

Pancreas. As previously mentioned, no discrete pancreas is present in the lamprey. A few small masses of cells have been described, buried in the substance of the liver and in the wall of the intestine. These may possibly represent pancreatic tissue. It is believed that they may be comparable to the **islands of Langerhans** of higher forms since no duct is present.

Thyroid gland. A **subpharyngeal gland,** sometimes referred to as the **endostyle,** is present in the *ammocoetes larva* of the lamprey. It lies beneath the floor of the pharynx, roughly between the first and fifth gill pouches. The subpharyngeal gland is a complicated structure which possibly functions as a mucous gland. Its orifice is associated with a system of ciliated grooves in the pharyngeal wall. Five types of cells have been described in the gland. At the time of metamorphosis certain of these cells lose their cilia, change their shape, and become arranged in the form of typical **thyroid follicles.** Because of this, the endostyle of such protochordates as amphioxus and tunicates has been regarded in the past as the forerunner and homologue of the thyroid gland of higher forms. Experiments in which radioactive iodine has been used as a tracer substance show that the endostyles of tunicates fail to concentrate iodine, whereas this element accumulates rapidly in certain cells of the ammocoetes subpharyngeal gland even before they become organized as thyroid follicles. Other cells apparently do not have this ability. These findings indicate that only a portion of the ammocoetes subpharyngeal gland, and not the entire organ, is the homologue of the thyroid gland and that the homologies of the endostyles of the protochordates with glands of higher forms are, therefore, questionable.

The fact that the thyroid gland first makes its appearance in the embryos of higher forms as a median, ventral diverticulum of the pharynx is also of special interest in this connection.

Parathyroid glands. In early stages of development in all vertebrates, small budlike masses of cells proliferate from both dorsal and ventral ends of the pharyngeal pouches. The number varies in different vertebrates and vertebrate groups. It is clear that in higher tetrapods certain of the epithelial buds give rise to the parathyroid glands. In cyclostomes, because of the small size, diffuse nature, and difficulty in extirpating the structures completely, it has not been conclusively determined whether any of them actually represent parathyroid tissue. Lampreys possess a very complete set of these small epithelial masses, since all pharyngeal pouches give rise to both dorsal and ventral buds. Their significance is unknown.

Adrenal glands. In *Petromyzon* there are two clearly distinguished series of bodies representing adrenal homologues. The first consists of small, irregular, lobelike structures situated along the postcardinal veins, renal arteries, and the arteries running dorsal to the opisthonephric kidneys. They may even extend into the cavities of these vessels. This series of small bodies is the **interrenal, or cortical, series.** The other, or **chromaffin series,** extends from near the anterior end of the gill region (opposite the second gill cleft) to the tail. Here the chromaffin bodies consist of small strips of tissue which extend along the course of the dorsal aorta and its branches.

Gonads. The gonads of both male and female lamprey have already been observed and their gamete-producing function reviewed. The fact that in the lamprey the urogenital sinus assumes different forms in male and female would lead one to infer that testicular and ovarian hormones are responsible for the phenomena. At the approach of sexual maturity in the male, the urogenital sinus becomes rather narrow and opens by means of a small pore at the end of a long tube which in some ways resembles a penis. In the female the urogenital sinus forms a large vestibule with a vulva and a rather wide opening.

Pituitary gland. The pituitary gland of the lamprey consists of the usual three component parts and is located between the nasopharyngeal pouch and the floor of the diencephalic portion of the brain. It is discussed below (page 23) in connection with the olfactory apparatus.

CIRCULATORY SYSTEM

We shall not study the entire circulatory system of the lamprey but confine ourselves instead to observations on the heart and the main blood vessels which carry blood to and from the heart.

The **heart** (Fig. 1.10) is a two-chambered organ located on the ventral side of the animal just posterior to the last pair of gill pouches and partially surrounded by the liver. It lies in the **pericardial cavity,** which is surrounded by a thick and tough **pericardium** of a purplish color. In the ammocoetes stage the pericardial cavity communicates with the rest of the coelom, but the connection disappears in the adult.

Clean away what remains of the gill region in the main portion of the specimen. The pericardium lies immediately posterior to this. Remove a portion of the body wall covering the pericardium, and then cut away as much as possible of the latter in order to expose the heart. The heart is to be removed carefully, together with the ends of the vessels which enter and leave it. Be sure to note dorsal and ventral relationships. The **atrium** lies on the left side of the **ventricle**, receiving blood from a rather small **sinus venosus**. Consult Fig. 1.10. After the heart has been exposed, loosen it by cutting the single **common cardinal vein** along the dorsal side of the pericardium. Also cut the small **ligament** which fastens the ventricle to the pericardial wall. Next, cut the sinus venosus free from the **hepatic** and **inferior jugular veins**. Loosen the proximal part of the **ventral aorta** where it leaves the heart, and remove a portion of it fastened to the **bulbus**. Place the heart in a finger bowl of water and examine it in detail.

The thin-walled sinus venosus, which lies in the crevice between atrium and ventricle, opens into the atrium through a slitlike aperture guarded by a pair of **sinuatrial valves**. The sinus venosus receives three vessels: (1) a large, single **common cardinal vein** on the dorsal

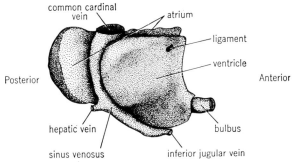

Fig. 1.10. Lateral view of heart of lamprey as seen from the right side. The posterior part of the atrium has been deflected to expose the sinus venosus to view.

side, (2) a small **inferior jugular vein** on its anteroventral side, (3) a small **hepatic vein** from the posterior side. The thin-walled atrium communicates with the ventricle by means of a small aperture guarded by **atrioventricular valves**. The ventricle, which lies on the right side of the atrium, is smaller than the atrium and possesses thick muscular walls. A bulbus aortae carries blood from the ventricle to the ventral aorta which in turn distributes it to the gills.

Make windows in atrium and ventricle in order to examine the internal structure of the heart. Wash the cavities free of coagulated blood, and examine the sinuatrial and atrioventricular apertures and valves. Slit the ventral aorta and bulbus longitudinally, and continue the cut into the ventricle. Spread apart the cut edges and look for a single set of **semilunar valves** in the bulbus. Be sure that you understand the direction in which blood courses through the heart of the lamprey.

If the sagittal section of the anterior end has been cut properly, it may still be possible to trace the arteries which arise from the ventral aorta and supply the gill region on the *right* side of the specimen.

In *Petromyzon marinus* the ventral aorta, which leaves the bulbus as a single vessel, bifurcates at the level of the fourth gill pouch (Fig. 1.11A). Four **afferent branchial arteries** arise from each of the paired anterior extensions, and four pairs are given off by the unpaired portion. The first of the eight pairs of afferent branchial arteries on each side supplies the gill lamellae of the anterior hemibranch. The last furnishes blood to the most posterior hemibranch. Each of the remaining vessels arises at the level of an interbranchial septum and divides almost immediately

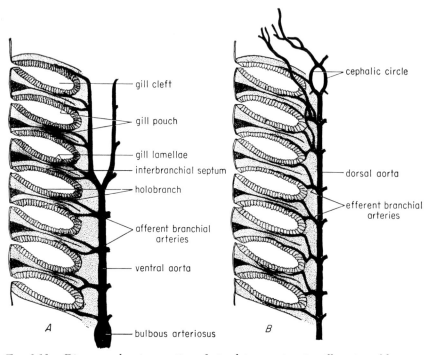

FIG. 1.11. Diagrams showing portion of circulatory system in gill region of lamprey, *Petromyzon marinus: A,* ventral aorta and afferent branchial arteries; *B,* dorsal aorta and efferent branchial arteries.

to supply the lamellae on either side of the septum. Thus each holobranch is furnished with the two branches of an afferent branchial artery. **Efferent branchial arteries,** corresponding in position to the afferent vessels, collect blood from the gill lamellae (Fig. 1.11*B*). They join the single, median **dorsal aorta.** The anterior end of this vessel is paired for a short distance, but the two portions come together again, thus forming what is referred to as the **cephalic circle.** From the circle arise arteries which supply the brain, eyes, tongue, and various parts of the head.

Dissection of the venous system in your specimen may not be feasible. The following points should be noted. Two inferior jugular veins unite to form the single vessel, previously noted, which enters the sinus venosus. Paired **anterior** and **posterior cardinals** are present. The common cardinals appear to have fused, or else the left one has degenerated in the adult so that but a single common cardinal enters the sinus venosus on its dorsal side (Fig. 1.10). A **hepatic portal vein** is present. It receives a branch from the head and contains a contractile **portal heart.** Blood from the liver is collected by a single hepatic vein, previously noted. No renal portal system exists in the lamprey. A **caudal vein,** which divides at the cloacal region, connects to the post-cardinal veins. Segmentally arranged veins from the kidneys and gonad enter the postcardinal veins as do those from the dorsal body wall.

NERVOUS SYSTEM AND SENSE ORGANS

The rather poorly developed **brain** of the lamprey lies just above and anterior to the tip of the notochord (Fig. 1.3).

Observe as many of the following structures as possible in the sagittal section of the anterior end of the lamprey.

The **telencephalon,** or foremost part of the brain, is on each side divided into an anterior **olfactory bulb** and a posterior **olfactory lobe.** The olfactory lobes are frequently referred to as **cerebral hemispheres.** Posterior to the olfactory lobes two small, median structures, an anterior **parietal body** and a posterior **pineal organ,** project from the roof of the **diencephalon.** They are almost microscopic in size and difficult to observe grossly. At the distal end of each a small eyelike structure is present in the lamprey. The pineal organ is the better developed of the two. It is, however, probably capable of little more than distinguishing light from dark. The **pituitary gland** is attached to the ventral side of the diencephalon. The **optic lobes** of the **mesencephalon** are poorly differentiated in the lamprey. An apparently unique feature is the presence of a vascular **mesencephalic choroid plexus** extending from the roof of the mesencephalon in the form of an everted sac. The **cerebellum** is represented only by a slight fold. The **medulla oblongata** is the only part of the brain that is really well developed. Its roof consists of a large, everted **posterior choroid plexus.** Ten pairs of **cranial nerves** are present in *Petromyzon.*

The **spinal cord** is a flat, ribbonlike structure of fairly uniform width throughout. The dorsal side is more or less convex, and the ventral side concave. **Dorsal roots** of **spinal nerves** are found to alternate with **ventral roots** so far as their origin from the spinal cord is concerned. The roots do not unite to form a common trunk as in higher forms.

The **olfactory apparatus** of the lamprey (Fig. 1.3) is a unique structure. The single dorsal **nostril** leads into a canal which connects posteriorly with a small **olfactory sac.** This lies just anterior to the

brain.   Its walls are composed of ridges covered over by a heavily pigmented **olfactory mucous membrane**.   A cartilaginous **olfactory capsule**
surrounds the olfactory mucous membrane.

The relation of the anterior end of the brain to the olfactory mucous
membrane, olfactory capsule, and nasopharyngeal pouch should be noted
in particular.   A *pair* of **olfactory nerves** passes posteriorly from the

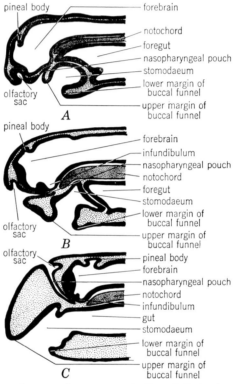

Fig. 1.12.   Diagrams showing three stages, *A, B,* and *C,* in the development of the
olfactory sac and nasopharyngeal pouch of the lamprey.   Note how the nasal aperture has shifted to the top of the head.   (*Based on Kuppfer and Dohrn.*)

olfactory mucous membrane, penetrates the olfactory capsule, and terminates in the anterior end of the brain.   If the median sagittal section has
been properly cut, the olfactory nerves will not be visible.   With a pair
of fine-pointed scissors cut through the olfactory capsule immediately in
front of the brain to a depth of $\frac{1}{16}$ to $\frac{1}{8}$ in., and remove the small piece
of tissue thus loosened.   The large, wide olfactory nerve will then be
exposed.

The fact that the single, median, olfactory mucous membrane is supplied by a *pair* of cranial nerves indicates that the olfactory organ of the lamprey is specialized rather than primitive and probably represents a fusion of paired structures. There is also some evidence from embryology to support this point of view.

From the anterior edge of the olfactory sac a long tube extends ventrally and posteriorly, passing beneath the anterior tip of the notochord to the level of the second gill pouch where it ends blindly. This is the **nasopharyngeal pouch.** Between the ventral part of the diencephalon of the brain and the nasopharyngeal pouch lies the small **pituitary gland** consisting of the usual component parts. It has been suggested (W. J. Leach, 1951, *J. Morphol.*, 89:271) that the nasopharyngeal pouch, which has no counterpart in higher vertebrates, may actually represent a portion of the embryonic mouth, or stomodaeal cavity, which has separated from the main part of the stomodaeum. The peculiar position of the nasal aperture and its unusual relation to the nasopharyngeal pouch, as compared with other vertebrates, are due to a shifting of these organs from their original ventral position during embryonic development (Fig. 1.12). Water is alternately forced into and out of the nasopharyngeal pouch and olfactory apparatus, the intake and outflow coinciding with respiratory movements in the gill region. In this manner water in contact with the olfactory mucous membrane is con-

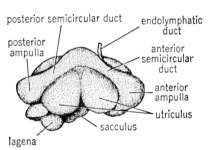

Fig. 1.13. Membranous labyrinth of lamprey. (*Modified from Krause.*)

stantly replaced, enabling the animal to detect chemical substances in solution in the water. In the lamprey neither olfactory sac nor nasopharyngeal pouch has any connection with the pharynx.

The **eyes** of the lamprey are primitive but well developed. In the ammocoetes larva they are undeveloped and lie hidden under the thick skin, which, however, thins out in the adult and becomes transparent. The **cornea** is not fused to the overlying skin and therefore lacks a corneal epithelium. The **lens** is permanently spherical, and suspensory ligament and ciliary apparatus are lacking. Furthermore, the size of the pupil is fixed.

The auditory (equilibratory) organs of the lamprey are considered to be degenerate. Only the **membranous labyrinth** of the inner ear is present (Fig. 1.13). Utricular and saccular regions are not distinct, and only two vertical **semicircular ducts** are present, each with an **ampulla** at its lower end. The inner ear does not lend itself well to ordinary dissection.

CHAPTER 2

THE SPINY DOGFISH (*Squalus acanthias*)

Classification:
Phylum: Chordata
Group: Vertebrata (Craniata)
Subphylum: Gnathostomata
Superclass: Pisces
Class: Chondrichthyes
Order: Selachii
Suborder: Squali
Family: Squalidae
Genus: *Squalus*
species: *acanthias*

NATURAL HISTORY

The name dogfish or skittle dog is applied to numerous species of small sharks because of their custom of pursuing prey in packs. They are active and voracious creatures which are very destructive to herring and other food fishes. Squid also seems to be a favorite article of diet. *Squalus acanthias*, the spiny dogfish, gets its name from the fact that a well-developed and very sharp spine is present in front of each of its two dorsal fins. It is abundant in almost all cool regions of the sea and even in some tropical waters. The fish is found on both sides of the Atlantic Ocean and is a special nuisance to fishermen since it often tears their nets, removes hooks from lines, and injures fish already caught. Dogfish are sometimes sought by fishermen because of the oil in their livers, which has a high vitamin content. As many as 20,000 have been taken in a single haul of the net. Customarily the fishermen remove the livers and cast the rest of the animal away. The flesh is of little commercial value but is used occasionally for food and sold under the name "gray-fish." Sharkskin is known as *shagreen* and is used for polishing woods of high quality.

Squalus acanthias has the gray color usually encountered among sharks. It comes near the shore and is, therefore, rather easily obtained by biological supply houses, which sell them to colleges and universities for dissection in courses in comparative anatomy.

24

The spiny dogfish is an ovoviviparous fish which gives birth to from five to nine young at a time. At the time of birth the young range from 9 to 10 in. in length and are the exact counterparts of their parents but in miniature. Mature specimens measure 3 to 4 ft. in length, the females usually being somewhat larger than the males. Hisaw, who made a special study of reproduction in *Squalus acanthias*, reports that it has a 2-year gestation period. In the Woods Hole region of Massachusetts, the animals migrate northward toward the coast of Newfoundland in late April and early May. Pregnant females caught at this time fall into two groups: those having "pups" with large yolk sacs (Fig. 2.1) and those in the so-called "candle stage." The latter have large undeveloped ova in their uteri. In October and November the fish again pass Woods Hole, migrating to the south. Those which carried pups in June have

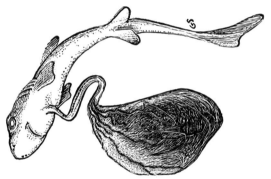

Fig. 2.1. Embryo of dogfish shark, *Squalus acanthias*, showing yolk sac attached to body by means of yolk stalk. (*Drawn by G. Schwenk.*)

given birth, or else the yolk sacs of the almost fully developed young have been practically absorbed, indicating that birth is about to occur. In the following spring the females which were in the candle stage the previous year are carrying pups, and those which have given birth to young are once more in the candle stage.

EXTERNAL FEATURES

Obtain a specimen of *Squalus acanthias* and place it in a dissecting pan. Examine the external features of the animal, noting the structures described below.

The **body** of the spiny dogfish is fusiform in shape (Fig. 2.2). It is of a grayish-green color on the dorsal side and yellowish-white on the undersurface. A few irregularly spaced white spots are present in the skin of young dogfish, but these tend to disappear as the animals grow older. Furthermore, they are less obvious in preserved specimens. The

head is broad and somewhat flattened in a dorsoventral direction. Posteriorly the body tapers gradually from a more or less cylindrical form to the laterally compressed **tail.** The skin is almost entirely covered with minute **placoid scales,** which point posteriorly (Fig. 2.3). The

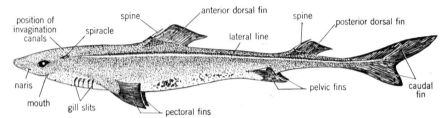

FIG. 2.2.   Lateral view of female dogfish, *Squalus acanthias.* (*Drawn by R. Schugt.*)

presence of these scales may be detected by rubbing the hand from posterior to anterior ends.   The **subterminal mouth** is on the ventral side of the head.   At the borders of the mouth the placoid scales are enlarged and modified to form the **teeth,** which are arranged in several rows.   At each corner of the mouth a **labial groove,** or **pocket,** extends forward toward the **nostril,** and posteriorly for a short distance.   Whether the labial pocket of *Squalus acanthias* is homologous with the oronasal groove of certain other elasmobranchs and of higher vertebrates has been questioned.   Each pocket marks the location of a **labial cartilage** (Fig. 2.9) which permits freedom of movement of the **lower jaw,** or **mandible** (**Meckel's cartilage**). Each nostril appears to be divided by a flap of skin so arranged as to direct water into one side of the nasal cavity and out the other (Fig. 2.4).

FIG. 2.3.   Enlarged photograph of skin of shark, *Squalus acanthias,* showing numerous placoid scales.

The anterior, paired **pectoral fins** have short bases and flexible surfaces. A cartilaginous **coracoid bar,** forming part of the **pectoral girdle** and lying between the pectoral fins, may be felt through the skin on the ventral side.   The posterior, paired **pelvic fins** are smaller than the pectoral appendages.   They, too, are connected ventrally.   A cartilaginous **ischiopubic bar** forms the **pelvic girdle,** which also may be detected through the skin. In males the medial border of each pelvic fin is elongated and modified into a **clasper** (Fig. 2.5) which bears a deep groove along its dorsomedial border. Folds of skin overlap the groove so that only a small portion is actually open to the outside. The groove is connected anteriorly with a large **siphon sac** (see page 50). The claspers serve as copulatory organs. Each is supported by cartilages. Near the end of the clasper and along its outer side is a sharp, grooved **spine**. On the inner side is a curved **hook** which presumably aids in making copulatory contact.

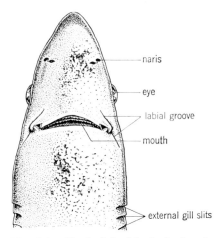

FIG. 2.4. Head of dogfish shark, *Squalus acanthias*, ventral view.

Two median **dorsal fins** are present, each bearing a strong, posteriorly directed spine on its anterior border. The **fin spine** is a highly modified placoid scale. The **caudal fin** forms an important part of the **heterocercal tail**. Note the discrepancy in size between the dorsal and ventral flanges. In this type of tail the skeletal axis bends upward to enter the larger dorsal flange. By holding the fins up to the light, it may be observed that they are supported by **fin rays**. These are thin rods of dermal origin.

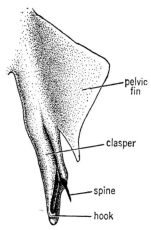

FIG. 2.5. Pelvic fin of male dogfish shark, *Squalus acanthias*, showing clasper in detail. (*After Petri.*)

A light-colored **lateral line** extends lengthwise along each side of the body from head to tail. The skin of the lateral line is slightly raised. Coursing through the dermis of the skin of the lateral line is the **lateral-line canal**, which opens to the outside at intervals through small microscopic **pores**. Cut through the skin across the lateral line at a point near the middle of the body. Examine the cut edge under a binocular dissecting microscope, and observe the lateral-line canal. The lateral-line system is an organ of special sense related to the aquatic mode of life. It occurs only in fishes and aquatic amphibians. Reception of deep vibrations and of pressure stimuli caused by currents or movements of the water, enabling the animals to orient themselves against currents, are among the functions ascribed to the lateral line. On the head are numerous **pores of the lateral-line system.** Some of these, arranged in rows (see page 76), are connected with branches of the lateral-line canal. Numerous other pores on the head represent the openings of an additional set of sense organs, the **ampullae of Lorenzini** (see page 76). It is believed that they may detect variations in temperature.

The **eyes** are located on the lateral sides of the head. Immovable upper and lower **eyelids** are present.

Five pairs of oblique openings on the sides of the head are the **external gill slits.** They communicate internally with the **pharynx.** Another pair of openings, called the **spiracles,** lies in a more dorsal position just posterior to the eyes. The spiracles actually represent the first pair of gill slits which has become modified. A **spiracular valve** projects posteriorly from the anterior wall of the spiracle. By movements of this valve the spiracle may be opened or closed.

Between the spiracles and near the median line are two small openings. They are the external apertures of the **invagination canals,** which connect the cavities of the **inner ears** with the outside.

On the ventral surface of the body between the pelvic fins is an opening, the **cloaca,** which is the common exit of the digestive and urogenital systems. Just within each lateral edge of the cloaca is an **abdominal pore** which leads directly into the body cavity. Probe for these. In young specimens they are usually closed. The function of the abdominal pores is obscure. The **anus** opens into the cloaca anteriorly. A cone-shaped papilla (**urogenital papilla** in the male and **urinary papilla** in the female), with a **urogenital** or **urinary pore** at its tip, projects into the cloacal cavity dorsal and posterior to the anus. The **oviducts** of the female also open into the cloaca by means of **genital pores,** located on either side of the urinary papilla.

SKELETAL SYSTEM

It is usually impracticable for students to clean and study the skeletons of dogfish which have been preserved in alcohol or formaldehyde. Specimens of skulls, visceral skeletons, vertebral columns, and even of entire skeletons may be obtained from biological supply houses and should be available for students who wish to study the skeletal system of *Squalus acanthias* firsthand.

The **skeleton** of the spiny dogfish is composed entirely of **cartilage** impregnated to varying degrees with lime salts. No true bone is present. It is made of two main portions: the axial and appendicular skeletons. As its name implies, the **axial skeleton** is that which forms the main axis of the body. It is divided into (1) the **spinal column**, which surrounds and protects the spinal cord; (2) the **skull**, composed in turn of (*a*) the **cranium**, or that portion which surrounds and protects the brain, (*b*) the **sense capsules**, which enclose and protect the auditory and olfactory organs, and (*c*) the **visceral skeleton**, supporting the jaws and gills. The **appendicular skeleton** is confined to the paired anterior **pectoral** and posterior **pelvic fins** together with their respective **girdles**, by means of which they are connected indirectly to the axial skeleton by muscles, connective tissue, and ligaments.

Axial Skeleton

VERTEBRAL COLUMN

The **notochord** is the primitive axial skeleton of vertebrates. In the shark the notochord is still present but has been partially replaced and invested by the cartilaginous **vertebral column**. The **vertebrae** do not show extensive modifications such as are to be found in most higher forms. There are only two regions in the vertebral column of the dogfish: a **body**, or **trunk**, **region** and a **tail**, or **caudal**, **region**.

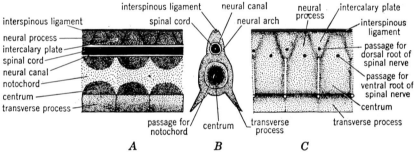

FIG. 2.6. Trunk vertebrae of dogfish shark: *A*, sagittal section through three vertebrae; *B*, end view of vertebra; *C*, lateral view of three intact vertebrae.

A typical body vertebra (Fig. 2.6) consists of a ventral **centrum**, both ends of which are deeply concave (*amphicoelous*). A small canal runs through the centrum from one concavity to the other. The remains of the notochord occupy the canal. The notochord is expanded at each concavity. From each ventrolateral border of the centrum extends a platelike **transverse process** (**basapophysis**), to the end of which a slender rib is attached.

The remainder of the vertebra above the centrum consists of a **neural arch** which encloses and protects the spinal cord. Each neural arch is made up of a triangular **neural process** on either side, with its broad base on the centrum. A small **foramen** for the passage of the *ventral root* of a spinal nerve is present near the base. The two neural processes meet dorsally forming the **neural spine**. A triangular **inter-**

calary plate fills in the space between two adjacent neural processes (Fig. 2.6A and C). It also contains a foramen, which, in this case, serves for the passage of the *dorsal root* of a spinal nerve. The two intercalary plates of a vertebra unite dorsally. A strong, tough, continuous **interspinous ligament** runs along the dorsal edge of the neural arches.

The tail, or caudal, vertebrae differ from the body vertebrae principally in that there are no transverse processes and a **ventral, or hemal, arch** lies below the centrum. The hemal arch surrounds the caudal blood vessels. The **caudal artery** is dorsal, and the **caudal vein** lies ventral to it.

Cut off the tail from your specimen at a point about 2 or 3 in. posterior to the cloaca. Make the cut at right angles to the axis of the animal. Examine the cut end of the tail and observe the various parts of the caudal vertebra thus exposed.

Skull

The **cranium** consists of a single piece of cartilage to which the **capsules** for the olfactory and auditory organs have fused. Openings, or foramina, for the passage of nerves and blood vessels going to and from the brain perforate the cranium at various places. The dorsal side is relatively flat and broad, whereas the ventral side is narrow (Figs. 2.7 and 2.8). At the anterior end is a scooplike projection, the **rostrum,** which has a large dorsal opening, the **precerebral cavity,** sometimes incorrectly referred to as the anterior fontanelle. During life the rostrum is filled with a gelatinous material. At its base are two large openings, the **rostral fenestrae.** These are continuous with the cavity of the cranium. On either side of the base of the rostrum is an **olfactory capsule** which partially surrounds and protects the **olfactory sac,** the organ for the sense of smell. On each side of the cranium is a large **orbit** in which the eye is accommodated during life. A prominent **supraorbital crest** marks the lateral edge of the cranium above the orbit. **Anterior** and **posterior orbital processes** project laterally and mark the ends of the supraorbital crest. A row of foramina paralleling the supraorbital crest serves for the passage of certain branches of the fifth and seventh cranial nerves. The large, rounded, posterolateral projections of the cranium are the **postotic processes.** The inner ears lie within these masses. An opening in the median line just posterior to the precerebral cavity is the **epiphyseal foramen** for the passage of the **epiphysis,** or **pineal body.** Farther back in the region of the auditory capsules is a fossa, or depression, in which lie two pairs of openings. The smaller, anterior ones are for the passage of the **invagination canals** of the inner ears; the larger, posterior openings are referred to as the **perilymphatic fenestrae.** Each perilymphatic fenestra enters the cavity surrounding the membranous labyrinth. During life the aperture is closed over by a membrane. A semifluid material lies over the membrane, above which is the skin. It is possible that this apparatus may transmit sound waves to the cavity below. The membrane may thus serve in the manner of the tympanic membrane of terrestrial vertebrates, but by no means should the two be considered as homologous structures. A large opening

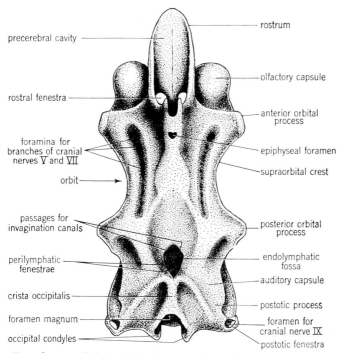

precerebral cavity

rostrum

olfactory capsule

rostral fenestra

anterior orbital process

foramina for branches of cranial nerves V and VII

epiphyseal foramen

orbit

supraorbital crest

passages for invagination canals

posterior orbital process

perilymphatic fenestrae

endolymphatic fossa

auditory capsule

crista occipitalis

postotic process

foramen magnum

foramen for cranial nerve IX

occipital condyles

postotic fenestra

Fig. 2.7. Dorsal view of skull of *Squalus acanthias*. (*After Senning, outline drawings for "Laboratory Studies in Comparative Anatomy," McGraw-Hill Book Company, Inc. By permission.*)

at the posterior end of the cranium is the **foramen magnum,** through which the spinal cord passes. Small projections on either side of the foramen magnum are the **occipital condyles** for articulation with the first vertebra. A slight ridge, the **crista occipitalis,** extends between the foramen magnum and the endolymphatic fossa.

On the ventral side of the cranium (Fig. 2.8) an **anterior orbital shelf** marks the anterior boundary of the orbit. Posterior to this the floor of the cranium narrows down to a heavy **infraorbital ridge.** In the median line opposite the posterior edges of the orbit is a foramen through which the **internal carotid arteries** enter the cranial cavity. Conspicuous foramina for the passage of the ninth and tenth cranial nerves are situated at the posterior lateral corners of the cranium.

Several foramina are located in the orbit. The **optic foramen** is a large anteroventral opening for the passage of the optic nerve. Numerous foramina on the dorsal side are for the branches of the fifth and seventh cranial nerves, previously mentioned. In the posteroventral corner of the orbit is another group of foramina. The largest, or

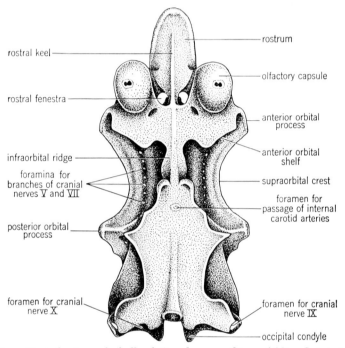

FIG. 2.8.   Ventral view of skull of *Squalus acanthias*. (*After Senning, outline drawings for "Laboratory Studies in Comparative Anatomy," McGraw-Hill Book Company, Inc. By permission.*)

trigeminofacial canal, is for the exit of nerves V and VII. Smaller openings are for cranial nerves III and VI and for blood and lymphatic vessels. A depression in this region represents the point of attachment of the **optic pedicel** (see page 77).

The remainder of the skull is called the visceral skeleton or splanchnocranium (Fig. 2.9). In the spiny dogfish there are seven cartilaginous **visceral arches** which almost completely surround the anterior end of the alimentary canal and support its walls in the gill region. These arches have been modified to perform various functions. The first, or **mandibular**, arch is somewhat complicated in structure. It has been modified on each side forming dorsal and ventral portions. The dorsal part is called the **palatopterygoquadrate cartilage,** and the ventral portion is known as **Meckel's cartilage.** These form the upper and lower jaws, respectively. The tissue covering these cartilages bears **teeth.** The angle of the mouth on each side lies at the point where palatopterygoquadrate and Meckel's cartilages join each other posterolaterally by a hinge joint. Each palatopterygoquadrate cartilage bears a dorsally

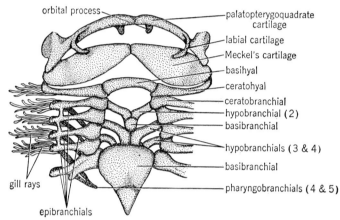

FIG. 2.9. Ventral view of visceral skeleton of *Squalus acanthias.* The hyomandibular cartilage is not shown.

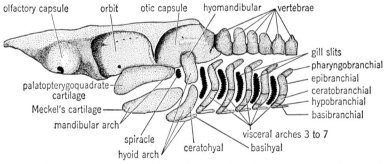

FIG. 2.10. Diagram showing relation of visceral arches of an elasmobranch to the chondrocranium, vertebral column, and gill slits.

directed **orbital,** or **palatine,** process which extends upward along the inner wall of the orbit.

The second, or **hyoid, arch** is also made up of dorsal and ventral portions. The dorsal part is the **hyomandibular cartilage.** It is attached to the **otic region** of the cranium. It serves as a suspensor of the jaws since both palatopterygoquadrate and Meckel's cartilages are joined to it by a ligamentous connection. This type of jaw suspension is known as the **hyostylic method.** Ventral to the hyomandibular cartilage is a **ceratohyal cartilage.** A median **basihyal cartilage** connects the cerato-hyals of the two sides. It supports the tongue. The hyomandibular and ceratohyal cartilages support the first **half gill,** or **hyoid hemibranch.**

The next four visceral arches support the remaining gills. The seventh, or last, visceral arch, however, is not associated with a gill. Each of the last five visceral arches is made up of several cartilages. Their detailed relations are illustrated in Figs. 2.9 and 2.10. The second, third, fourth, fifth, and sixth visceral arches bear slender cartilaginous **gill rays** which are embedded in the septa of the gills to which they give support. No gill rays are associated with the seventh visceral arch.

Appendicular Skeleton

PECTORAL GIRDLE AND FINS

The **shoulder,** or **pectoral,** girdle of the spiny dogfish (Fig. 2.11) is a U-shaped cartilage supporting the anterior paired fins; it is located just posterior to the gill region. It is connected to the axial skeleton only

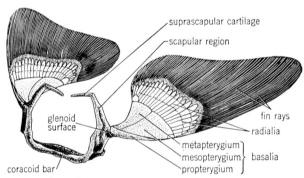

FIG. 2.11. Anterolateral view of pectoral girdle and fin of *Squalus acanthias.*

indirectly. The girdle consists of a single **scapulocoracoid cartilage.** The **coracoid bar** makes up the ventral portion. A rather long **scapular process** extends dorsally on each side beyond the **glenoid region,** the point of articulation of the pectoral fin. A distinct **suprascapular cartilage** is attached to the free end of each scapular process. A **foramen** for the passage of nerve fibers going to the fin lies just mediad the glenoid articulation.

The base of the pectoral fin proper consists of three cartilages known as **basalia.** The smallest and most lateral is the **propterygium;** next to it lies the large, triangular **mesopterygium;** last is the medial **metapteryg-ium.** Numerous cartilaginous **radialia** extend beyond the basalia. Each is made up of two or three segments. Fibrous dermal **fin rays** (**ceratotrichia**) extend beyond the radialia and give support to the main part of the fin.

Pelvic Girdle and Fins

The **pelvic girdle** is of much simpler structure than the pectoral. It is made up of a transverse **ischiopubic bar,** corresponding to the coracoid bar of the pectoral girdle, and a small **iliac** process which projects dorsally to a slight extent. The iliac process is comparable to the scapular process of the pectoral girdle.

Each **pelvic fin** (Fig. 2.12) consists of two **basal cartilages, or basalia,** which join the pelvic girdle at the **acetabular region.** They include a short, lateral **propterygium** and a long medial **metapterygium,** extending

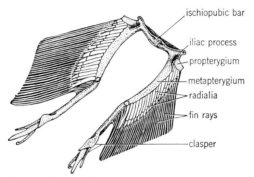

ischiopubic bar

iliac process

propterygium

metapterygium

radialia

fin rays

clasper

Fig. 2.12.   Pelvic girdle and fin of male *Squalus acanthias.*

posteriorly. Numerous **radialia** extend outward from the basalia. In males, the skeleton supporting the clasper is a continuation of the metapterygium and probably represents a modified radial cartilage. Its distal end is divided into several pieces. Dermal fin rays support the remainder of the fin.

MUSCULAR SYSTEM

The muscular system of the dogfish is rather simple compared with that of higher vertebrates. Nevertheless, it shows certain marked advances over the rather primitive arrangement observed in cyclostomes.

Trunk Musculature

Mark off an area on one side of your specimen extending about 1½ in. anterior and 1½ in. posterior to the first dorsal fin. Make a cut through the skin extending from middorsal to midventral lines. Do not cut too deeply. Grasp the cut edge with the fingers, and strip off the skin in

this region without further use of the scalpel.   If you attempt to cut the
skin from the body by means of a knife, you may slash into the muscles.
The scalpel may be used, however, to loosen any tough strands of connective tissue.

The body wall beneath the skin is composed of muscles.   These are
known as **parietal muscles** as opposed to the **visceral branchial muscles,**
which are located on the ventral surface of the head and in the gill
region.

The parietal muscles are arranged in zigzag bands around the body
(Fig. 2.13).   Each muscular band is known as a **myotome** or **myomere.**

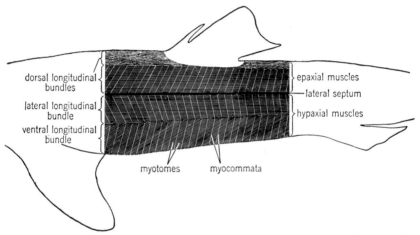

Fɪɢ. 2.13.   Lateral view of portion of body wall of dogfish, *Squalus acanthias,*
showing zigzag arrangement of the myotomes.   The skin has been removed to
show the muscle fibers beneath.

The myotomes are separated from each other by connective-tissue septa
called **myocommata.** Each myotome is made up of many parallel
muscle fibers which run from one myocomma to the next.   A white band
of connective tissue, called the **linea alba,** along the midventral line
separates the myotomes of the two sides of the body.   A tough **lateral
septum,** lying directly beneath the lateral line, separates the myotomes
into dorsal **epaxial** and ventral **hypaxial regions.**

Even though the myocommata take a zigzag course, the muscle fibers
in the myotomes, particularly those in the epaxial region, continue to
run in a longitudinal direction.   The **epaxial muscles** on each side are
arranged in the form of two or three **dorsal longitudinal bundles** extending from the base of the skull to the end of the tail.   They form rather
large muscle masses, used primarily in bending the body from side to
side in swimming.   The **hypaxial muscles** are divided into **lateral** and

ventral longitudinal bundles. The lateral longitudinal bundle lies just ventrad the lateral septum and is attached anteriorly to the scapular process. It is darker than the other muscles. Anterior to the pelvic fins its fibers take a slightly oblique course anteriorly and upward, but posteriorly they course in a horizontal direction. The ventral longitudinal bundle, which in turn is divided into two parts, overlaps the lateral bundle to a slight degree. The ventral longitudinal bundle is attached anteriorly to the ventral region of the pectoral girdle. Its fibers are arranged obliquely in an anteroventral direction. This is indicative of the direction in which the "pull" caused by contraction of the muscle fibers is being exerted. In some elasmobranchs the portion of the ventral longitudinal bundle on either side of the linea alba is further differentiated into a long but narrow **rectus abdominis muscle** in which the fibers are longitudinally arranged.

Branchial Musculature

Remove the skin from the ventral surface of the head and one side of the gill region. If this is done carefully the superficial muscles between the pectoral girdle and eye will be exposed.

The muscles which move the jaws and visceral arches are referred to as **branchial muscles.** They are voluntary striated muscles derived from the splanchnic mesoderm of the hypomere and *not* from myotomes. The branchial muscles begin anteriorly at the mandibular arch and run in series to each of the successive visceral arches. The outer, or superficial, muscles function as **constrictors** of the pharynx. They tend to close the gills and mouth during respiratory movements. There are six dorsal and six ventral constrictors, lying above and below the gills, respectively (Fig. 2.14). Each constrictor is separated from the next by a band of connective tissue, arranged vertically and known as a **raphe.**

In *Squalus acanthias* the dorsal constrictor of the first, or mandibular, arch is a small muscle which lies anterior to the spiracle. It has its origin on the otic capsule and inserts on the palatopterygoquadrate bar. The **adductor mandibulae,** which in elasmobranchs lies outside the angle of the mouth and acts in closing the jaws, is a derivative of the first dorsal constrictor. The first ventral constrictor forms the rather broad **intermandibularis muscle** which originates from a midventral raphe. Its fibers pass forward on either side to insert on Meckel's cartilage. The constrictors of the remaining visceral arches are bounded anteriorly and posteriorly by the gill slits. The second, lying between the first typical gill slit and the spiracle, is a large muscle with rather distinct dorsal and ventral portions which pass anteriorly above and below the jaws. The dorsal portion is known as the **epihyoideus muscle.** It has its origin on the otic capsule and its insertion on the hyomandibular cartilage. The anterior portion of the second ventral constrictor gives rise to the **inter-hyoideus muscle** which is attached to the hyoid arch and lies just above the intermandibularis. The last four constrictors are simply arranged, their dorsal and ventral portions being rather similar in appearance.

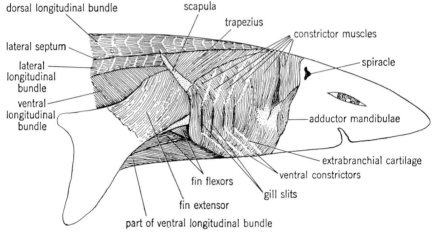

FIG. 2.14. Superficial muscles of shoulder and head of dogfish, *Squalus acanthias*. (*Original by Howell, J. Morphol.,* **54**:401. *By permission of the Wistar Institute of Anatomy and Biology.*)

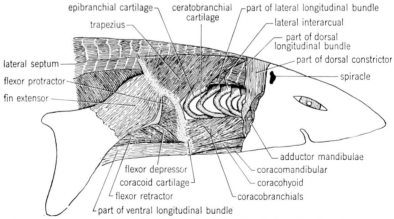

FIG. 2.15. Deeper muscles of shoulder and head of dogfish, *Squalus acanthias*. (*Original by Howell, J. Morphol.,* **54**:401. *By permission of the Wistar Institute of Anatomy and Biology.*)

Other branchial muscles, covered for the most part by the constrictors, serve as **levators** of the visceral arches. The first levator is the **levator maxillae**, which acts in raising the upper jaw. It passes from the lateral surface of the otic capsule to insert on the upper edge of the palatopterygoquadrate cartilage. The second is the levator of the hyoid arch. It lies directly under the epihyoideus. The **trapezius** (**cucullaris**) belongs to the levator group and probably represents the posterior portion of the remaining levators. It originates from dorsal fascia and overlying skin and extends in a ventrocaudal direction to insert on the epibranchial cartilage of the last visceral arch as well as on the ventral portion of the scapula. Four small **lateral interarcual muscles** originate from pharyngobranchial cartilages of visceral arches 3, 4, 5, and 6 and are inserted on the corresponding epibranchial cartilages (Fig. 2.15). Since the trapezius and lateral interarcuales insert on epibranchial cartilages in series, it is believed that they represent specialized portions of a single levator group. The remaining representatives of the branchial musculature include more deeply situated **dorsal** or **medial arcuales**, which connect adjacent pharyngobranchial cartilages. We shall not study the details of the muscles in this region.

Hypobranchial Musculature

In elasmobranchs the hypaxial portions of the first few myotomes posterior to the gill region send buds or branches anteriorly and ventrally to form the **hypobranchial musculature**. The hypobranchial muscles are actually continuations of the ventral longitudinal muscle bundles. They lie in the region between the coracoid bar and the mandible and are dorsal to the intermandibularis muscle. The first of these in *Squalus acanthias* are the paired **common coracoarcuales**, arising from the coracoid bar and inserting on the strong connective tissue comprising the floor of the pericardial cavity. Cut through the intermandibularis along its midventral line, and deflect the cut edges of this muscle. Just above it lies the **coracomandibular muscle** (Fig. 2.15), originating from the fascia at the anterior end of the coracoarcuales and inserting on the symphysis of the mandible. Dorsal to the coracomandibular lie the paired **coracohyoids**, coming from the coracoarcuales and passing to the basihyal and ceratohyal cartilages. At this point it is well to locate the thyroid gland, which is a darkish flattened mass just in back of the central portion of the lower jaw. It lies between the anterior ends of the coracomandibular and coracohyoid muscles. Finally, above the coracohyoids are several **coracobranchial muscles**, which originate from fascia above the coracoarcuales and insert on the ceratohyal and other hypobranchial cartilages.

Appendicular Musculature

One of the most important advances in the muscular system of vertebrates takes place in connection with the appearance of paired appendages first found in the pectoral and pelvic fins of elasmobranch fishes.

During early development, when the myotomes are growing ventrally in the body wall, buds grow out from them into folds from which the pectoral and pelvic fins arise (Fig. 2.16). They develop into the muscles which move the fins. These muscles are, therefore, derivatives of the myotomes of the trunk. Since the muscles are modified to course in different directions, their original metameric arrangement may not be apparent.

Two types of appendicular muscles are generally recognized, *i.e.*, **extrinsic** and **intrinsic**. The former attach the girdle, fin, or limb to the axial skeleton directly or indirectly. They originate in the axial musculature and are inserted on some skeletal element within the limb. Extrinsic muscles serve to move the entire appendage. Intrinsic muscles have both origin and insertion on parts of the limb or fin skeleton itself,

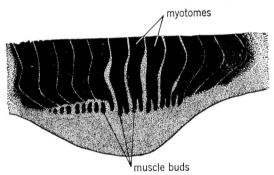

FIG. 2.16. Developing appendage of elasmobranch fish, *Pristiurus*, showing muscle buds arising from the myotomes. (*After Rabl.*)

serving to move parts rather than the appendage as a whole. Actually, the distinction between extrinsic and intrinsic muscles in fishes is not of too great importance, since the appendicular muscles are all derived from myotomes. In *Squalus acanthias* the extrinsic muscles are well defined, but intrinsic muscles are poorly developed. Remove the skin from both sides of a pectoral and a pelvic fin. It is more desirable to study the musculature of the pelvic fin in a female, since the muscles associated with the clasping organ in the male may confuse the relationships. The dorsal, or extensor, muscle of the pectoral fin consists of a single sheet, some fibers of which have their origin on the scapula while others originate from the fascia covering the hypaxial myotomes. These fibers insert, respectively, on the propterygium and on the distal radialia and connective tissue covering the dermal fin rays. Other fibers originate from fascia covering the medial surface of this sheet and all three of the basal cartilages. They also insert on the radialia and connective tissue covering the fin rays. The ventral, or flexor, musculature of the pectoral fin is more elaborately developed. It makes up the anterior and ventral parts of the fin and consists of three divisions, all of which originate from various regions of the pectoral girdle. The **flexor protractor** inserts on the anterior border of the propterygium. The **flexor depressor** passes to the anterior half of the mesopterygium and to the radialia and dermal fin rays distal to it. The **flexor retractor** inserts on the posterior half of the mesopterygium and on all the metapterygium.

The various intrinsic muscles are grouped so as to move the pectoral fin in different directions.

The muscles moving the pelvic fins are also divided into dorsal, or extensor, and ventral, or flexor, groups. The dorsal muscle consists of superficial and deep portions. The superficial portion originates from the connective-tissue fascia of the hypaxial myotomes and from the iliac region of the pelvic girdle; the deeper portion originates from the metapterygium. Both insert on the radialia and connective tissue covering the dermal fin rays. The ventral muscles likewise form two masses, one originating from the ventral side of the ischiopubic bar and linea alba and passing to the metapterygium, the other originating on the metapterygium and inserting on the radialia and dermal fin rays. Complications are introduced in the pelvic musculature of male elasmobranchs because of the presence of clasping organs.

COELOM

Place your specimen in a dissecting pan with the ventral side up. Again locate pectoral and pelvic girdles by feeling for them with the fingers. Now make a median ventral incision extending from the cloaca to a point about 2 in. posterior to the pectoral girdle. It will be necessary to cut through the pelvic girdle to do this. Next make a cut through the angle of the mouth on the right side, cutting through the cartilages in this region. Continue the cut through the center of the external gill slits and through the pectoral girdle, and then swing over to the midline to meet the midventral incision previously made. Deepen the cut in the gill region so that it extends into the mouth, pharyngeal, and esophageal cavities. Be careful to watch the angle at which your scalpel is directed, otherwise you may cut into the pericardial cavity in which the heart lies. When you cut into the esophagus it will be necessary to sever the proximal part of the right gonad in order to make the incision as directed. The abdominal viscera and gills are now exposed for identification and study.

The **body cavity**, or **coelom**, in *Squalus acanthias* is actually composed of two cavities: the **pleuroperitoneal**, or **abdominal**, **cavity**, in which the abdominal viscera are located; and the **pericardial cavity**, in which the heart lies. A muscular and membranous partition, the **septum transversum,** almost completely separates the two. The pericardial cavity is not to be exposed at this time. It will be studied in connection with the dissection of the heart (page 54).

Inside the pleuroperitoneal cavity it will be noted that the body wall is lined with a smooth, shiny membrane, the **parietal peritoneum.** Reflected over the surface of the viscera is the **visceral peritoneum.** The parietal peritoneum and the visceral peritoneum, which covers the alimentary canal, are connected to each other along the middorsal line of the abdominal cavity by a **dorsal mesentery.** This is actually a two-layered sheet, continuous dorsally with the two halves of the parietal peritoneum. The relationships of these layers are indicated in Fig. 2.17.

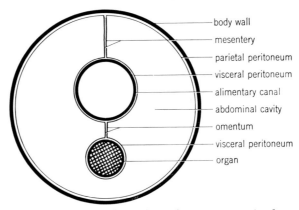

FIG. 2.17. Diagram showing relationship of a mesentery and an omentum to parietal and visceral peritoneum.

With the differentiation of the alimentary tract into various regions, appropriate names are applied to certain portions of the dorsal mesentery. Thus, the term **mesogaster** is used to denote the part of the dorsal mesentery which supports the stomach. A **ventral mesentery** connecting the gut with the ventral body wall is usually present during developmental stages. This, however, disappears before long in most cases. In some regions a part of the alimentary canal is connected to an adjacent organ or part by a mesenterylike band of tissue, called an **omentum.** The names of the various omenta are indicative of the structures which they connect. In the spiny dogfish the following mesenteries and omenta should be noted as the various visceral organs are identified:

1. The **mesogaster,** suspending the stomach from the middorsal wall of the coelom.
2. The **mesentery proper,** supporting the intestine.
3. The **mesorectum,** supporting the rectal gland and large intestine.

4. The **gastrosplenic omentum,** from stomach to spleen.
5. The **gastrohepatoduodenal omentum,** roughly divided into two parts:
    (*a*) the **hepatoduodenal** portion, extending from liver to duodenum, and
    (*b*) the **gastrohepatic** part, joining stomach to liver and duodenum. The
    bile duct and certain blood vessels course through the hepatoduodenal
    portion.

The gonads, which project into the body cavity, are suspended from
the dorsal body wall by two-layered membranes similar to the mesentery
of the gut. Those supporting the ovaries are called **mesovaria;** those
suspending the testes are **mesorchia.**

DIGESTIVE SYSTEM

Without cutting any further, identify the various parts of the digestive
system.

The **teeth,** previously mentioned, have no roots but are closely united
to the tissue covering the jaw cartilages. This is the **acrodont** method
of tooth attachment. All the teeth are similar in shape, the dentition,
therefore, being of the **homodont** type. The teeth are arranged in rows,
each functional tooth having behind it a series of reserve teeth. If a
tooth is lost or destroyed, it is replaced by a reserve tooth. Since re-
placement may take place an indefinite number of times, the dentition is
said to be **polyphyodont.**

The **mouth,** or **oral cavity,** lies just within the borders of the jaws. On
its floor lies the immovable **tongue,** supported by the cartilaginous **hyoid
arch.** Posterior to the mouth is the **pharynx** with six pairs of openings
to the outside. The first pair, called the **spiracles,** are rounded openings
on the dorsal side. The five pairs of **internal gill slits** open laterally.
The **visceral arches,** which support the gills, bear numerous projections,
the **gill rakers.** These serve to strain out food particles, which are thus
prevented from entering the gill chambers.

The posterior end of the pharynx (Fig. 2.18) is constricted and enters
the short **esophagus** which leads directly to the **cardiac end** of the
stomach. This is a large J-shaped structure, the shorter limb of which,
known as the **pyloric end,** terminates in a muscular thickening called the
pylorus, or **pyloric valve.**

The location of the pyloric valve marks the beginning of the **small
intestine.** The first part, called the **duodenum,** is only a short tube which
connects posteriorly with the remainder of the small intestine. This is
a rather wide, straight structure, the surface of which shows a spiral line
which marks the point of attachment of the **spiral valve,** located within
this portion of the small intestine.

A finger-shaped **rectal gland** opens into the intestine by means of a

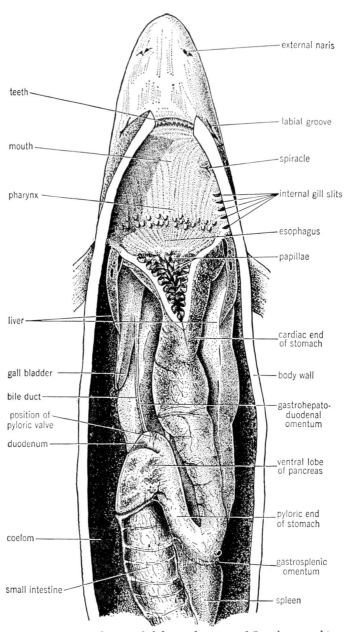

FIG. 2.18.   Ventral view of abdominal viscera of *Squalus acanthias.*

duct. Its function apparently is to remove large amounts of sodium chloride from the blood (J. W. Burger and W. N. Hess, 1960, *Science*, **131**:670). Homology of the rectal gland with the caecum of higher forms is doubtful. The point at which the duct of the rectal gland enters the intestine marks the division between **small** and **large intestines**. The narrow large intestine is very short. It opens through the **anus** into the **cloaca**. The terms large and small intestine may seem ambiguous here. They are used, however, because of their homologies with similarly named structures of higher forms in which the large intestine is of greater diameter than the small intestine.

The **liver** of *Squalus acanthias* is very large. It consists of elongated right and left lobes and a small **median lobe**. The **gall bladder**, easily recognized because of its greenish tinge, is embedded along the entire length of the median lobe of the liver on its right side. The **bile duct**, or **ductus choledochus**, leaves the gall bladder at its *anterior* end, passes posteriorly through the hepatoduodenal omentum to the dorsal side of the duodenum, and then courses through the duodenal wall for some distance before entering the cavity of the duodenum. Make a longitudinal slit in the gall bladder and, by using a probe, determine the point where the bile duct leaves it.

The **pancreas** is a whitish organ composed of two lobes lying in the bend where the stomach joins the duodenum. The **dorsal lobe** is long and narrow, lies dorsal to the pylorus, and extends as far posteriorly as the spleen. It is connected by a short **isthmus** to the rounded and flattened **ventral lobe**, which lies just below the duodenum. The **pancreatic duct** is small in diameter. It leaves the posterior margin of the ventral lobe to enter the wall of the duodenum, through which it courses for almost an inch before opening in the duodenal cavity.

Although the **spleen** is an organ belonging to the circulatory system, it forms such a conspicuous part of the abdominal viscera that mention should be made of it here. It is a dark triangular structure, loosely attached to the posterior bend of the stomach, where cardiac and pyloric portions join by means of the **gastrosplenic omentum**.

Note again the mesenteries and omenta found in association with the digestive system and listed on pages 42 and 43.

The next thing to be studied is the lining of the digestive tract. Continue posteriorly the cut already made in the ventral wall of the anterior end of the esophagus. As far as possible confine your incision to the midventral line. When you come to the region of the duodenum, cut the omentum connecting the ventral lobe of the pancreas with the stomach. It will then be noted that in the ventral part of the duodenal region the dorsal and ventral lobes of the pancreas are connected by a narrow isthmus. Cut through the isthmus, separating the two lobes from each other. The duodenum will now be exposed so that a mid-ventral incision can easily be made. The cut should lie between the two lobes of the pancreas. The small intestine should now be slit carefully so as to expose the spiral valve. Cut through the intestinal wall, but not too deeply. Then grasp the cut edges with the fingers and pull them apart gently. Continue the midventral incision to the cloaca.

The digestive tract often contains partially digested food and other debris. Take your specimen to the sink and wash out the contents of the digestive tract under running water.

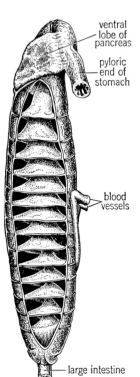

ventral lobe of pancreas

pyloric end of stomach

blood vessels

large intestine

FIG. 2.19. Small intestine of *Squalus acanthias* cut open to show spiral valve. (*Drawn by J. Dohm.*)

The lining of the esophagus and upper portion of the stomach, commonly called the **cardiac end,** bears numbers of posteriorly directed **papillae,** which tend to prevent the contents of the stomach from passing back into the pharynx and mouth. Farther back, the lining of the stomach is thrown into rather heavy **longitudinal folds.** The size of the folds varies with the degree to which the stomach is contracted. In a stomach gorged with food the longitudinal folds may disappear temporarily.

Note carefully the thickened muscular wall at the junction of stomach and duodenum. This is the **pyloric valve,** mentioned above. It is actually a sphincter muscle. Now examine the structure of the **spiral valve,** confined to that portion of the small intestine beyond the duodenum (Fig. 2.19). It is arranged in the manner of a spiral staircase. Determine the number of turns that it takes. The spiral valve serves to retard the passage of food through the small intestine, thus facilitating the completeness of the digestive processes and affording a large surface for secretion of enzymes and absorption of the products of digestion.

Now find the ducts of the pancreas, gall bladder, and rectal gland. Be able to demonstrate these, and the points where they open into the alimentary canal, to the instructor. Both pancreatic and bile ducts course for some distance in the intestinal wall. They may often be seen by holding the portion of the duodenal wall in question up to the light. It may be necessary to scrape off some of the epithelial lining of the duodenum in order to see these ducts clearly. The pancreatic duct, which leaves the ventral lobe of the pancreas, is usually hidden by the first fold of the spiral valve.

RESPIRATORY SYSTEM

Turn back the floor of the mouth which you had cut previously, and examine the gills and gill region.

Respiration in the dogfish is carried on entirely by means of vascular **gill lamellae.** Except for the almost vestigial lamellae of the pseudo-branch in the spiracle (page 48), which receives oxygenated blood, the gill lamellae are supplied with unoxygenated blood which takes oxygen from the water bathing them and gives off carbon dioxide.

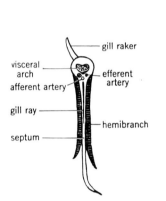

Fig. 2.20. Diagram showing structure of elasmobranch gill.

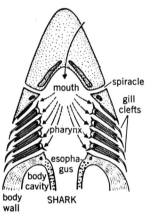

Fig. 2.21. Respiratory mechanism of dogfish shark (diagrammatic). Arrows indicate direction of water currents. (*From Storer, "General Zoology," Mc-Graw-Hill Book Company, Inc. By permission.*)

There are six pairs of **gill pouches,** the **spiracles** being considered as the first pair. The gills are made up of rows of lamellae which radiate from the membranous covering of the cartilaginous bars known as **visceral arches** (Figs. 2.20 and 2.21). The gills are supported by numerous cartilaginous **gill rays** which extend from the visceral arches into the **interbranchial septa.** Each interbranchial septum thus contains a single visceral arch at its base, with its respective gill rays. The **hyoid arch** is present anterior to the second gill pouch (first typical gill slit). It bears gill lamellae on its posterior surface only. Just as in the lamprey, such a single set of lamellae, or **half gill,** is termed a **hemibranch.** An entire gill, or **holobranch,** is made up of two hemibranchs enclosing between them an interbranchial septum. In *Squalus acanthias* there are nine hemibranchs but only four holobranchs on each side. Thus the last gill pouch bears lamellae only on its anterior wall. Nevertheless, there are five cartilaginous visceral arches posterior to the hyoid arch. No lamellae are associated with the last visceral arch. **Gill rakers** project into the pharynx from the inner surfaces of the visceral arches, including the last.

The gill lamellae of the dogfish (Fig. 2.20), unlike those of the lamprey, are closely attached to the interbranchial septa. The septa, however, extend laterally past the outer edges of the lamellae and are continuous with the skin, helping to form the protecting flaps which guard the external openings of the gill pouches.

Water, taken into the mouth, passes through the internal gill slits, bathes the lamellae, and then passes out of the external gill slits. Since the vestigial lamellae in the spiracle receive blood that has already been oxygenated, they form what is sometimes called a **pseudobranch, or false gill.**

UROGENITAL SYSTEM

Since in the dogfish, as in all vertebrates, the organs of reproduction and those for the elimination of nitrogenous wastes are so closely related to each other, they will be considered together.

The Male

The **opisthonephric kidneys** form a pair of long, strap-shaped bodies lying against the dorsal body wall above the parietal peritoneum on both sides of the median line. The dorsal aorta and postcardinal veins lie between them. The kidneys extend almost the entire length of the body cavity. Each opisthonephros is composed of an anterior, slender portion, the **cranial opisthonephros,** and a posterior, thicker **caudal opisthonephros** (Fig. 2.22). The posterior part is apparently the chief functional excretory organ of the adult animal.

The testes are rather small, pale bodies lying dorsal to the anterior part of the liver, each one being attached to the middorsal body wall by a double peritoneal fold, the **mesorchium.** A few small, delicate ducts, the **efferent ductules,** course through the mesorchium, connecting the tubules of the testes with certain anterior kidney tubules of the cranial opisthonephros. Since the cranial opisthonephros is concerned more with transportation of sperm than with excretion, it is sometimes referred to as the **epididymis.** It may be homologized with a portion of the epididymis (caput epididymis) of higher forms.

A large **archinephric duct** extends along the entire ventral face of the kidney. In mature males its anterior portion is highly convoluted.

The tubules of the opisthonephros connect with the archinephric duct which has the dual function of serving for the passage of both urinary wastes and spermatozoa.

In the region of the caudal opisthonephros the archinephric duct straightens out and is considerably enlarged. This portion is referred to as the **seminal vesicle.** Each seminal vesicle opens at its posterior end into a ventrally situated **sperm sac,** the cavities of the two sperm sacs uniting medially to form the **urogenital sinus.** This is the space inside the small **urogenital papilla,** which projects into the cloaca. The urogenital sinus opens to the outside at the tip of the papilla. Slit open one of the sperm sacs and remove the white **seminal fluid** with which it is filled and which contains great numbers of **spermatozoa.** Probe for the opening of the seminal vesicle where it enters into the sperm sac.

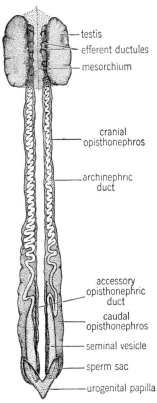

testis

efferent ductules

mesorchium

cranial opisthonephros

archinephric duct

accessory opisthonephric duct

caudal opisthonephros

seminal vesicle

sperm sac

urogenital papilla

Accessory opisthonephric ducts are also present in the caudal opisthonephros. They lie just dorsal to the seminal vesicles and enter the sperm sacs through minute pores near the openings of the seminal vesicles. Two or three of these fine, threadlike ducts are often present. To find the main accessory duct, cut through the parietal peritoneum along the lateral edge of the caudal opisthonephros on one side of the animal. Carefully strip off the peritoneum from the ventral surface of the kidney in this region. Now gently elevate the seminal vesicle from the kidney tissue. The accessory duct will be found as a fine, threadlike structure immediately dorsal to the seminal vesicle.

Fig. 2.22. Ventral view of urogenital organs of mature male *Squalus acanthias.*

Squalus acanthias is an ovoviviparous species with internal fertilization. Copulation is accomplished by means of clasping organs (Fig. 2.5), which are modifications of the medial portions of the pelvic fins of males, used for transport of spermatozoa. Each clasper is provided with a median groove, the middle portion of which actually serves as a closed tube, since the edges overlap in the manner of a scroll. The anterior opening into the clasper is termed the **apopyle;** the posterior exit is the **hypopyle.** Spermatozoa enter the apopyle, which is situated close to the cloaca. In sharks and dogfish a sac, the **siphon,** with heavy muscular walls lies just beneath the skin in the posterior, ventral, abdominal region. Its anterior portion ends blindly, but posteriorly it communicates with the apopyle. Look for the siphon sac in your specimen. It is located near the midline at the posterior end of the abdomen. Its cavity may have been exposed when you made the midventral incision. The cavity of the siphon sac may easily be recognized by its ochre-yellow color. Make a longitudinal slit from one end of the siphon sac to the other. Find the opening which communicates with the apopyle, and insert a probe into the opening. Determine the point at which the probe emerges.

Direct observations indicate that the siphon is used with some force in the ejection of spermatozoa. Under normal conditions the apopyle is open, and sea water is drawn into the siphon sac. The clasper tube gradually fills with spermatozoa. During the copulatory act the clasper is bent in such a manner as to close the apopyle. Contraction of the siphon sac forces water down the clasper tube, ejecting the spermatozoa already there through the hypopyle into the uterus of the female.

It is probable that during copulation only one clasper is inserted into the cloaca of the female. This has been noted during observation of copulation of *Scyllium,* another dogfish, in an aquarium. The coition lasted for 20 minutes. Motion pictures of rays, taken during the act of mating, have also revealed that but a single clasper is inserted at a time. Unqualified data are lacking, however; the difficulty of observing such a process under natural conditions is obvious.

The Female

The opisthonephric kidneys of the female are similar to those of the male, with narrow cranial portions and larger caudal regions. Since the archinephric duct of the female serves only for the passage of urinary wastes, it is smaller than that of the male. It courses in a straight line along the ventral face of the kidney. An accessory duct is also usually present in the caudal opisthonephros of the female. Accessory ducts and archinephric ducts course posteriorly to enter the **urinary sinus** within the small, median, **urinary papilla** which projects into the cloaca. Strip the peritoneum from the ventral side of the opisthonephros in the same manner as with the male, and look for archinephric and accessory opisthonephric ducts. These are usually much more difficult to find in the female than in the male because of their more slender character.

The ovaries of a mature female are lobulated bodies, located dorsally on either side of the anterior end of the body cavity (Fig. 2.23). The lobulated character of the surface of the ovary is due to the presence of large eggs, located in sacs called **ovarian,** or **Graafian, follicles.** These cannot be observed grossly in immature females in which the ovaries are small, smooth-walled structures. Each ovary is attached to the dorsal body wall by a peritoneal fold, the **mesovarium.** On the midventral line and near the anterior end of the body is a folded, rather loose membrane with a single longitudinal slit, the **ostium tubae,** on its *dorsal* aspect. The ostium tubae leads to a short duct which soon divides into right and left portions. These **oviducts, or Mül-**

lerian ducts, extend dorsolaterally and then posteriorly. Vestiges of the ostium and oviducts can be observed even in males of this species. At their anterior ends the oviducts are narrow tubes. A short distance posteriorly each bears a slight enlargement, the **shell gland,** which secretes a thin membrane over the eggs as they pass down the oviduct. The oviducts become narrow again as they pass posteriorly but then suddenly enlarge to form the **uteri.** The cavity of each uterus opens into the cloaca on either side of the pointed median urinary papilla. This region of the cloaca is often termed the **urogenital sinus,** and the openings of the uteri are spoken of as the **genital openings** or **pores.** The large mesenterylike membranes which suspend the oviducts and uteri of mature females are known as **mesotubaria.** In immature females* the oviducts are slender tubes coursing along the ventral face of the opisthonephric kidneys. No mesotubaria are present during the immature stage.

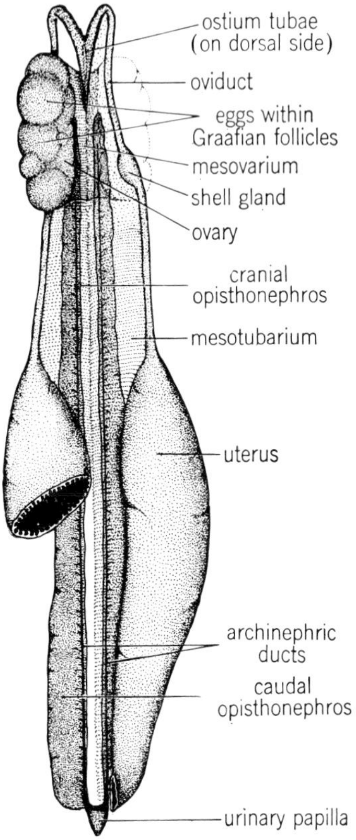

The ovaries are not connected with any duct whatsoever. When the eggs are ripe, they break out of the Graafian follicles, pass through the wall of the ovary, and drop into the body cavity.

Fig. 2.23. Ventral view of urogenital organs of mature, pregnant female *Squalus acanthias.* One ovary is shown only in outline, and part of one uterus has been removed in order to expose structures lying dorsal to them.

They make their way passively to the anterior end and are engulfed by the ostium tubae. Passage down the right or left oviduct seems to be a matter of chance. Spermatozoa in the upper reaches of the oviduct

---

* In the event that immature females are supplied for dissection, a group of several students should have a pregnant female available for study of the mature reproductive system.

fertilize the eggs as they pass through this region. Development of the embryos takes place in the uterus. In *Squalus acanthias,* which is **ovoviviparous,** a beautifully clear, amber-colored, temporary, membranous **shell** at first surrounds several eggs in the uterus. The shell is secreted by the shell gland. The eggs undergo early development within the shell. At about the time that the transient external gills of the embryo are being absorbed, the shell breaks down. Numerous villuslike folds develop in the lining of the uterus during pregnancy. They are in close contact with blood vessels in the yolk sac of the embryo, and an exchange of metabolic substances takes place between the circulatory systems of the mother and her developing young.

ENDOCRINE SYSTEM

It is not convenient at this point to locate all the organs belonging to the endocrine system, since several of them are found in close relation to parts not yet studied. They will, however, be mentioned at appropriate places in the following pages. Nevertheless, it is convenient to describe them here in order that the student may refer to them as a group.

Gonads. The ovaries and testes of *Squalus acanthias* have already been studied in connection with the urogenital system. In addition to their gamete-producing function, the gonads are endocrine glands, secreting **sex hormones** of primary importance in regulating the development and function of the **accessory sex organs** and **secondary sex characters.** The actual endocrine elements of the gonads cannot be discerned in gross dissections. Furthermore, the tissues responsible for secretion of sex hormones in fishes are not known with certainty.

Pancreas. The gross structure of the pancreas was studied in connection with the digestive system. As in the case of the gonads, the pancreas serves a dual function. In its relation to the digestive tract it functions as an exocrine gland, pouring its pancreatic-juice secretion, which is rich in digestive enzymes, into the duodenal portion of the intestine. The endocrine tissue of the pancreas consists of numerous groups of special cells, the **islands of Langerhans,** scattered throughout its substance. These have no ducts, and the secretion which they produce enters the blood-vascular system directly. It is necessary to study sections of the pancreas under the microscope in order to observe the islands of Langerhans.

Thyroid gland. The thyroid gland of *Squalus acanthias* is a rather dark, flattened mass of tissue lying in the floor of the mouth just posterior to the middle of the cartilage of the lower jaw, or symphysis of the mandible. It will be observed later on, when the circulatory system is studied, just anterior to the point where the ventral aorta bifurcates into the first pair of afferent branchial arteries.

Parathyroid glands. Some small bodies in the pharyngeal region of the dogfish may represent parathyroid tissue, but this has not been determined with certainty.

Adrenal glands. Two sets of structures in elasmobranchs represent the homologues of the cortical and medullary portions of the adrenal glands of mammals. The first of these, the **interrenal bodies,** homologous with the adrenal cortex of mammals, lie between the posterior ends of the opisthonephric kidneys. In the dogfish they consist of an unpaired mass of tissue, which in the living animal has a yellowish color. The **chromaffin bodies,** homologous with the adrenal medulla in mammals, are small paired masses located on the intersegmental branches of the dorsal aorta on either side of the vertebral column. Some of the anterior bodies may be elongated and united. Their close relationship to the sympathetic ganglia is evident in elasmobranchs.

Pituitary gland. The pituitary body, or gland, will be studied after the brain has been removed from the skull. It is a conspicuous structure, attached to the ventral side of the diencephalon and lying just posterior to the optic chiasma. In the center is the **infundibulum** with its laterally placed **inferior lobes.** A thin median stalk extends posteriorly from between the inferior lobes and expands dorsally to form the thin-walled **saccus vasculosus.** This is found only in aquatic animals and may possibly have a sensory function associated with life in the water. Attached to the ventral side of the saccus vasculosus is the **hypophysis,** or **pituitary gland.** The **posterior lobe** of this structure in the dogfish is diffuse and cannot be identified readily. The pituitary gland lies in a depression of the skull called the **sella turcica.**

Thymus gland. The actual existence of thymus tissue in elasmobranchs is far from clear. Some authorities claim that small masses of tissue derived from all except the first pair of pharyngeal pouches represent thymus tissue. It is doubtful whether the thymus possesses an endocrine function.

Pineal body. The **epiphysis,** or **pineal body,** consists of a slender stalk extending upward from the posterior portion of the diencephalon. Whether it is an endocrine organ is doubtful. In specimens of *Squalus acanthias* prepared for dissection by biological supply houses, the pineal body is frequently destroyed when a hole is made in the cranium to permit formaldehyde to enter the cranial cavity in order to preserve and harden the brain.

CIRCULATORY SYSTEM

A special specimen in which certain parts of the circulatory system have been injected with colored latex should be available for study of the circulatory system. In such specimens the tail has been partially severed and the arterial system injected through the caudal artery.   An incision through the ventral body wall has usually been made in order to inject the hepatic portal vein and its tributaries.   If this procedure has been followed, the heart and the afferent branchial arteries leading from the heart to the gills will remain uninjected, since the injected latex cannot pass through vessels of capillary dimensions.

The Heart

As removal of the heart from the injected specimen would seriously interfere with a complete study of the circulatory system, at least at this stage, it is better first to study the heart in your old specimen and then, after having determined its relations, to return to the injected specimen for a complete study of its arterial and venous connections.

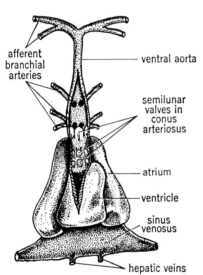

afferent branchial arteries

ventral aorta

semilunar valves in conus arteriosus

atrium

ventricle

sinus venosus

hepatic veins

FIG. 2.24. Ventral view of heart of dogfish, *Squalus acanthias.* The ventricle and conus arteriosus have been cut open to show the arrangement of the semilunar valves in the conus.

If previous directions have been followed, the skin should have been removed from the ventral and left sides of the head and gill region. Layer by layer, carefully remove the muscles between the pectoral girdle and mandible until the pericardial sac is exposed. Now cut through the pectoral girdle in the middle and continue the midventral incision forward, being careful not to injure any of the underlying vessels. The cavity thus exposed is the pericardial cavity. It is roughly triangular in shape and is almost completely filled by the heart. Trim away the tissue comprising the ventral wall of the pericardium so as better to observe the heart.

Dorsal to the posterior end of the heart is a rather large opening which leads posteriorly into a short passage running along the ventral side of the esophagus for a distance of about 1 in. This is the **pericardio-peritoneal canal** which connects the pericardial and pleuroperitoneal, or abdominal, cavities. The heart itself (Fig. 2.24) is made up of a series of parts, of which only two, the **atrium** and **ventricle**, are considered to be **true chambers**.

The sinus venosus is the most posterior part. It is a thin-walled, triangular structure extending transversely across the posterior wall of the pericardial cavity to which it is attached. On either side a large **Cuvierian sinus (duct of Cuvier, common cardinal vein)** opens into the sinus venosus. Posteriorly two **hepatic veins** bring blood to the sinus venosus from the liver. The cavity of the sinus venosus connects to the atrium through a **sinuatrial opening** which is guarded by a **sinuatrial valve.** This consists of two folds continuous with the lining of the atrium. They are so arranged that blood can pass freely into the atrium but cannot pass in the opposite direction because of closure of the valves.

The **atrium** is a large thin-walled sac. It contains but a single cavity which opens ventrally through an **atrioventricular opening** into the ventricle. The opening is guarded by the **atrioventricular valve.**

The **ventricle** is relatively small in size but has heavy muscular walls, since it propels blood to all parts of the body. **Tendinous cords** within the ventricle are attached to the opposite walls. They prevent the ventricle from expanding beyond its capacity.

The cavity of the ventricle is continuous with that of the **conus arteriosus.** This is a short, muscular tube, the cavity of which is triangular in cross section. Inside the conus arteriosus are three sets of **semilunar valves** to be observed later. Anterior to the conus arteriosus and continuous with it is the **ventral aorta** from which arise the **afferent branchial arteries** which distribute blood to the gills. Blood passes through the parts of the heart in the following sequence: sinus venosus, atrium, ventricle, conus arteriosus. When it enters the ventral aorta from the conus arteriosus, it has entered the arterial system.

Clean away the muscles and connective tissue around the conus arteriosus and ventral aorta until they are clearly exposed. The ventral aorta bifurcates at its anterior end a short distance posterior to the mandibular arch. Look for the **thyroid gland,** previously described, in this vicinity.

Blood Vessels

Blood vessels which carry blood away from the heart are called **arteries;** those bringing it back to the heart are called **veins.** Whether a blood vessel carries oxygenated or unoxygenated blood has nothing to do with the terminology. Arteries are stronger and their walls are more muscular than veins. In birds and mammals, particularly those with long extremities, many of the medium-sized veins of the forelimbs and hind limbs are provided with paired **semilunar valves** on the inner walls. They prevent backflow of blood in the veins and are generally located distal to the point where a tributary enters a larger vessel. In the dogfish many of the veins are primitive structures and are more properly called sinuses. Arteries and veins are connected by minute capillaries.

Arterial System

Five pairs of **afferent branchial arteries** leave the ventral aorta. Trace each of these out toward the gills for some distance. The first two arise from a common trunk formed on each side by a bifurcation of the ventral aorta. The more anterior of the two supplies the hyoid hemibranch; the second goes to the first holobranch, thus supplying the second and third hemibranchs. The third afferent branchial artery, which is easily located, comes off the ventral aorta at a point approximately one-third of the distance from the conus arteriosus. It supplies the second holobranch composed of hemibranchs 4 and 5. The last two afferent branchial arteries arise from the ventral aorta near its junction with the conus arteriosus. Sometimes they arise independently, but they frequently spring from a common trunk. These arteries are more difficult to find than the others, since they are embedded in the muscular tissue just dorsal and lateral to the anterior end of the conus arteriosus. They supply the third and fourth holobranchs, respectively. Since no gill lamellae are present on the posterior wall of the last gill pouch, no vessel from the ventral aorta supplies this region.

After having traced each of these vessels to a point about 1 in. from its origin, loosen them from adjacent tissues and remove the entire heart and ventral aorta with the afferent branchial arteries attached. Place in a finger bowl of water. It will be necessary to cut through the Cuvierian sinuses and hepatic veins in order to free the heart.

Make windows in atrium, ventricle, and sinus venosus by cutting away a small portion of the wall of the heart in each region. Examine the sinuatrial and atrioventricular openings and valves. Slit the conus arteriosus longitudinally and examine it under a binocular dissecting microscope to identify the three sets of **semilunar valves**. They are usually seen best if the conus arteriosus is covered with water. Consult Fig. 2.24 in order to aid in their identification. Each consists of three pocketlike structures. The anterior set is located at the front of the conus, and its three components are larger than those of the others.

Now take your injected specimen and remove the skin from the ventral side of the head and gill region. Expose the heart as before but DO NOT REMOVE IT. Before proceding further consult Fig. 2.25 in order to understand the location of the **hypobranchial arteries**. Now trace each afferent branchial artery on the animal's left side to its distal end, being careful to avoid damaging the hypobranchial arteries. The latter have been injected with latex and are easily distinguished from the uninjected afferent branchial arteries.

After having completed this part of your dissection make a midventral incision through the body wall as before and cut through the gill region on the animal's **right** side as in the uninjected specimen. This will leave the entire left side intact for dissection and determination of the relationships between afferent and efferent branchial arteries.

Within the gill lamellae the afferent branchial arteries branch into minute, thin-walled capillaries. It is here that blood takes oxygen from the water and gives off carbon dioxide.

Carefully remove the mucous membrane from the roof of the mouth and pharynx and find four **efferent branchial arteries** which receive blood from the gills. The blood vessels in the gills are essentially intra-arterial capillaries connecting the afferent branchial arteries with branches of the efferent branchial arteries. Trace the efferent branchial arteries out toward the gills as far as possible, cutting away thin slices of cartilage as you go in order to expose them clearly. Note that at the dorsal border of each internal gill slit each efferent branchial artery is formed by the union of a small **pretrematic artery** and a much larger **posttrematic artery.** The capillaries within the lamellae of a given hemibranch combine to form a single vessel which is called a pretrematic or posttrematic artery, depending upon whether the hemibranch is on the anterior or posterior wall of the *gill pouch.* In this manner each interbranchial septum is found to carry both a pretrematic and a posttrematic artery (Fig. 2.25). Several large **cross connections** are present between these vessels. Blood in the pretrematic artery draining the ninth hemibranch passes entirely through cross connections into the posttrematic branch of the fourth efferent branchial artery. The efferent branchial arteries bend posteriorly and then unite in the middorsal line to form the **dorsal aorta.**

Next turn your attention to the arteries in the head region. These are rather complex in arrangement. From about the middle of the first pretrematic artery arises a large **afferent spiracular artery** which courses dorsally under the skin to supply the pseudobranch, or rudimentary gill lamellae, of the spiracle. This artery may best be found by removing the skin from an area immediately posterior to the spiracle, where it occupies a rather superficial position. For some reason the afferent spiracular arteries often remain uninjected. An **efferent spiracular** (**spiracular epibranchial**) **artery** carries blood away from the spiracle. It courses in an anteromedial direction, giving off an **ophthalmic** (**optic**) **artery** to the eyeball, and then joins the **internal carotid artery** described below. From the *ventral* end of the first efferent branchial loop, or the point where the pretrematic and posttrematic branches of the first efferent branchial artery join each other ventrally, a small vessel arises and passes forward for a short distance in the lower jaw. This is the **external carotid artery,** sometimes referred to as the **mandibular artery.**

Just before the pretrematic and posttrematic branches of the first efferent branchial artery unite *dorsally,* the pretrematic artery gives off a conspicuous **hyoidean epibranchial artery** which passes toward the midline. It is joined by a small vessel, the **radix of the aorta** which springs from the first efferent branchial artery near its junction with the

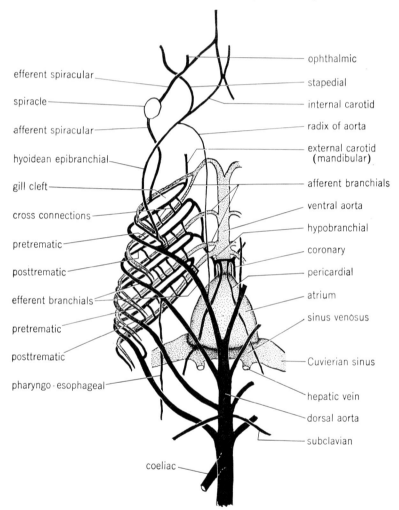

efferent spiracular

spiracle

afferent spiracular

hyoidean epibranchial

gill cleft

cross connections

pretrematic

posttrematic

efferent branchials

pretrematic

posttrematic

pharyngo-esophageal

coeliac

ophthalmic

stapedial

internal carotid

radix of aorta

external carotid
(mandibular)

afferent branchials

ventral aorta

hypobranchial

coronary

pericardial

atrium

sinus venosus

Cuvierian sinus

hepatic vein

dorsal aorta

subclavian

FIG. 2.25. Diagram showing arteries in the left gill region of *Squalus acanthias* as seen from the dorsal side. The length of the arteries at the anterior end has been exaggerated for the sake of clarity. Capillary connections between afferent and efferent arteries have been omitted. (*Modified from Daniel.*)

dorsal aorta. Soon after receiving the radix the hyoidean epibranchial gives off a branch, the **stapedial artery,** which passes to the region where the hyomandibular cartilage joins the otic region of the cranium. The continuation of the hyoidean epibranchial is the **internal carotid**

artery. The internal carotids of the two sides come together in the midline, penetrate the skull through a foramen, and then diverge. Each internal carotid is soon joined by the efferent spiracular artery, mentioned above, and continues forward to the brain.

On each side of the roof of the mouth and pharynx is a **pharyngo-esophageal artery.** It arises from the second efferent branchial artery not far from the point where the pretrematic and posttrematic branches join and supplies the dorsal region of the pharynx and esophagus.

From the *ventral* ends of the second and third efferent branchial loops, where pretrematic and posttrematic arteries join, vessels are given off which soon unite to form a **hypobranchial artery** on each side. There is some variation in this region among different specimens. Each hypobranchial artery courses posteriorly, ventral to the pharynx and visceral arches. As it reaches the level of the anterior end of the conus arteriosus it divides into two branches. The more dorsal branch, the **pericardial artery,** courses through the pericardium, supplying its walls, and continues on to the esophagus and adjacent tissues. The proximal parts of the pericardial arteries of the two sides are united *dorsal* to the conus arteriosus by a transverse vessel. The ventral branch of the hypobranchial artery on each side is the **coronary artery** which supplies the wall of the ventricle of the heart itself.

Now direct your attention to the dorsal aorta in the region where it is joined by the efferent branchial arteries. It courses straight backward to the tail, where it is continued as the **caudal artery.** Numerous paired and unpaired arteries come from the dorsal aorta. The first paired arteries are the **subclavians,** which arise from the aorta between the junction of the third and fourth pairs of efferent branchial arteries (Fig. 2.25). Each subclavian gives off a small **lateral artery,** which passes posteriorly along the body wall underneath the lateral line. This artery lies close to the skin. It will be necessary to remove some of the muscles of the body wall in order to expose it. A **ventrolateral artery** comes from the subclavian at a level about halfway between the lateral line and midventral line and extends posteriorly. Beyond the point where the ventrolateral artery comes off, the subclavian continues into the pectoral fin as the **brachial artery.**

Numerous paired **parietal arteries** arise along the whole length of the aorta to supply the body wall. Many small **renal arteries** likewise arise from the aorta in the region of the opisthonephric kidneys to supply these structures with oxygenated blood. At the level of the pelvic fins a pair of **iliac arteries** comes from the aorta. A branch from each iliac extends anteriorly to anastomose with the ventrolateral artery mentioned above.

Four unpaired arteries (Fig. 2.26) arise from the dorsal aorta to supply the abdominal viscera. The first and largest of these is the

coeliac artery, which comes from the aorta a short distance posterior to the subclavian arteries at a level with the anterior end of the body cavity. Near its origin the coeliac gives off branches which supply the esophagus, the cardiac end of the stomach, and the gonads. It then

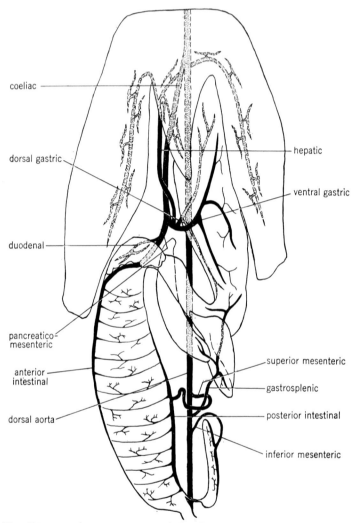

coeliac

dorsal gastric

hepatic

ventral gastric

duodenal

pancreatico-
mesenteric

anterior
intestinal

dorsal aorta

superior mesenteric

gastrosplenic

posterior intestinal

inferior mesenteric

Fɪɢ. 2.26. Diagram showing portion of the dorsal aorta and its unpaired branches which supply the viscera of *Squalus acanthias,* ventral view.

continues for some distance before it again branches. The coeliac artery enters the gastrohepatic omentum and branches into three main arteries: (1) the **gastric,** which soon divides into **dorsal** and **ventral branches** supplying the stomach; (2) the small **hepatic artery,** which courses anteriorly along the bile duct to supply the liver; (3) the large **pancreaticomesenteric artery**, which passes along the dorsal side of the pyloric valve, giving off branches to the pyloric region of the stomach and to the pancreas. A **duodenal branch** supplies the duodenum, but the main vessel continues along the *right side* of the small intestine, where it is known as the **anterior intestinal artery**. This vessel gives off branches corresponding to the places of attachment of the spiral valve.

The second and third unpaired arteries arise from the aorta close together just posterior to the level of the spleen. The more anterior of the two is the **superior mesenteric artery**, which courses along the *left side* of the small intestine as the **posterior intestinal artery** and gives off branches at the points of attachment of the spiral valve. The **gastrosplenic artery** arises just posterior to the point of origin of the superior mesenteric artery. It crosses the latter and extends anteriorly to supply the spleen and lower end of the stomach. The last unpaired branch of the aorta is the **inferior mesenteric artery**, which arises somewhat anterior to the iliac arteries to supply the rectal gland. Occasionally two inferior mesenteric arteries are encountered.

Venous System

Systemic veins. The systemic veins (those returning blood to the heart from the body proper) of the dogfish are, for the most part, spaces in the tissues without definite walls and are generally referred to as **sinuses.**

Although, in dissecting, it is more convenient to trace the veins from the sinus venosus as a starting point, the direction of blood flow toward the sinus venosus should be constantly kept in mind. All the systemic veins of the dogfish ultimately drain into the sinus venosus. Make a *transverse* cut in the ventral wall of the sinus venosus. Take your specimen to the sink and wash out any blood contained within it. Examine the inside of the sinus venosus and note the openings of the two **hepatic veins** along its posterior border, one on either side of the midline. Insert probes into the hepatic veins, directing them posteriorly, and note that they enter the liver. Now follow the probes by cutting into the liver substance. The large cavities thus exposed are the **hepatic sinuses.** Each sinus extends posteriorly almost the entire length of the liver lobe.

Beginning at the lateral boundary of the pericardium and curving in a dorsal direction around the esophagus is a lateral continuation of the sinus venosus on either side, known as the **Cuvierian sinus, duct of Cuvier,** or **common cardinal vein.** Continue the transverse cut previously made in the sinus venosus into the *left* Cuvierian sinus. Several large veins enter this structure. Identify these vessels and probe for their openings. Consult Fig. 2.27. From the head region on each side come two main sinuses: a smaller, median, ventral, **inferior jugular sinus** and a large dorsolateral **anterior cardinal sinus.** The inferior jugular drains blood from the floor of the mouth, the region ventral to the visceral arches, and the pericardial region. The anterior cardinal sinus lies dorsal to the visceral arches. It receives blood from the **postorbital sinus,** which lies between the posterior border of the eye and the first hemibranch. The postorbital sinus is in communication with the large **orbital sinus** which encircles the eye. An **interorbital canal,** which lies in the floor of the skull, connects the posterior borders of the two orbital sinuses. It does not lend itself well to dissection. A **hyoidean sinus,** located just in front of the hyoidean hemibranch, connects the anterior cardinal and inferior jugular sinuses.

Now direct the probe into the left **postcardinal sinus.** This enters the posterolateral part of the Cuvierian sinus through a large opening, being joined as it does so by the anterior cardinal sinus. Lift up the viscera on the left side of the body and note that the probe has entered a large sac at the anterior end of the abdominal cavity. This is the postcardinal sinus. The posterior portion of the postcardinal sinus swerves toward the midline. Make a longitudinal slit in the postcardinal sinus, remove the probe, and wash out the contents of the sinus in running water. Examine the inner surface and note that the postcardinal sinus communicates with its partner on the right side by means of a rather large aperture. A large **genital sinus,** which drains the gonad on each side, connects with the postcardinal sinus by means of **genital** (**ovarian or spermatic**) **veins** along its ventrolateral aspect.

Between the kidneys lies a pair of **postcardinal veins.** These receive

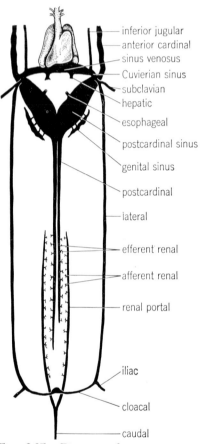

inferior jugular
anterior cardinal
sinus venosus
Cuvierian sinus
subclavian
hepatic
esophageal

postcardinal sinus

genital sinus

postcardinal

lateral

efferent renal

afferent renal

renal portal

iliac

cloacal

caudal

Fig. 2.27. Diagram of systemic veins and renal portal system of *Squalus acanthias*, ventral view.

blood from **efferent renal veins** in the opisthonephric kidneys. Each postcardinal vein courses straight forward to enter the postcardinal sinus. It receives, en route, small, intersegmental **parietal veins** from between the myotomes.

On the inner surface of the body wall on either side, a large **lateral vein** courses anteriorly and enters the Cuvierian sinus. It receives small intersegmental **parietal veins** from between the myotomes along its length. Each lateral vein is formed posteriorly by the union of a **cloacal vein** from the cloacal region and an **iliac vein** from the pelvic fin. The cloacal veins from the two sides join each other in the midline. Slit open the lateral vein in this region and probe for the iliac and cloacal veins. Anteriorly each lateral vein is joined by a **subclavian vein** formed by the union of a **brachial vein** from the pectoral fin and a **subscapular vein** from the pectoral girdle.

Portal systems. A portal system of veins is one which begins in capillaries and again breaks up into capillaries before the blood which it contains reaches the heart. In *Squalus acanthias* there are two portal systems, the **renal portal** and the **hepatic portal.** A third portal system associated with the pituitary gland has been described for some vertebrates.

Renal portal system. In the renal portal system the venous blood collected from the tail passes through a network of capillaries in the opisthonephric kidneys. In order to locate the caudal and renal portal veins, cut off cleanly near its base what remains of the tail of the dogfish. Examine the cross section of the caudal vertebra thus exposed. Two vessels will be observed, enclosed by the hemal arch. The upper one is the **caudal artery;** the more ventral one is the **caudal vein.** Insert a probe in the caudal vein and direct it anteriorly. Dissect away the tissue ventral to the probe, following the probe to the abdominal cavity. At about the middle of the cloacal region the caudal vein divides into right and left **renal portal sinuses** (Fig. 2.27). Trace these forward with the aid of the probe and determine the relations of the renal portal veins to the kidneys. They lie dorsolateral to the opisthonephric kidneys, giving off small **afferent renal veins** to these structures. **Efferent renal veins,** which join the postcardinal veins, collect the blood after it has passed through the capillaries in the kidneys.

Hepatic portal system. The hepatic portal system of veins drains the various parts of the digestive tract and spleen. The hepatic portal vein of the spiny dogfish is formed by the converging of four vessels (Fig. 2.28). The first of these is the very small **duodenal vein,** often poorly injected. It courses along the lower end of the bile duct, draining the duodenum, the anterior part of the small intestine, and the ventral lobe of the pancreas. A large **gastric vein** on the left drains the main part of the stomach by means of **dorsal** and **ventral gastric branches.** The large **lienomesenteric vein** drains the rectal gland and the left side of the small intestine, where it is known as the **posterior intestinal vein.** This vessel receives branches from the places of attachment of the spiral

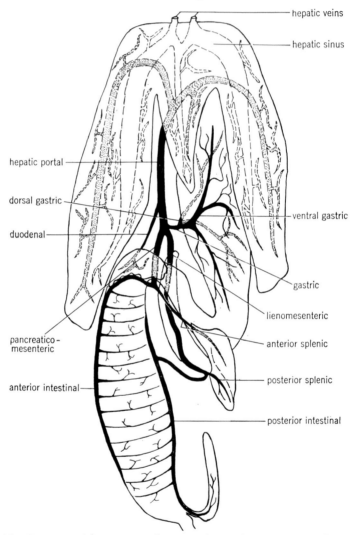

FIG. 2.28. Diagram of hepatic portal vein and its tributaries in *Squalus acanthias,* ventral view.

valve. It is joined by a **posterior lienogastric vein (posterior splenic)** from the posterior end of the spleen and the adjacent stomach region. The main part of the lienomesenteric vein passes through the dorsal lobe of the pancreas, receiving **pancreatic veins** en route. The large

pancreaticomesenteric vein is formed by an **anterior intestinal vein,** draining the right side of the small intestine and points of attachment of the spiral valve, and an **anterior lienogastric vein (anterior splenic)** from the anterior end of the spleen and the gastrosplenic omentum.

The large **hepatic portal vein** enters the liver, where it ultimately branches into innumerable capillarylike **sinusoids.** The blood is collected by small veins, which join **hepatic sinuses,** finally entering the sinus venosus of the heart through the **hepatic veins** previously observed.

Review the entire circulatory system of the spiny dogfish and understand the manner in which blood is carried to and from the gills. Be able to trace the course of blood anywhere in the body.

NERVOUS SYSTEM

A large, separate dogfish head should be provided to be used entirely for study of the brain, spinal cord, cranial nerves, the more anterior spinal nerves, and the major sense organs. The dissection is delicate and requires considerable patience. Care should be taken not to cut or tear away any of the cranial nerves or branches. The opening usually present in the top of the head of preserved specimens has been made deliberately to permit formaldehyde to enter the cranial cavity in order better to preserve the brain. The **epiphysis,** or **pineal body,** is generally destroyed when the opening is made.

In this dissection the brain and spinal cord should be completely exposed. However, confine your dissection of the cranial and spinal nerves to the *right* side. This will leave the olfactory capsule, eye, and inner ear on the *left* side intact for further detailed study of these sense organs. If the instructor prefers, the sense organs may be studied in the uninjected or injected specimens previously dissected.

First remove the skin from the dorsal side of the head and as far laterally as the external gill slits. The most superficial of all the cranial nerves is the **hyomandibular branch** of the **facial nerve (VII).** Expose this nerve first so as to be sure not to destroy it inadvertently. It lies immediately posterior to the spiracle.

Next remove the muscles of the head in the vicinity of the chondrocranium and cut away thin slices of cartilage until the brain is exposed. It will be necessary to destroy the inner ear on the right side in this dissection. Details of ear structure should be noted for future reference, however. Watch carefully for **cranial nerves,** some of which course through the dorsal part of the orbit. Refer to Figs. 2.29 and 2.30. Be particularly careful not to destroy the very slender **trochlear nerve (IV).** Find this nerve but do not clear away the surrounding tissues until the dissection is almost complete. The trochlear nerve emerges from the posterodorsal part of the mesencephalon, or optic lobes, and passes through a foramen on its way to the superior oblique eye muscle which it innervates.

Dorsal Aspect of Brain
(Fig. 2.29)

The brain of *Squalus acanthias* is made up of three main parts: the **forebrain,** or **prosencephalon;** the **midbrain,** or **mesencephalon;** and the **hindbrain,** or **rhombencephalon.**

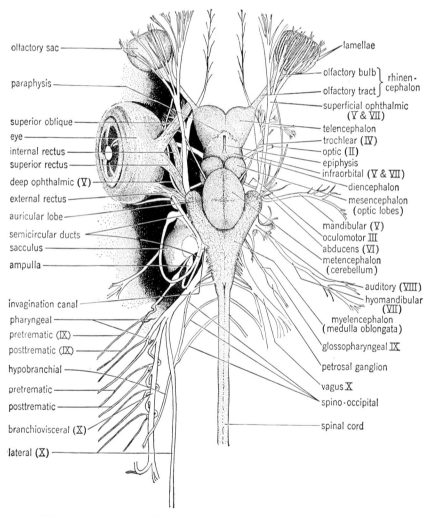

FIG. 2.29.   Dorsal view of brain, sense organs, and cranial nerves of *Squalus acanthias.*

The prosencephalon has two main divisions. The first is the **telencephalon,** the anterior part of which is the **rhinencephalon,** composed of **olfactory lobes.** These lie immediately behind the **olfactory sacs.** The cavity of each olfactory sac opens to the outside through the **nostril,** or **naris.** Its inner wall contains a number of folds called **lamellae.** The rhinencephalon on each side is composed of an **olfactory bulb,** connected at its anterior end with the olfactory sac, and a narrow **olfactory tract** which extends posteriorly to the cerebral hemisphere. The bulb and tract together constitute the **olfactory lobe.** The paired **cerebral hemispheres** make up the rest of the telencephalon. The rounded an-

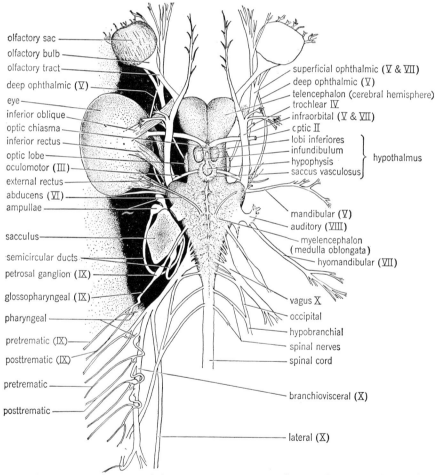

Fig. 2.30. Ventral view of brain, sense organs, and cranial nerves of *Squalus acanthias.*

terior portion of each is sometimes called the olfactory lobe. Posterior to the telencephalon lies the second portion of the forebrain, the **diencephalon**, or **thalamencephalon**. It is roofed over by a thin vascular membrane, the **tela choroidea**. Vascular folds of the tela choroidea extend into the cavity, or third ventricle, below, forming the **anterior choroid plexus**. A flattened fold, the **paraphysis**, anterior to the anterior choroid plexus, extends dorsally, overlapping the cerebral hemispheres to some extent. Its function is unknown. From the posterior dorsal portion of the diencephalon a slender stalk extends upward. This is the **pineal body**, or **epiphysis**, referred to above, which has probably been destroyed in your specimen.

The mesencephalon comes next in order behind the diencephalon. Its roof is called the **optic tectum**. This appears in the form of two rounded **optic lobes**, or **corpora bigemina**, which are centers for the visual sense.

The anterior part of the rhombencephalon is referred to as the **metencephalon**. Its dorsal part consists of a large, oval-shaped structure, the **cerebellum**. This partially overlaps the mesencephalon in front. The remaining portion of the hindbrain, which is also partly covered by the cerebellum, is the **myelencephalon**, or **medulla oblongata**. A pair of prominent, irregular projections, the **auricular lobes** (**restiform bodies**), is present at the anterior end of the medulla oblongata on the dorsal side. These are actually parts of the metencephalon, although several authors regard them as parts of the medulla oblongata. They serve as equilibratory nerve centers, correlating muscular movements in relation to impulses arising in sensory nerves connected with the inner ears. The inner ears of elasmobranchs are primarily organs of equilibration. Posteriorly the myelencephalon tapers down to connect with the **spinal cord**, or **myelon**, which extends back to the tail. The medulla oblongata is roofed over by a thin, vascular **tela choroidea**. Folds of the tela choroidea extend into the cavity, or fourth ventricle, below, to form the **posterior choroid plexus**.

The ventral aspect of the brain (Fig. 2.30) will not be studied at this point. After all the cranial nerves have been identified and a practical examination on this material has been given, the brain will be removed and its ventral surface studied in detail (page 74).

Summary

    I. Prosencephalon (forebrain)
        A. Telencephalon
            1. Rhinencephalon (olfactory lobes)
            2. Cerebral hemispheres
        B. Diencephalon ('tween brain)
    II. Mesencephalon (midbrain)

III. Rhombencephalon (hindbrain)
   A. Metencephalon (cerebellum)
   B. Myelencephalon (medulla oblongata)
IV. Myelon (spinal cord)

Cranial Nerves

Although it is usually stated that there are ten pairs of cranial nerves in the dogfish, there are actually eleven. The most anterior of these, the **terminal nerve (O)**, is often omitted from descriptions. The distribution of the cranial nerves is of interest, since it is similar to that of higher vertebrates except for certain portions which are associated with the aquatic mode of life.

The **terminal nerve (O)** in *Squalus acanthias* is rather difficult to find. It is a very small nerve coursing along the entire medial side of the olfactory tract. Although a pair of terminal nerves has been found in representatives of all classes of vertebrates except cyclostomes and birds, it is best developed in the elasmobranch fishes. It is a **sensory nerve** bearing one or more ganglia. Its function is not clear.

The **olfactory nerve (I)** on each side is composed of a great number of separate fibers so small that they can scarcely be seen by the unaided eye. In their aggregate they are known as the olfactory nerve. The fibers are located in the lamellae of the olfactory sac and terminate in the olfactory bulb, mentioned previously. The olfactory nerve is a **somatic sensory nerve.**

The **optic nerve (II)** is a large white cord which has its origin in the retina of the eye. It passes through the various coats of the eye to the ventral side of the diencephalon. The fibers of each optic nerve cross to the opposite side of the brain. In doing so they form an X-shaped figure, the **optic chiasma.** The fibers terminate in the optic lobes. The term **optic tract** is the name given to the portion of the nerve between the chiasma and the optic lobe. The optic nerve is generally referred to as a **special somatic sensory nerve.** Since the retina of the eye is derived in the embryo from a lateral extension of the diencephalon, the optic nerve really should not be included in the category of cranial nerves. Unlike other cranial nerves, it grows from one part of the brain to another and thus is actually a **fiber tract** of the brain.

The **oculomotor nerve (III)** is usually thought of as a **somatic motor nerve.** Actually it carries some **preganglionic autonomic fibers** as well as a few **somatic sensory proprioceptive fibers.** The nerve arises from the ventral surface of the mesencephalon. It passes into the orbit, where it divides into four branches going to the inferior oblique and the superior, inferior, and internal rectus eye muscles. Its distribution is indicated in Fig. 2.34. The autonomic fibers enter the eyeball via a small **ciliary branch.**

The **trochlear nerve** (**IV**) is primarily a **somatic motor nerve** which, like the oculomotor, bears a few **proprioceptive somatic sensory fibers.** It emerges from the posterodorsal side of the mesencephalon where that part of the brain joins the cerebellum. The trochlear nerve passes into the orbit to innervate the superior oblique eye muscle.

The **trigeminal nerve** (**V**) is a **mixed nerve,** being composed of **somatic sensory** and **visceral motor fibers.** It comes from the lateral side of the medulla oblongata along with the seventh and eighth cranial nerves. These nerves at their bases are inextricably fused. The trigeminal nerve has three main branches: **ophthalmic, mandibular,** and **maxillary.** The ophthalmic branch is divided into **superficial** and **deep** portions.

The fibers of the **superficial ophthalmic** and those of the similarly named branch of nerve VII are inseparably intermingled. They pass forward along the inner wall of the eye socket, or orbit, above the muscles of the eyeball. The trigeminal nerve supplies sensory fibers to the skin. The facial fibers innervate the ampullae of Lorenzini and pores of the lateral-line system on the dorsal surface of the snout. The superficial ophthalmic nerve bears only **somatic sensory fibers.**

The **deep ophthalmic** (**profundus**) passes between the superior and external rectus muscles, sending a **ciliary branch** to the eye, and then continues forward along the inner surface of the eyeball. It leaves the orbit through a foramen and joins the superficial ophthalmic branch, being distributed along with it to the dorsal and lateral surfaces of the snout. The deep ophthalmic is entirely a **somatic sensory nerve.**

The **mandibular branch** of the trigeminal nerve runs along the posterior wall of the orbit. It passes ventrally and innervates the skin of the lower jaw as well as the muscles of the mandibular arch, including the levator maxillae, adductor mandibulae, and the first superficial ventral constrictor. It contains both **somatic sensory** and **visceral motor fibers.**

The fibers of the **maxillary branch** run together with those of the **buccal branch of nerve VII.** Together they form the large **somatic sensory infraorbital nerve,** a broad white band extending forward on the floor of the orbit. Near the anterior part of the orbit the infraorbital nerve divides into three main branches. The smallest and most lateral of these passes to the skin lateral and anterior to the eye. The largest and most medial branch courses forward toward the tip of the snout. The middle branch, composed of numerous rather short fibers, passes to the angle of the mouth. The easiest way to identify these branches is to remove the skin from the ventral surface of the snout and to note their superficial distribution. The fibers of the maxillary nerve innervate the skin on the ventral surface of the snout. Those of the buccal nerve supply the infraorbital lateral-line canal and ampullae of Lorenzini in the same region.

The trigeminal nerve should be thought of as the nerve of the mandibular, or first visceral, arch, from which both upper and lower jaws are derived. The large **Gasserian ganglion** of the trigeminal nerve lies in the mass of tissue from which the trigeminal, facial, and auditory nerves arise lateral to the medulla oblongata.

The **abducens nerve (VI)**, the origin of which will not be observed until the ventral surface of the brain is studied, is, like the other nerves going to the eye muscles, a **somatic motor nerve** carrying a few **proprioceptive somatic sensory fibers**. It emerges from the ventral side of the medulla oblongata and runs forward and laterally to enter the orbit, where it supplies the external rectus eye muscle.

The **facial nerve (VII)**, part of which in its distribution is closely associated with the trigeminal nerve, contains **somatic sensory, visceral sensory,** and **visceral motor fibers**. It has three main branches, the first two of which are composed only of somatic sensory fibers supplying the lateral-line system and ampullae of Lorenzini. The **superficial ophthalmic branch,** as previously noted, courses with the similarly named branch of nerve V. The **buccal branch,** together with the maxillary branch of nerve V, forms the large **infraorbital nerve.** These branches of the seventh nerve are not present in higher vertebrates, having disappeared in the course of evolution with emergence of life from water to land. A third branch, the **hyomandibular,** which contains fibers of the facial nerve alone, bears a **geniculate ganglion** at its base. It is the nerve of the second, or hyoid, arch, distributed to the side of the head immediately behind the spiracle. It is a mixed nerve supplying somatic sensory fibers to the mandibular and hyomandibular lateral-line canals as well as to the ampullae of Lorenzini in this region, and visceral motor fibers to the superficial constrictor muscles of the hyoid arch. Visceral sensory fibers are also supplied to the lining of the mouth by means of a small **palatine branch** which comes from the geniculate ganglion. It passes to the roof of the mouth, giving off a branch to the spiracle.

The **auditory nerve (VIII)**, which is purely **somatic sensory,** connects to the lateral side of the medulla oblongata along with the roots of nerves V and VII. It is a short nerve extending from the inner ear to the brain. Branches come from the ampullae of the semicircular ducts (page 80) as well as from sacculus and utriculus.

The **glossopharyngeal nerve (IX)**, which is considered to be the most typical of the cranial nerves, is a mixed nerve emerging from the lateral side of the medulla oblongata under the inner ear. It bears a swollen **petrosal ganglion** a short distance from the brain. Beyond the ganglion it divides into three main branches. The first, or **pretrematic (hyoid),**

branch is a **visceral sensory nerve** supplying the first hemibranch. The second, or **posttrematic (branchial), branch** is composed of **visceral sensory** and **visceral motor fibers**. The sensory fibers are distributed to the second hemibranch and the motor fibers to the muscles associated with the third visceral arch. The third, or **pharyngeal, branch,** containing **visceral sensory fibers** alone, goes to the lining of the pharynx. Another small branch, sometimes called the **supratemporal nerve** and composed of **somatic sensory fibers,** passes from the petrosal ganglion through the auditory capsule to the supratemporal lateral-line canal and anterior part of the lateral line proper.

The **vagus nerve (X)** is a **mixed** nerve, consisting of a large trunk which arises from the lateral edge of the medulla oblongata by a number of roots. The vagus soon gives off a large **somatic sensory lateral (dorsal) branch** which passes under the main lateral-line canal to the tail. The vagus proper continues as the **branchiovisceral nerve** to supply the remaining four gill pouches and the viscera. Four **branchial branches** come off this nerve to supply the last four visceral pouches. They course across the floor of the anterior cardinal sinus. Each branchial nerve bears a small ganglion from which arise three branches: a small **visceral sensory pharyngeal branch,** which goes to the lining of the pharynx; an anterior **visceral sensory pretrematic branch,** supplying the anterior hemibranch of the gill pouch; and a **posttrematic branch,** composed of both **visceral sensory** and **visceral motor fibers,** passing to the posterior hemibranch. The visceral motor fibers of the posttrematic branches of the vagus supply the muscles of the fourth to seventh visceral arches in succession. Since no hemibranch is present on the posterior wall of the last gill pouch, the last posttrematic branch passes to muscles in that region. The (branchio)visceral branch continues posteriorly and more deeply to enter the body cavity where it sends branches to the heart, digestive tract, and other viscera. Trace the branch going to the heart. Note that it curves forward, coursing in the inner part of the body wall. Find the point where it enters the heart tissues.

Spinal Nerves

Paired metameric **spinal nerves** come from the spinal cord at regular intervals along its entire length. Each spinal nerve arises from the cord by two **roots, dorsal** and **ventral.** In such lower forms as *Squalus acanthias* the dorsal root carries **somatic sensory, visceral sensory,** and **visceral motor fibers;** the ventral root is composed of both **somatic motor** and **visceral motor fibers.** The ventral root passes through a foramen in the cartilaginous neural arch of the corresponding vertebra and is located somewhat anterior to the dorsal root which passes through the intercalary plate. The two roots then join to form a spinal nerve. Between the point of junction and the foramen through which it emerges, the dorsal root bears a swelling, the **dorsal root ganglion.**

In the region of the *pectoral fin* the third, fourth, fifth, and sixth spinal nerves extend posteriorly and ventrally. When they reach the level of the pectoral girdle, they join each other by means of cross connections to form the **cervicobrachial plexus,** from which branches go to the fins. The seventh to eleventh spinal nerves pass to the level of the fin and then branch. One branch goes to the muscles of the ventral body wall, and the other to the fin.

Each *pelvic fin* is supplied by nine or ten spinal nerves. The most posterior ones may be connected by cross-branches to form the **lumbosacral plexus.**

Between the first typical spinal nerve and the vagus on each side, two or three small roots arise from the medulla oblongata. These are referred to as the **spino-occipital nerves.** Some authorities are of the opinion that they represent the ventral roots of certain anterior spinal nerves, the dorsal roots of which have been taken over by, and incorporated within, the vagus nerve. The roots unite to form the **occipital nerve.** This joins the vagus for a short distance and then diverges from it. It is soon joined by the first two spinal nerves. The **hypobranchial nerve** formed by their union crosses over the branchiovisceral branch of the vagus and then turns ventrally to supply the muscles in the floor of the mouth. It is possible that the hypobranchial nerve is homologous with the twelfth cranial nerve (hypoglossal nerve) of more advanced vertebrates.

Peripheral Autonomic Nervous System

The term *peripheral nervous system* is applied to the nerves and ganglia which are connected with the brain and spinal cord. We have spoken of these as cranial and spinal nerves. Parts of the peripheral nervous system are composed of **autonomic fibers,** which are motor fibers distributed to those parts of the body under involuntary control. This portion of the peripheral nervous system is often referred to as the **peripheral autonomic system.** Its fibers pass to the heart and to smooth muscles and glands all over the body. In higher forms it has been clearly shown that this part of the nervous system is subdivided functionally and anatomically into **sympathetic** and **parasympathetic portions.** These elicit opposite responses. The hypothalamic region of the diencephalon is believed to be the center of control of the autonomic fibers. It is not practicable for the student to make a gross study of the peripheral autonomic fibers of the dogfish. Investigations have shown that both sympathetic and parasympathetic elements are present, but they do not show complexities as do those of higher forms. The sympathetic portion seems to be confined to the abdominal region, there being no cranial sympathetic fibers that have been demonstrated. It is represented anteriorly by a series of consecutive **sympathetic ganglia** on both sides of the middorsal line of the pleuroperitoneal cavity, embedded in the dorsal wall of the postcardinal sinus and the anterior end of the opisthonephric kidney. The ganglia form connections with spinal nerves and are in close association with the chromaffin bodies. The fibers associated with these ganglia have a rather diffuse arrangement, and no true longitudinal sympathetic trunks are evident. Preganglionic para- sympathetic fibers are present in the oculomotor (III), facial (VII), glossopharyngeal (IX), and vagus (X) nerves. Those of the vagus pass to the esophagus and stomach but do not seem to go to the intestine or to the urogenital organs.

Ventral Aspect of the Brain
(Fig. 2.30)

The ventral aspect of the brain of *Squalus acanthias* should not be studied by the student until after the cranial nerves and anterior spinal nerves have been studied. The brain may then be removed and its ventral surface examined.

Cut the spinal cord transversely an inch or two posterior to the brain. Sever each of the cranial and spinal nerves as close to the brain and spinal cord as feasible. Now carefully lift the brain from the cranial cavity. Be particularly careful in loosening from the cranium the region on the ventral side of the diencephalon and mesencephalon. This por- tion of the brain lies in a depression, the **sella turcica**, from which it is loosened with some difficulty. Place the brain, after removal, in a finger bowl of water, and observe the ventral surface.

Certain conspicuous features mark the ventral side of the brain, par- ticularly in the region of the diencephalon. The **optic chiasma** is an X-shaped structure where the two **optic nerves** cross each other on the ventral side of the diencephalon. Fibers from the chiasma pass pos- teriorly and dorsally to enter the optic lobes. They form the **optic tracts.** Posterior to the chiasma the ventral portion of the diencephalon forms a large projection, the **hypothalamus.** In its center is the **infundib- ulum**, with its **inferior lobes** on either side. The narrow infundibulum, which appears as a thin median stalk, extends posteriorly to form a saclike structure, the **saccus vasculosus.** The ventral part of the saccus vasculosus is attached to the small **hypophysis**, or **pituitary gland**, which often breaks off and remains in the sella turcica of the skull when the brain is removed.

The points of origin of two pairs of slender cranial nerves, the **oculo- motor** (**III**) and **abducens** (**VI**), arising from the ventral side of the brain, may be clearly seen on the ventral aspect. The oculomotor nerves emerge from the ventral part of the mesencephalon posterior to the hypothalamus and pass laterally. The abducens nerves emerge from the ventral side of the medulla oblongata near the median line, coursing in an anterolateral direction.

Cavities of Brain and Spinal Cord
(Fig. 2.31)

Slice away the top of the brain very carefully, and examine the cavities within. In the region of the brain the original cavity of the dorsal hollow nerve cord is conspicuously modified to form the large cavities, or ventricles, of the brain. The **lateral, or first** and **second, ventricles** are in the telencephalon. They extend forward as narrow channels through the olfactory tracts into the olfactory bulbs. Posteriorly each lateral ventricle opens by an **interventricular foramen (foramen of Monro)** into the **third ventricle,** which is the cavity within the diencephalon. The third ventricle, as previously noted, is covered by a tela choroidea, vascular folds of which make up the anterior choroid plexus. The cavity within the medulla oblongata is the **fourth ventricle.** It also is covered by a tela choroidea, folds of which form the posterior choroid plexus. In higher vertebrates a narrow canal, the **cerebral aqueduct (aqueduct of Sylvius),** connects the third and fourth ventricles. In *Squalus acanthias* the cerebral aqueduct is much expanded on either side, forming large cavities in the optic lobes. These are known as the **optic ventricles,** or, together, as the **mesocoele.** A large cavity in the cerebellum of the dogfish is called the **metacoele.** It is actually a dorsal continuation of the fourth ventricle. The portion of the fourth ventricle in the medulla oblongata is often referred to as the **myelocoele.** It is continuous posteriorly with the minute **central canal** of the spinal cord.

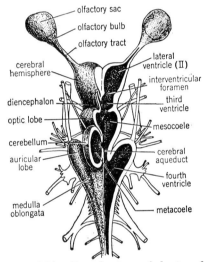

FIG. 2.31. Dorsal view of brain of *Squalus acanthias* with part of wall removed to show the cavities of the brain.

(labels: olfactory sac; olfactory bulb; olfactory tract; cerebral hemisphere; diencephalon; optic lobe; cerebellum; auricular lobe; medulla oblongata; lateral ventricle (II); interventricular foramen; third ventricle; mesocoele; cerebral aqueduct; fourth ventricle; metacoele)

SENSE ORGANS

In addition to such major sense organs as the olfactory apparatus, eye, and ear, fishes possess certain sense organs the functions of which seem to be associated with the aquatic mode of life. These include the lateral-line system and the ampullae of Lorenzini. The latter are to be found only in elasmobranchs.

Ampullae of Lorenzini

Scattered over the surface of the head are numerous small pores which represent the openings of the **ampullae of Lorenzini** (Fig. 2.32). A crystalline mucus may be forced to exude from them if pressure is applied. Each pore leads to a small **canal of Lorenzini,** which terminates in a lobulated, bulblike expansion, the **ampulla,** containing sensory cells. These cells are supplied by delicate nerve strands coming from branches of the facial nerve (VII). The ampullae of Lorenzini have, in the past, been believed to be associated with perception of pressure and vibrations in the water. More recent studies, however, indicate that they may have a thermosensory function.

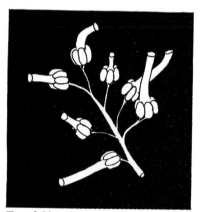

FIG. 2.32. A group of sensory ampullae of Lorenzini.

Lateral-line System

The lateral-line system in *Squalus acanthias* is made up of a number of canals which lie beneath the skin (Fig. 2.33). They open to the surface by numerous **pores.** Sensory receptors, called **neuromasts,** are located in the canals. The **lateral-line proper** extends the length of the body from head to tail. It lies over the lateral septum which separates the epaxial and hypaxial muscles of the body wall. At about the level

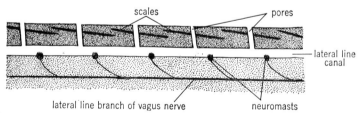

FIG. 2.33. Diagram showing relation of neuromasts to lateral-line canal and lateral branch of vagus nerve, as found in most fishes.

of the spiracles the two lateral canals communicate with each other by a **supratemporal,** or **commissural, canal.** Anterior to this point each canal branches. A **supraorbital canal** runs forward dorsal to the eye; an **infraorbital canal** lies between the eye and the spiracle and runs forward below the eye; a **hyomandibular canal** passes backward from the infra-orbital canal to the hyoid-arch region and ventral surface of the snout; a **mandibular canal** lies in the lower jaw. It is believed that the lateral-line system functions in making the animal aware of deep vibrations in the water and of currents or movements of the water, including those caused by movements of the animal itself.

The neuromasts of the lateral-line proper are supplied by small twigs coming from the lateral branch of the vagus nerve (X); those of the canals of the head region receive their nerve supply from branches of the seventh and ninth cranial nerves.

Olfactory Apparatus

Each naris on the ventral side of the snout opens into a blind pouch, the **olfactory sac.** A flap of skin over the naris directs water in one side and out the other. Inside the olfactory sac are many small plates, or **lamellae,** which are covered by the sensitive olfactory epithelium. The numerous fibers of the olfactory nerve lie embedded in the lamellae. They form synapses with fibers in the olfactory bulb, previously described.

Eye

The eye lies in a socketlike depression in the side of the skull, a concavity referred to as the **orbit.** Cut away the skin from around the eye on the opposite side of the head from that on which you dissected the cranial nerves. Clean away any connective tissue that may be present, and examine the structures in back of the eye in the orbit.

Six eye muscles are attached to the eye and help to keep it in place (Fig. 2.34). Two of these muscles, located at the anterior end and originating from the anterior part of the orbit, are called **oblique muscles.** The **superior oblique** is attached to the anterior dorsal side of the eyeball, the **inferior oblique** being attached to the anteroventral side. Four muscles which have their origin in the posterior part of the orbit are known as the **rectus muscles.** The **superior rectus** is attached to the dorsal side of the eyeball at practically the same place as the superior oblique. The **inferior rectus** passes to the ventral side of the eyeball, inserting at the same point as the inferior oblique. An **external rectus muscle** is attached to the posterior surface of the eyeball at about its center. The **internal rectus** extends most anteriorly of all the rectus muscles. It is attached to the medial side of the eyeball under the superior oblique muscle. A cartilaginous **optic pedicel,** located among the rectus muscles, helps to hold the eyeball in place. The various cranial nerves which supply the eye muscles should be recalled at this time.

Cut away all the eye muscles at their points of origin, and sever the optic pedicel and the optic, oculomotor, trochlear, and abducens nerves, as well as the two ends of the deep ophthalmic branch of the trigeminal nerve. Remove the eye and again examine its surface.

The **conjunctiva** is the outermost covering of the front of the eyeball (Fig. 2.35). It is continuous with the lining of the immovable eyelids and is not included among the true coats of the eye, being but a modification of the epidermal layer of the skin. The outer coat of the eye is the **fibrous tunic.** This is composed of two regions: a posterior, opaque region called the **sclerotic coat,** or **sclera,** and a transparent portion in front of the eyeball, called the **cornea.** The cornea and conjunctiva are

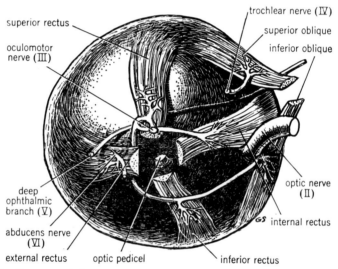

FIG. 2.34. Posteromedial view of left eyeball of *Squalus acanthias*, showing nerve supply to the six eye muscles. (*Drawn by G. Schwenk.*)

fused. Cut a window in the dorsal side of the eyeball in order to examine the inner structure of the eye. Place the eye in a finger bowl of water.

The three coats making up the wall of the eyeball should be evident, particularly in the posterior portion. The outermost coat is the **sclera,** already alluded to. Next to it is the heavily pigmented **choroid coat.** The innermost, greenish-yellow layer is the **retina,** which is often collapsed in preserved specimens. The retina contains the sensory light-receptor cells and is, therefore, the actual sensory portion of the eye. A thickened, vascular portion of the choroid coat, called the **suprachoroid layer,** lies between the choroid and sclerotic coats on the medial aspect of the eyeball. It is present only in those elasmobranchs having an optic pedicel.

Toward the front of the eye the choroid coat and a nonsensory part of the retina separate from the sclera and form a curtainlike structure called the **iris.** In the center of the iris is a round hole, or opening, called the **pupil.** The choroid coat and the nonsensory portion of the retina immediately in back of the iris form a series of radiating folds which make up the **ciliary body** to which the large **crystalline lens** is attached by means of a **suspensory ligament.** Accommodation is accomplished by moving the lens rather than by changing its shape as in higher vertebrates.

The sensory portion of the retina extends forward toward the front of the eye as far as the ciliary body. The irregular border of this part of the retina is called the **ora serrata.** The nonsensory portion of the retina already referred to, which cannot be distinguished in gross preparations, continues forward beyond the ora serrata, covering the posterior surface of the ciliary body and the iris, thus forming a part of both these structures.

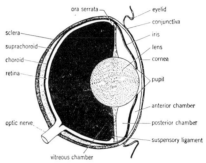

Fig. 2.35. Diagrammatic sagittal section through eye of dogfish.

The **blind spot** may be observed in the posteroventral part of the inside of the eyeball. It is the point of origin of the optic nerve. Sensory light-receptor cells, found in other parts of the sensory portion of the retina, are lacking at the blind spot.

When the dogfish is alive the lens is attached to the ciliary body and to the margin of the pupil. In preserved specimens the attachment is usually broken. The **anterior chamber** of the eye lies between iris and cornea. The small space between the lens and the iris is called the **posterior chamber.** A transparent fluid, the **aqueous humor,** fills the anterior and posterior chambers. The large cavity in back of the lens, the **vitreous chamber,** is filled with a jellylike mass, the **vitreous humor.**

Ear

In fishes there are no external ears or middle ears. Only an **inner ear** is present. The dissection of the inner ear of the spiny dogfish is delicate and requires patience. Locate the opening of the left invagination canal unless this has been destroyed previously. Expose the ear by very carefully removing thin slices of cartilage from the cranium between the invagination canal and the spiracle. Keep a close watch for the appearance of small translucent tubes in the cartilage.

The inner ear of the spiny dogfish (Fig. 2.36A and B) is a delicate membranous structure embedded in cartilage in a set of channels and a rather large central cavity, collectively known as the **cartilaginous labyrinth.** Anterior, posterior, and **horizontal semicircular canals** are present in the cartilaginous labyrinth. Within these canals and central cavity lies the **membranous labyrinth,** consisting of three **semicircular ducts,** each with an ampulla at its lower end, together with a **vestibule** made up of **saccular** and **utricular** regions. The anterior and horizontal ducts join a delicate chamber, the **anterior utriculus,** dorsally. Their ampullae, which are placed close together, also join the anterior utriculus ventrally. Both ends of the posterior canal join a chamber which is considered by some authorities to be a second, or **posterior, utriculus.** The **sacculus** is a pear-shaped structure which lies between the two utriculi. It opens to the top of the head by the **invagination canal** which is *not* homologous with the endolymphatic duct of higher vertebrates as often stated. On the ventral side of the sacculus a blunt projection, the **lagena,** extends posteriorly. The cavities of the sacculus and utriculi communicate with each other by small apertures.

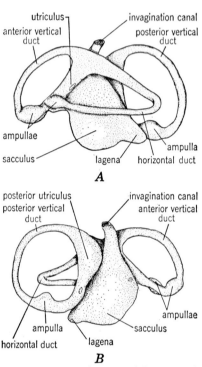

Fig. 2.36. Membranous labyrinth of *Squalus acanthias: A,* lateral view of left ear; *B,* medial view of left ear.

The membranous labyrinth is filled with fluid. This is usually referred to as **endolymphatic fluid,** but it is probable that in elasmobranchs it is composed largely of sea water. Sand grains from the exterior may enter the sacculus through the opening of the invagination canal. These, together with crystals of calcium salts, are gathered together in a rather large, loose mass, the **otolith.** The inner ear of the spiny dogfish is primarily an organ of equilibration, but it is possible that it may play a role in sound reception of a sort (page 31). Movements of the endolymph and the otolith stimulate sensory endings in the ampullae and vestibule, thus informing the animal of its position in the water.

CHAPTER 3

THE MUD PUPPY (*Necturus maculosus*)

Classification:
Phylum: Chordata
Group: Vertebrata (Craniata)
Subphylum: Gnathostomata
Superclass: Tetrapoda
Class: Amphibia
Subclass: Caudata
Order: Proteida
Family: Proteidae
Genus: *Necturus*
species: *maculosus*

NATURAL HISTORY

The mud puppy, or water dog, is a caudate amphibian frequently studied in courses in comparative anatomy as an example of a primitive terrestrial vertebrate. Members of the genus *Necturus* are found throughout North America east of the 100th meridian. *Necturus maculosus* is the most widely distributed species. This large salamander, adult specimens of which vary in length from 11 to 18 in., is commonly found in the Mississippi River system from the Arkansas River and northern Alabama northward into Canada and eastward into the mountainous regions of North Carolina, Virginia, West Virginia, and Pennsylvania. Its range includes the Great Lakes and St. Lawrence River and their tributaries in Manitoba, Ontario, and Quebec; the Hudson River drainage system; and the Susquehanna and Delaware Rivers. *Necturus* spends its entire life in the water and, unlike most amphibians, does not metamorphose, retaining its external gills throughout life. This condition, in which larval characteristics persist during adult life, is referred to as **neoteny.** The neotenic condition is considered to be degenerate rather than primitive. Amphibians which retain their gills throughout life and fail to undergo metamorphosis are called **perennibranchiates.**

Necturus is frequently caught with hook and line by fishermen, many of whom believe the animal to be poisonous. Actually it is harmless.

Even a bite by *Necturus* is of little consequence, since the teeth are small and are not apt to cause skin abrasions.

Necturus feeds on crayfish, worms, and aquatic insects and their larvae. The animal is of little or no economic value, although occasionally it is used as food for human beings. These amphibians are sluggish creatures which usually forage at night.

Fertilization is internal in *Necturus*. In the autumn gelatinous masses of spermatozoa, the **spermatophores**, are deposited by the male on underwater objects. By movements of the lips of the cloaca of the female, the tips of the spermatophores are taken into the cloacal orifice. A saclike mass of tubules, the **spermatheca**, opens into the posterodorsal wall of the cloaca of the female. Here the spermatozoa are stored. In the following spring, as the eggs pass down the oviducts into the cloaca prior to laying, they are fertilized by the stored spermatozoa. Neither amplexus nor copulation occurs in *Necturus* or other salamanders. The eggs, which appear as pale yellow spheres, are deposited individually on the undersides of stones or other submerged objects. Sometimes nests are prepared underwater in a sunny place in the sand. As many as 150 eggs may be laid. They take from 6 to 9 weeks to hatch. At the time of hatching, the larvae measure approximately ¾ in. in length. It takes from 7 to 8 years for the animals to reach maturity, and they may live as long as 23 years or more.

EXTERNAL FEATURES

Obtain a preserved and injected specimen of *Necturus*. Place it in a dissecting pan and observe its external features. If possible, make

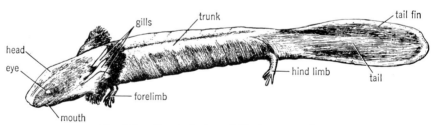

Fig. 3.1.   External view of *Necturus maculosus.*

observations on a living specimen in an aquarium. During life the animal is rusty brown in color and has a mottled appearance.

The body of *Necturus* is somewhat indistinctly divided into three regions: **head, trunk,** and **tail** (Fig. 3.1). Head and trunk are flattened in a dorsoventral direction, but the tail is laterally compressed. It bears a **tail fin** which, unlike the fins of fishes, is not supported by finrays.

The **skin** is smooth, devoid of scales, and very slimy because of the numerous mucous glands which it contains. In preserved specimens the mucus has coagulated, giving the animal a grayish appearance. **Lateral-line organs** are present, even in the adult.

Necturus has two pairs of weak limbs. The **pectoral limbs, or fore-legs,** are divided into **upper arm, forearm, wrist,** and **hand;** the **pelvic,** or **hind limbs** are made up of **thigh, shank, ankle,** and **foot.** Each limb has but four **digits** (fingers or toes), although the five-fingered (penta-dactyl) condition is considered to be primitive. The first digit is the one which has disappeared in *Necturus*. The limbs are used effectively in crawling about on the bottoms of lakes, ponds, and streams. On land, however, they are of little value, since the decreased buoyancy of the body when surrounded by air makes it impossible for the weak limbs to support it for any length of time.

The head contains a **terminal mouth,** bordered by **lips.** The upper jaw extends *over* the lower jaw. A pair of **nostrils,** or **external nares,** lies at the anterior end of the snout. The nostrils are rather far apart. Each communicates with the mouth cavity through an **internal naris** (**choana**). This is an important advance over the condition observed in most fishes, in which the nostrils are nothing more than blind sacs. The **eyes** are relatively small and without lids. No external sign of an ear is present.

Gills are located on either side at the posterolateral border of the head. They are **external gills,** derivatives of the integument, and not homologous with the internal gills of fishes. The gills of *Necturus* number three on each side. Each terminates in a large number of delicate **filaments,** which have a plumelike appearance when extended in the water. As mentioned previously, the gills are retained throughout life. Two **gill slits** are present on each side. They are located between the bases of the first and second and the second and third gills and connect the pharynx with the outside. It is doubtful whether water passes through the gill slits of *Necturus*.

Just in back of the hind limbs on the midventral line is the **cloacal opening,** through which the products of digestion, excretion, and repro-duction pass.

SKELETAL SYSTEM

It is usually impracticable for students to prepare a skeleton of *Necturus* for study. Mounted skeletons should be in the laboratory for observation.

The **bony skeleton** of *Necturus* is primitive but, nevertheless, of a much higher level of organization than that of the shark or dogfish. The skeleton is composed of **axial** and **appendicular** portions. The **axial skeleton** includes the **skull, vertebral column, ribs,** and **sternum;** the **appendicular skeleton** includes the bony framework of the **limbs** and **limb girdles.**

Axial Skeleton

VERTEBRAL COLUMN AND RIBS

The **vertebrae** of *Necturus*, like those of fishes, are typically **amphicoelous,** the **centra** being hollow at either end. The spinal column is composed of four regions: **cervical, trunk, sacral,** and **caudal.** The cervical portion consists of a single vertebra, the **atlas,** which articulates with the skull. Its anterior face bears a pair of small concavities, the **condylar facets,** for reception of the **occipital condyles.** The atlas does not bear ribs.

The trunk vertebrae are all of similar structure (Fig. 3.2). There are usually 17 trunk vertebrae in *Necturus*. Above the centrum is a **neural arch,** which encloses the **neural,** or **vertebral, canal** in which the spinal

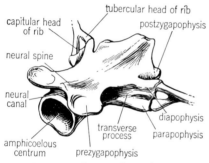
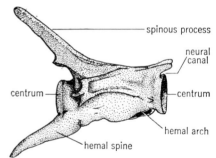

FIG. 3.2.   Trunk vertebra of *Necturus*. (*Drawn by R. Archer and G. Schwenk.*)

FIG. 3.3.   Lateral view of caudal vertebra of *Necturus*.

cord lies. The **neural arch** is composed of two **neural processes** which meet above the neural canal, forming a slight dorsal projection, the **neural spine.** Paired **prezygapophyses** and **postzygapophyses** project from the anterior and posterior ends of the neural arch, respectively. The prezygapophyses of one vertebra articulate with the postzygapophyses of the vertebra immediately anterior to it. **Articular facets** are present on the zygapophyses, those of the prezygapophyses facing upward and those of the postzygapophyses facing downward. A **transverse process** extends laterally from each side of the vertebra. It is composed of two parts, a **diapophysis** coming from the neural arch and a **parapophysis** from the centrum. Small **ribs** are attached to the transverse processes. Each rib is forked, presenting two surfaces for attachment to the vertebra. The upper limb of the fork constitutes the **tubercular head,** the lower limb being the **capitular head.** These articulate with the diapophysis and parapophysis, respectively.

Only one vertebra is usually present in the sacral region, although the actual number of sacral vertebrae shows some variation among different specimens. The ribs of the sacrum are stout structures which are united with the pelvic girdle.

The caudal vertebrae (Fig. 3.3) are numerous. Most of them lack ribs. In addition to the usual parts, the caudal vertebrae bear **hemal arches** on their ventral sides. These are comparable to the neural arches on the dorsal side. The caudal vein and artery are enclosed within the hemal arches. The first caudal vertebrae do not possess hemal arches but may carry rudimentary ribs. Toward the end of the tail the caudal vertebrae become very much reduced.

STERNUM

The origin of the **breastbone,** or **sternum,** in evolution is obscure. According to one theory, the earliest indication of a sternum is to be found in *Necturus,* in which it is referred to as the **archisternum.** This is rather difficult for the student to identify and is usually lost in ordinary skeletal preparations. It consists of a few cartilages which appear in the intermuscular connective-tissue septa (myocommata) in the ventral thoracic region. Fusion of some of the archisternal elements may possibly explain how the sternum of higher forms originated.

SKULL

The **skull** (Figs. 3.4 and 3.5) consists of the **cranium** and **sense capsules,** surrounding and protecting the brain and sense organs, and the **visceral skeleton,** associated in development with the anterior part of the alimentary canal. The skull of *Necturus* is composed partly of cartilage and partly of bone.

During development the cranium is at first cartilaginous and, together with the sense capsules, forms a **chondrocranium** which, although incomplete on the dorsal side, is comparable to the chondrocrania of cyclostomes and elasmobranchs. As development progresses, the cartilage is replaced in part by bones (cartilage bones). Dermal, or membrane, bones, which do not go through a cartilage stage in development, form a roof over the greater part of the chondrocranium. Dermal bones may also cover or invest other parts of the chondrocranium. Such bones are derived from the dermis of the skin and are believed to represent the bony dermal scales of fishes.

The visceral skeleton of *Necturus,* as in *Squalus acanthias,* is at first laid down in cartilage. The first, or **mandibular, visceral arch** becomes divided into an upper **palatopterygoquadrate cartilage** and a lower **Meckel's cartilage.** Although the posterior part of the palatopterygo-quadrate bar is replaced by bone (quadrate bone), the remainder becomes invested by membrane bones. This is also true of Meckel's cartilage. The remaining parts of the visceral skeleton of *Necturus* retain their original cartilaginous character or disappear. In adult animals cartilage bones and membrane bones are not readily distinguishable. Furthermore, in dried skulls even the bony and cartilaginous elements are difficult to tell apart. Soaking the skull in water will often reveal which parts are bony and which are cartilaginous. Where bones are joined to one another, the lines of fusion are referred to as **sutures.**

At the posterior end of the cranium where it articulates with the vertebral column are two **exoccipital bones,** each bearing on its posterior face a protuberance, the **occipital condyle,** which articulates with the **atlas,** or first vertebra. Dorsally the two exoccipitals are separated by a small cartilaginous **synotic tectum** and ventrally by a narrow cartilaginous **basioccipital arch.** The large opening between the two exoccipital bones is the **foramen magnum,** where brain and spinal cord become continuous. Lateral to each exoccipital is an **opisthotic bone,** extending from the dorsal to the ventral side of the skull, articulating dorsally with the **squamosal** and **parietal** and ventrally with the **parasphenoid.** Most of the posterior dorsal part of the skull is covered with a pair of **parietal bones** which meet in the midline. These articulate anteriorly with paired **frontal bones** which partially overlap them. The anterior end of the skull is bordered by two small V-shaped **premaxillary bones** with which the frontals articulate. One limb of the V partly overlaps the frontal. **Teeth** project from the ventral side of the premaxillaries. A **vomer bone** lies posterior to each premaxillary along the lateral margin of the skull. From the anterolateral portion of the opisthotic on each side extends a slender **squamosal bone.** It lies lateral to the parietal and meets the **quadrate** anteriorly. A small **pro-otic** bone is present on each side between the squamosal and parietal. It is separated from the opisthotic by a small cartilage.

On the ventral side of the skull (Fig. 3.5) an unpaired parasphenoid bone extends forward from the exoccipitals. Anteriorly it is flanked on either side by the vomer bone which lies beneath the nasal capsule. The vomer bones bear teeth. A cartilaginous **ethmoid plate** lies anterior to the parasphenoid between the two vomers. A **palatopterygoid** (**pterygoid**) bone passes posteriorly from each vomer. Its anterior portion bears teeth. Posteriorly it articulates with the quadrate. The latter forms a projecting process near the middle of the lateral border of the skull. The quadrate serves as the point of articulation of the lower jaw.

The skull of the mud puppy lacks nasal and maxillary bones. The

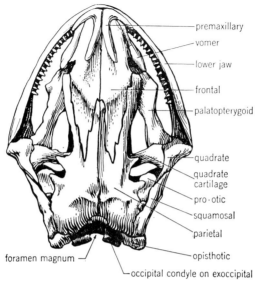

FIG. 3.4. Dorsal view of skull of *Necturus*. (*Drawn by R. Archer and G. Schwenk.*)

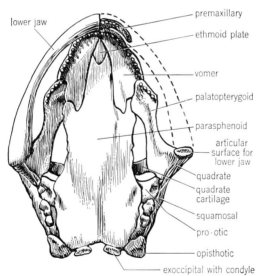

FIG. 3.5. Ventral view of skull of *Necturus*. (*Drawn by R. Archer and G. Schwenk.*)

orbit, which accommodates the eye, is *not* surrounded by bony elements in *Necturus.*

The **lower jaw** of the mud puppy consists of three bones on each side arranged about the cartilaginous core called **Meckel's cartilage.** A **dentary bone** bearing teeth forms the greater part of the outer surface of the anterior end. A small **splenial bone,** also bearing teeth, is located near the middle of the inner surface. The third bone, or **angular,** makes up the greater part of the inner surface. Its posterior end passes below the dentary to the outer surface of the jaw. The posterior end of Meckel's cartilage is expanded. This is the portion of the lower jaw which articulates with the quadrate. The two halves of the lower jaw are rather loosely united in front.

Despite the fact that numerous cartilage bones and dermal bones are present in the skull of *Necturus,* some of the original chondrocranium persists. It is usually not practicable to study separately the chondro-cranial remnants, since it involves removal of the membrane bones. Portions already noted, however, include the synotic tectum, the basi-occipital arch, the ethmoid plate, the small cartilage lying between the pro-otic and opisthotic bones, and Meckel's cartilage of the lower jaw.

The **nasal** and **otic capsules,** which are originally separate cartilages, contribute to the chondrocranium. The nasal capsules are fragile and usually destroyed in preparation of skulls. The cartilaginous otic cap-sules are largely replaced by the pro-otic and opisthotic bones. On the medial side of each otic capsule is a large **foramen** through which blood vessels and nerves pass. A ventrolateral opening is the **fenestra ovalis,** which is plugged by the **stapes bone.** A **columellar process** is attached to the stapes at one end and by means of a suspensor-stapedial ligament to the squamosal bone on the other.

For convenience, the remnants of the chondrocranium, as well as the various cartilage and membrane bones of the skull of *Necturus,* are listed below.

Cartilages	*Cartilage bones*	*Membrane bones*
Nasal capsules	Exoccipitals	Parietals
Ethmoid plate	Pro-otics	Frontals
Synotic tectum	Opisthotics	Vomers
Basioccipital arch	Quadrates	Premaxillaries
Meckel's cartilage	Stapes	Squamosals
		Parasphenoid
		Palatopterygoids (?)
		Dentary
		Splenial
		Angular

The arches which support the gill region of *Necturus* are cartilaginous. A reduction in number, in comparison with the primitive condition, has occurred. The hyoid arch and the three following visceral arches are represented, however (Fig. 3.6).

The **hyoid arch** which lies just in back of the lower jaw consists of two cartilages on each side, a small medial **hypohyal** and a larger, lateral **ceratohyal.** The next visceral arch, often called the **first branchial arch,** is likewise composed of two cartilages, a medial **first cerato-branchial** and a lateral **epibranchial.** Between the ceratobran-chials and hypohyals is a single median **copula,** or **basibranchial cartilage.** A small **second basi-branchial** lies posterior to the union of the first ceratobranchials in the midline. Branchial arches 2 and 3 (visceral arches 4 and 5) are much reduced, since the ceratobranchial elements are very small or are altogether lacking. The second and third epibranchials are represented, however, by small cartilaginous bars lying in succession behind the first epibranchial.

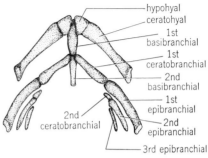

FIG. 3.6. Hyoid apparatus of *Necturus.*

Appendicular Skeleton

PECTORAL GIRDLE AND LIMBS

The **pectoral girdle** (Fig. 3.7) is an arch of cartilage and bone which supports the forelimbs. It is composed of two halves which are not united but which overlap each other ventrally. Each half consists of a

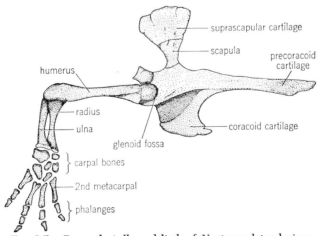

FIG. 3.7. Pectoral girdle and limb of *Necturus,* lateral view.

single skeletal element in which regions can be recognized. The ventral part, which is cartilaginous, has anterior **precoracoid** and posterior **coracoid regions.** A depression, the **glenoid fossa**, on the lateral border serves as the point of articulation of the arm with the girdle. A narrow bony region, the **scapula**, projects dorsally. To its distal border is attached a broad **suprascapular cartilage.** The pectoral girdle forms no direct connection with the vertebral column.

The single bone of the upper arm is the **humerus.** It bears a **deltoid crest** on its lower surface for muscle attachment. Two bones, **radius** and **ulna**, are in the forearm. They can be distinguished from each other since the proximal end of the ulna projects beyond the elbow joint as the **olecranon process.** The radius is on the thumb side. Six or seven very small bones arranged in three rows make up the **wrist**, or **carpal, bones.** Two are proximal, consisting of a **radiale** on the side of the radius and an **ulnare** on the ulnar side. A small **intermedium** is generally fused to the ulnare. Three **carpal** bones are **distal.** A single **centrale** lies between the proximal and distal rows. Four **metacarpals** are present in the hand. The first digit, or **thumb** (**pollex**), is absent. Digits 2, 3, and 5 contain two **phalanges** each. The fourth contains three.

Pelvic Girdle and Limbs

The **pelvic girdle** (Fig. 3.8) is almost entirely cartilaginous. It consists of a **puboischium** and an **ilium.** The puboischium is a flat plate on

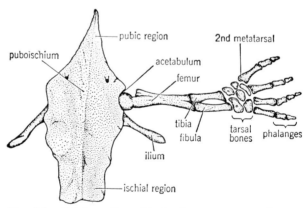

Fig. 3.8.   Pelvic girdle and limb of *Necturus*, ventral view.

the ventral side of the animal. Its anterior end represents the **pubis**, and the posterior end the **ischium.** Part of the ischial region may be bony. The puboischium bears a depression, the **acetabulum**, on either side for the reception of the head of the femur. A bony rod extends dorsally from each lateral side of the puboischium. This is the **ilium.**

It is fastened to the strong rib of the sacral vertebra. The actual number of sacral vertebrae, as mentioned previously, shows some variation among different specimens.

The pelvic limb is much like the pectoral limb in structure. The upper leg, or thigh, contains a single bone, the **femur.** Two bones, **tibia** and **fibula,** are in the shank. The tibia corresponds to the radius and the fibula to the ulna. Six **tarsal,** or **ankle,** bones are present, arranged in a manner similar to that of the carpals. The terms **tibiale** and **fibulare** are applied to the two bones of the proximal row lying opposite the tibia and fibula, respectively. There are three **distal tarsals** and a **centrale,** the latter lying between the proximal and distal rows. The foot contains four **metatarsal** bones, the first, or **hallux,** being lacking. As in the hand, each digit has two **phalanges** except the fourth, in which there are three.

MUSCULAR SYSTEM

The muscles of *Necturus* do not deviate very greatly from the primitive condition. This is particularly true of those in the trunk and tail regions. In the pectoral and pelvic regions modifications have occurred in connection with the evolution of tetrapod limbs.

Remove the skin from the head and trunk regions. First cut through the skin along the middorsal line on your specimen, and then loosen it laterally on both sides down to the midventral line. Avoid damaging the muscles which lie directly under the skin. It is not necessary to attempt to remove the skin covering the external gills.

Trunk Musculature

The muscles of the two sides of the body are distinct from each other. A thin connective-tissue partition, the **linea alba,** separates the muscles of the two sides along the midventral line. Toward the dorsal side a horizontal septum divides the muscles into dorsal **epaxial** and ventral **hypaxial** regions (Fig. 3.9). The lateral septum is more dorsal in position than that of *Squalus acanthias.* As a result the epaxial musculature is reduced. The muscles consist of a series of metameric, blocklike **myotomes,** or **myomeres,** each extending all the way from the middorsal to the midventral lines. The myotomes are separated from one another by connective-tissue partitions, the **myosepta,** or **myocommata.** The greater part of the epaxial region has become modified to form a single muscular unit, the **longissimus dorsi (dorsalis trunci)** on each side. Here the muscle fibers course in a longitudinal direction. The deeper portion of the epaxial region forms a series of short **intersegmental bundles** passing from one vertebra to the next. The hypaxial muscles have differentiated into three layers. The outermost layer is the **external oblique.** Its fibers course obliquely, slanting in a posteroventral direction. Carefully remove a portion of this layer. Under the external oblique find the **internal oblique muscle,** in which the fibers slope in an anteroventral direction. Remove part of this layer extending over an area of three or four myotomes, and note the third and innermost layer, the **transversus,** in which the fibers are arranged almost in a circular, or vertical, direction. Cut away a portion of the transversus and determine that it lies directly over the **parietal peritoneum** lining the outer part of the body cavity. On either side of the linea alba is a thin, superficial,

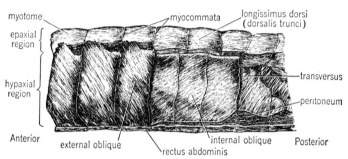

Fig. 3.9. Muscles of portion of trunk region of *Necturus,* lateral view. In the fourth, fifth, and sixth segments from the left the external oblique layer has been removed to show the underlying internal oblique layer. In the seventh and eighth segments both external and internal oblique layers have been removed to expose the transversus. The ventral portions of the internal oblique and transversus have been removed to show the underlying peritoneum.

rectus abdominis muscle. It extends from the pubis to the pectoral region. Its longitudinally directed fibers are interrupted at regular intervals by myocommata.

Muscles of the Head and Gill Region

Arrange your specimen so that the ventral side is toward you, and examine the superficial muscles on the ventral side of the head (Fig. 3.10). There are two of these. Each passes laterally from the midventral raphe to the bone of the lower jaw. These are **branchial muscles.** The more anterior of the two is the **intermandibular.** The **interhyoid** lies posterior to it. Cut through these muscles slightly to the right of the midventral raphe and deflect the cut edge in order to examine the **hypobranchial muscles** which lie directly above. These consist of a pair of **geniohyoids** on either side of the midline. Their fibers extend longitudinally from the front of the lower jaw to the second basibranchial cartilage.

Now examine the dorsal surface of the head (Fig. 3.11). The

anterior end of the longissimus dorsi can be observed attached to the posterior end of the skull.   A **levator mandibulae** covers the greater part of the top of the skull.   It is divided into anterior, external, and posterior portions.   The **anterior levator mandibulae** lies near the middorsal line; the **external levator mandibulae** is located behind the eye; the smaller **posterior levator mandibulae** lies under the external levator

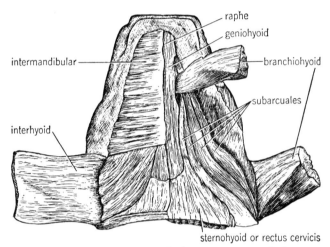

FIG. 3.10.   Muscles of head of *Necturus*, ventral view.

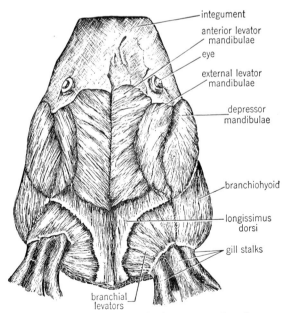

FIG. 3.11.   Muscles of head of *Necturus*, dorsal view.

mandibulae. All three components insert on the lower jaw, thus serving to close the mouth. Two additional branchial muscles lie between the external levator mandibulae and the gills. The more anterior of the two is the **depressor mandibulae.** Its fibers pass from the visceral arch behind the hyoid to the posterior part of the lower jaw near the point where it articulates with the quadrate. The other is the **branchiohyoid.** This has the same origin as the depressor mandibulae but passes to the ceratohyal. Several small muscles lie above the gill region. These are the **branchial levators,** or levators of the gills. They pass from the skin to the remaining visceral arches and serve to raise the gills. Now cut across the middle of the branchiohyoid and deflect the cut ends. Several small **subarcual muscles,** passing from one visceral arch to another, lie dorsal to the geniohyoids and branchiohyoids. Three small **branchial depressors,** which lower, or depress, the gills, pass from the ventral portions of the posterior visceral arches to the bases of the external gills.

Muscles of the Pectoral Girdle and Forelimb
(Fig. 3.12)

Immediately behind the gills is the **cucullaris muscle.** It originates from fascia and inserts on the scapula near the glenoid cavity. Posterior to the cucullaris lies the **dorsalis scapulae.** It originates on the suprascapula, covers most of the scapula, and passes to the humerus. Still another muscle, the **latissimus dorsi,** is situated posterior to the dorsalis scapulae. It arises by several slips from myocommata and fascia in the epaxial region and inserts on the proximal end of the humerus. A small muscle, the **pectoriscapularis,** lies anterior and ventral to the cucullaris and inserts on the scapula. It partially covers another muscle, the **sternohyoid (rectus cervicis),** which is the anterior continuation of the **rectus abdominis.** Deeper muscles in this region include the **levator scapulae** and **serratus anterior.** They originate from the epaxial muscles and insert on the scapula. On the ventral side of the body in the pectoral region three additional muscles may be observed. The first of these, the **pectoralis,** passes from the linea alba to the ventral side of the proximal end of the humerus. A **supracoracoid muscle** lies anterior to the pectoralis which partly overlaps it. It extends from the coracoid cartilage of the pectoral girdle and also inserts on the humerus. The third muscle, the **precoracohumeralis,** is a slender muscle, lateral in position, extending from the precoracoid cartilage to the humerus. Between the two precoracohumeralis muscles lies the **sternohyoid,** previously mentioned.

On the ventral surface of the foreleg proper is the **humeroantibrachialis,** often referred to as the **biceps.** It passes from the proximal end of the humerus to the radial side of the forearm. A larger muscle, the **coracobrachialis,** lies behind the humeroantibrachialis. It passes from the coracoid cartilage to insert on the distal end of the humerus. On the dorsal surface of the upper arm is the **anconeus.** It originates from several slips, or heads, from the coracoid, scapula, and proximal part of the humerus. The aconeus inserts on the ulna.

The muscles of the forearm are grouped into two divisions. An **extensor digitorum communis** lies on the dorsal surface, and a **flexor digitorum communis** is found on the ventral side. Both extensor and

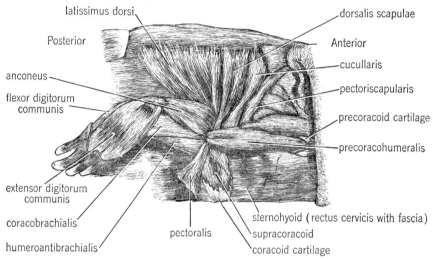

FIG. 3.12. Superficial muscles of right pectoral girdle and forelimb of *Necturus,* ventrolateral view.

flexor muscles are separated into various small components which insert on the digits.

Muscles of the Pelvic Girdle and Hind Limb

In *Necturus* two separate muscles pass from the midventral line to the hind limb (Figs. 3.13A and B). The more anterior of the two is the **puboischiofemoralis externus.** It passes from the anterior end of the pubis to the proximal end of the femur. Posterior to the puboischio-femoralis externus lies the **puboischiotibialis.** This muscle originates on the puboischiac plate of the pelvic girdle and inserts along the shaft of the tibia. It lies anterior to a glandular mass, the **anal,** or **cloacal, gland,** located anterolaterad the cloacal opening. Remove this gland. Dorsal to it are two muscles, the fibers of which are longitudinally arranged. The more medial muscle is the **ischiocaudalis.** It originates on the posterior part of the ischium and inserts on the tail. Laterad the ischiocaudalis is the **caudopuboischiotibialis**. This muscle originates on the fascia covering the puboischiotibialis muscle and inserts on the tail. Just above this muscle lies the **caudofemoralis**, which passes from the femur to the tail. These three pairs of muscles are used in bending the tail in different directions.

Several additional muscles of the pelvic girdle are found toward the dorsal side of the body. The most anterior of these is the **puboischio-femoralis internus**. It originates from the dorsal side of the pelvic girdle near the acetabulum and inserts on the shaft of the femur. Immediately behind it, still on the dorsal side, is a slender **iliotibialis**. In back of this

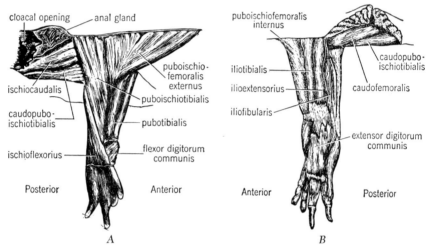

FIG. 3.13. Superficial muscles of left pelvic girdle and hind limb of *Necturus: A*, ventral view; *B*, dorsal view.

lies the **ilioextensorius**. These two muscles, which originate on the iliac region of the pelvic girdle, insert on the tibia. The last of the dorsal muscles is the **iliofibularis**, passing from the ilium to the fibula. A small triangular-shaped **iliofemoralis** arises from the base of the ilium and passes to the posterior border of the femur. On the ventral side of the above group of muscles is the **pubotibialis**, originating on the pubo-ischiac plate and inserting on the proximal end of the tibia. The **puboischiotibialis** partly covers this muscle. Last comes the **ischio-flexorius**, passing from the puboischiac plate to the fascia of the lower leg.

The muscles of the lower leg, as in the case of the forearm, consist of a dorsal **extensor digitorum communis** and a ventral **flexor digitorum communis**. Each is divided into separate, smaller elements which pass to the digits.

COELOM

Expose the **coelom,** or body cavity, of your specimen by making a longitudinal incision in the ventral body wall slightly to the left of the median line and extending from the cloaca to the transverse fold of skin in the gill region. Raise the body wall lateral to the incision and note the **mesohepar,** a ventral mesentery attaching the liver to the ventral body wall. At each end of the incision cut the body wall laterally in both directions for about ¾ in. After observing any blood vessels coursing through the mesohepar, cut this membrane loose from the ventral body wall. The flaps thus formed may be cut off or laid back and pinned down. The internal organs should now be exposed to view.

Observe that it appears as though two cavities had been opened: a small anterior one, just posterior to the gill region, containing the heart; and a large posterior cavity, containing all the other viscera. The cavity in which the heart lies is the **pericardial cavity;** that containing the remaining viscera is the **pleuroperitoneal cavity.**

The body cavity, or coelom, in *Necturus* is thus divided into two separate compartments. The pericardial cavity is surrounded by a membranous **pericardium (parietal pericardium).** This is continuous with the **visceral pericardium,** or **epicardium,** which is closely applied to the surface of the heart itself.

A partition, the **septum transversum,** or **false diaphragm,** separates the pericardial and pleuroperitoneal cavities. The large veins bringing blood to the heart from the abdominal viscera pass through the septum transversum. The outer wall of the pleuroperitoneal cavity is lined with **parietal peritoneum.** A **visceral peritoneal layer** is reflected over the surface of the organs in the pleuroperitoneal cavity (see Fig. 2.17).

Note that the lungs extend into the pleuroperitoneal cavity and lie in close proximity to the digestive organs. In the cat, which we shall study next, the lungs lie in separate portions of the coelom, the pleural cavities.

DIGESTIVE SYSTEM

Although some of the organs belonging to the digestive system have already been exposed, we shall first direct our attention to the mouth cavity.

Mouth. The mouth opening is bordered by heavy, soft **lips** which, although immovable, are capable of closing the mouth completely. Cut backward from the angles of the jaw. On the right side extend the incision far enough to cut through all the visceral arches. Lay back the lower jaw. The anterior part of the cavity thus exposed is the **mouth cavity.** The posterior portion, in the region of the gills, is the **pharynx.**

Two rows of **teeth** are present in the upper jaw (Fig. 3.5). The first row is short, being confined to the premaxillary bones. The other is longer and situated on the vomers and palatopterygoids. The teeth of the lower jaw are located on the dentary and splenial portions of the mandible. When the mouth is closed, the single row of teeth on the lower jaw fits into the groove between the two rows on the upper jaw.

The **internal nares**, or **choanae**, lie lateral to the most posterior vomerine teeth. They appear as small slits and are often difficult to find in preserved specimens because of the coagulated mucus which obscures them.

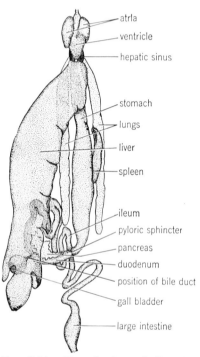

atrla
ventricle
hepatic sinus
stomach
lungs
liver
spleen
ileum
pyloric sphincter
pancreas
duodenum
position of bile duct
gall bladder
large intestine

FIG. 3.14. Ventral view of digestive organs and lungs of *Necturus*.

The **tongue** lies in the floor of the mouth. It is immovable in *Necturus* and is supported by the hyoid cartilages.

Pharynx. The mouth cavity is continued posteriorly as the pharynx. The wall of the pharynx on each side opens to the exterior through two **gill slits**, one behind the other. Note the **visceral arches**, which are cartilaginous bars covered with mucous membrane, between which the gill clefts are located. On the visceral arches observe the short, blunt projections on each side. These are the **gill rakers**, not so well developed nor so functionally efficient as those of the dogfish, but serving as an aid in retaining food. No internal gills homologous with those of fishes are present in *Necturus*. The gills are entirely external and are modifications of the integument. A small longitudinal slit in the floor of the pharynx, about 1 in. posterior to the tip of the tongue, is the **glottis**. It leads to the **lungs**, which are described below. The glottis is bordered by a pair of small **lateral cartilages**.

Esophagus. The **esophagus** of *Necturus* is short and serves merely to connect the pharynx with the stomach. It lies dorsal to the pericardium and passes through the septum transversum.

Stomach. The **stomach** (Fig. 3.14) is an elongated sac lying on the left side of the pleuroperitoneal cavity. Its posterior end is marked by a constriction, the **pyloric sphincter.** The stomach is suspended from the dorsal body wall by a mesentery, the **mesogaster.**

Intestine. The first part of the **small intestine,** between the pylorus and the entrance of the bile duct, is the **duodenum.** It bends rather sharply to the right and then passes posteriorly. The coiled portion of the small intestine beyond the duodenum is the **ileum.** It terminates at the posterior end of the coelom in a short, expanded portion, the **large intestine,** which in turn joins the **cloaca.** The latter opens to the outside through the **cloacal aperture.** The small intestine is supported by the **mesentery proper,** which is continuous with the mesogaster. The portion of the dorsal mesentery suspending the large intestine is the **mesorectum.**

Liver. The **liver** of *Necturus* is a large organ filling up a good share of the pleuroperitoneal cavity. Its margins are notched at various points, giving it a lobulated appearance. A ventral mesentery, the mesohepar, or **falciform ligament** of the liver, previously noted, attaches the ventral face of the organ to the midventral body wall. A **gastro-hepatic ligament** passes from the anterior end of the stomach to the dorsal side of the liver. A small, thin-walled **gall bladder** is located on the dorsal aspect of the right side of the liver near its posterior end. The **bile duct,** or **ductus choledochus,** passes from the gall bladder to the duodenum. It is surrounded by pancreatic tissue.

Pancreas. Lying in the loop between the duodenum and stomach is the irregularly shaped, whitish **pancreas.** It is partially enclosed in the hepatoduodenal ligament which connects duodenum and liver. Several small ducts from the pancreas join the bile duct or enter separately into the duodenum.

RESPIRATORY SYSTEM

In addition to the external gills previously referred to and the vascular integument, *Necturus* possesses a pair of **lungs** which may be used to some extent in respiration (Fig. 3.14). In this respect *Necturus* shows a decided advance over the dogfish.

On either side of the stomach in the anterior portion of the pleuroperitoneal cavity is an elongated, thin-walled, translucent lung. The lungs are *not* enclosed in separate portions of the coelom, as in the case of mammals. Hence the term pleuroperitoneal is an appropriate name for this portion of the body cavity. The lungs of *Necturus* are unusually long, simple, thin-walled sacs which may extend posteriorly even past the end of the liver.

The **glottis,** previously mentioned, located in the midventral part of the pharynx, leads to a small **larynx.** At the base of the larynx is a short, narrow **trachea** from which the lungs arise directly, without the intervention of bronchi.

The walls of the lungs, although smooth, are highly vascular. The blood vessels, in times of emergency, supplement those of the gills and skin in taking up oxygen and getting rid of carbon dioxide. Blood going to the lungs under ordinary conditions has been oxygenated in the gills. It is probable that the lungs are effective only when the oxygen supply of the water in which the animal lives is depleted and the gills and skin are unable to obtain sufficient oxygen. Although *Necturus* is permanently aquatic, it comes to the surface at irregular intervals to replenish the air in the lungs. The passage of air from the outside to the lungs takes the following course: external nares, nasal passages, internal nares, mouth, pharynx, glottis, larynx, trachea, and lungs.

EXCRETORY SYSTEM

Without removing any of the digestive organs, study the excretory and reproductive systems. Borrow a neighbor's specimen to study an individual of the opposite sex.

The **kidneys** of *Necturus* are of the **opisthonephric type.** They consist

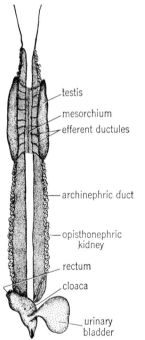

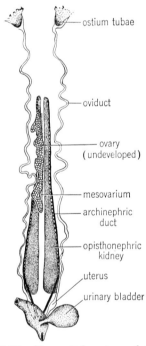

FIG. 3.15. Urogenital system of male *Necturus*, ventral view.

FIG. 3.16. Urogenital system of female *Necturus* during the nonbreeding season, ventral view. The left ovary has been removed to show the opisthonephros above.

of a pair of brown, narrow, elongated organs which lie in the posterior part of the body cavity close to the dorsal body wall (Figs. 3.15 and 3.16). The anterior end is narrower than the posterior end. The kidneys of the female are shorter than those of the male. Each is *entirely* surrounded by visceral peritoneum, a condition not usually encountered in vertebrates. Along the lateral border of each opistho-nephros lies the **archinephric duct.** It passes to the cloaca. The archi-nephric duct of the female is of finer structure than that of the male, in which it serves to transport spermatozoa in addition to urinary wastes.

A large, saclike **urinary bladder** comes off the ventral wall of the cloaca. A ventral mesenterylike band, the **median ligament of the bladder,** passes from the urinary bladder to the ventral body wall. The archinephric ducts have no connection with the bladder. Urinary wastes pass from the opisthonephric kidneys and archinephric ducts to the cloaca and thence to the bladder, which serves as a temporary storage place. The bladder is evacuated from time to time.

REPRODUCTIVE SYSTEM

In the male *Necturus* the reproductive and excretory systems are inti-mately connected, but in the female this relationship does not exist.

The Male

The **testes** are a pair of elongated bodies, each attached to the middorsal body wall by a mesenterylike membrane, the **mesorchium.** The size of the testes varies during different seasons of the year, reaching a maximum just prior to the breeding period. A few delicate tubules, the **efferent ductules,** pass from the testes through the mesorchium to the medial border of the kidney (Fig. 3.15). Here they form connec-tions with certain anterior kidney tubules. Spermatozoa thus pass from the testes through the efferent ductules to kidney tubules. The tubules in turn join the convoluted archinephric duct, which thus serves as a **ductus deferens** in transporting spermatozoa to the cloaca. The archinephric ducts open independently into the dorsolateral part of the cloaca anterior to the opening of the urinary bladder.

The Female

The **ovaries** of the female vary greatly in size and appearance during different seasons of the year. When filled with ripe eggs just prior to the breeding season, they occupy a considerable portion of the pleuro-peritoneal cavity. Each ovary is an elongated structure suspended from the dorsal body wall by a peritoneal fold, the **mesovarium.** A white, thick-walled, convoluted **oviduct,** or **Müllerian duct,** lies laterad each ovary (Fig. 3.16). Each oviduct is attached to the dorsal body wall by a membrane, the **mesotubarium**. The kidney lies within this two-layered membrane. The oviducts pass forward dorsal to the lung to the anterior end of the pleuroperitoneal cavity, where each opens by means of a slitlike **ostium tubae** into the body cavity.

The posterior end of each oviduct is somewhat enlarged to form a **uterus**. The uteri open into the sides of the cloaca lateral to the opening of the urinary bladder.

When eggs are fully ripened, the **follicles** in which they lie rupture, and the eggs pass directly into the pleuroperitoneal cavity. They are engulfed by the ostia and then pass in a rotary manner down the long, convoluted oviducts, where they receive an albuminous coating. A few may be stored temporarily in the uteri, from which they pass to the outside through the cloaca and cloacal aperture.

The method by which internal fertilization is accomplished in *Necturus* has been discussed previously (page 82).

ENDOCRINE SYSTEM

There are eight glandular structures in *Necturus*, some of which have been described above, usually considered to belong to the endocrine system.

Gonads. The ovaries and testes, already mentioned, in addition to their function of producing gametes, secrete **sex hormones** which are of importance in controlling the development of secondary sex characters and the development, maintenance, and function of the accessory sex organs. The exact cellular elements which secrete these hormones in amphibians are not clearly understood.

Pancreas. Besides secreting enzymes used in digestion, the pancreas serves as an endocrine organ. Certain groups of cells which can be identified in histological preparations of the pancreas secrete a hormone, **insulin,** into the blood stream. They are called the **islands of Langerhans.** Insulin plays an important part in the metabolism of carbohydrates and fats. The anatomical relations of the pancreas have been described above.

Thyroid gland. In *Necturus* the **thyroid gland** consists of a small mass of tissue located along the sides of the second basibranchial cartilage and partly covered by the branchiohyoid muscles.

Parathyroid glands. Small masses of cells derived embryonically from visceral pouches come to lie ventral and lateral to the aortic arches. Two or three such structures in *Necturus* are considered to be homologous with the **parathyroid glands** of higher forms. Not much investigation has been carried out on their functions in amphibians.

Adrenal glands. The **adrenal glands** of caudate amphibians are not discrete structures such as those of salientians and higher vertebrates. **Interrenal** (cortical) and **chromaffin** (medullary) components are more or less intermingled. Small isolated masses of tissue are present, usually in association with sympathetic ganglia. These are considered to be the homologues of the adrenals of higher forms. Gross observation of these masses in *Necturus* is difficult.

Pituitary gland. The various components of the **pituitary body** of *Necturus* are not clearly evident upon gross dissection. The pituitary body lies ventral to the diencephalon of the brain (Fig. 3.20B). Histological examination reveals the usual three-lobed structure.

Thymus gland. Uncertainty exists as to whether or not the **thymus** should be included in the category of endocrine structures. Derived from the dorsolateral portions of the visceral pouches in amphibians, the thymus consists of small masses of tissue lying laterad the aortic arch region and dorsal to the parathyroid elements.

Pineal body. Another structure often included among the endocrine organs is the **pineal body,** which extends dorsally from the roof of the diencephalic portion of the brain. Homologies with a third, median eye, found in rudimentary condition in several vertebrates, are suggestive in explaining the existence of this unusual structure of doubtful function.

CIRCULATORY SYSTEM

The circulatory system of *Necturus* consists of a three-chambered **heart** and numerous blood vessels. These include **arteries, arterioles, capillaries, venules,** and **veins.** In addition, **lymphatic vessels** and **glands,** as well as the **spleen,** make up parts of the circulatory system.

Heart

The **heart,** lying in the pericardial cavity, consists, as in other amphibians, of two thin-walled **atria** and a single muscular **ventricle** (Fig. 3.17). The atria lie anterior and dorsal to the ventricle. In *Necturus* the cavities of the two atria are separated only by a thin, perforated **interatrial septum.** Dorsal to the heart and attached to the septum transversum is a large, thin-walled **sinus venosus,** which collects blood from all parts of the body except the lungs. It opens into the right atrium through the **sinuatrial aperture,** which is guarded by a **sinuatrial valve.** Two large **common cardinal veins,** or **ducts of Cuvier,** join the sinus venosus. They are located dorsal to the pericardial cavity, and one enters each side of the sinus venosus (Fig. 3.19). A pair of large **hepatic sinuses** joins the posterior part of the sinus venosus dorsal to the ventricle (Figs. 3.17 and 3.19). The hepatic sinuses lead from the liver and pass through the septum transversum. A pair of **pulmonary veins** from the lungs comes together to form a common vessel which courses dorsal to the hepatic veins and enters the left atrium. The two atria have a common opening into the ventricle. This is guarded by an **atrioventricular valve**. A single vessel, the **conus arteriosus**, leaves the ventricle, and from it blood is distributed to the gills and hence to all parts of the body. Just anterior to the conus is an expanded **bulbus arteriosus** which actually represents the proximal portion of the ventral aorta. Anterior to the bulbus the **ventral aorta** branches, as described in the following section, distributing blood to the gills.

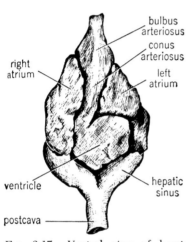

FIG. 3.17. Ventral view of heart of *Necturus*.

Carefully slit open the ventricle on its ventral side with a fine-pointed pair of scissors, and continue the cut into the conus arteriosus. Clean out any coagulated blood from the interior, and examine the inside of the ventricle, preferably under water, using a binocular dissecting microscope. Look for a row of pocketlike **semilunar valves** at the point where the conus leaves the ventricle. Although most amphibians have a longitudinal septum in the conus arteriosus, dividing its cavity into two separate channels, such a septum is lacking in *Necturus*.

The heart of *Necturus*, even though it is not a typical example of a three-chambered heart, shows an important advance over that observed in the dogfish shark. A **double circulation** of blood passes through it. Oxygenated blood coming from the lungs via the gills enters the left atrium. Blood entering the right atrium from the sinus venosus is mixed. It consists of unoxygenated blood coming from most parts of the body and some oxygenated blood from the skin and lining of the mouth. The system of vessels coming from the lungs to the heart, and those leading from the heart to the lungs, is referred to as the **pulmonary circulation**. That which is distributed to the body in general and then returned to the heart via the sinus venosus is called the **systemic circulation**. The pulmonary circulation of *Necturus* is atypical, since the blood in the pulmonary arteries under normal conditions has already been oxygenated in the gills. This indicates that the lungs of *Necturus* normally function but little as respiratory organs and are probably used chiefly in times of emergency.

Although many amphibians have developed a rather complicated system of values and partitions which ostensibly serve to keep the two blood streams in the heart fairly well separated, the heart of *Necturus*, with its perforated interatrial septum, and lacking a longitudinal septum in the conus, cannot be very effective in this respect. This is really of little importance because under ordinary circumstances blood is sent to the gills for aeration after leaving the heart. It is possible, however, for blood to bypass the gills by coursing directly through the branchial arteries (see below).

At this point it is important to note that the three-chambered condition of the heart first appears in the true lungfishes of the superorder Dipnoi.

Arterial System

Clean away any muscles in front of the pericardium and find the vessels leading from the ventral aorta to the gill region.

Afferent Branchial Arteries

The ventral aorta, which is very short, divides almost immediately into right and left trunks (Fig. 3.18). Each of these in turn gives off two branches. The anterior branch on each side passes to the first gill. The posterior branch passes laterally for a short distance and then splits into anterior and posterior branches which pass to the second and third gills, respectively. The three vessels going to the gills are the **afferent branchial arteries.**

The first afferent branchial artery gives off a small **external carotid artery** at the base of the gill. It passes medially and then turns forward to supply the floor of the pharynx and mouth. The external carotid artery actually has connections with the first **efferent branchial artery** but its main connection is with the first afferent branchial artery as noted. Within each gill the afferent branchial artery sends up a branch, the **afferent branchial loop,** which gives off numerous small capillary vessels to the gill filaments. Blood in these vessels is collected by other small vessels which unite to form another vessel, the **efferent branchial loop,** which returns blood to the efferent branchial artery. A short vessel at the base of each gill connects each afferent branchial artery to its respective efferent branchial artery. This is actually part of the original aortic arch which serves as a **gill bypass,** referred to above. Unlike the condition in fishes, therefore, the aortic arches are continuous and are not distinctly separated into afferent and efferent portions by a capillary network. Blood may either course directly through them or go through the branchial loops (Fig. 3.18).

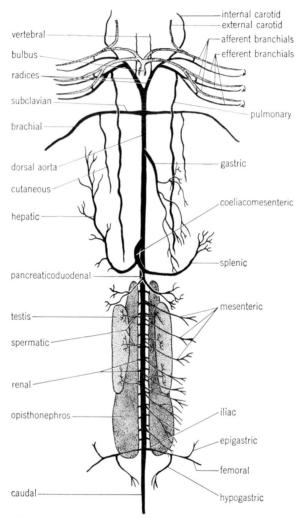

FIG. 3.18.   Ventral view of arterial system of *Necturus*.

Efferent Branchial Arteries

Now remove the mucous membrane from the roof of the mouth and pharynx. A large pair of vessels, the radices of the aorta, will be exposed. Trace the left radix to its origin, and note that it is formed by the union of efferent branchial arteries. It may be necessary to use a binocular dissecting microscope in tracing these vessels.

Blood is collected from the gill region by three **efferent branchial arteries** corresponding to the three gills. Each vessel parallels a corresponding afferent branchial artery with which, as already noted, it forms a direct connection, the **gill bypass,** as well as an indirect connection by way of the branchial loop with its afferent and efferent branches. The second and third efferent branchial arteries join each other to form a single vessel which is then joined by the first efferent branchial artery. The combination of the three vessels on each side, as just described, results in the formation of a large **radix aortae.** The two radices pass medially and posteriorly and then join to form the **dorsal aorta.** This vessel lies under the vertebral column and passes to the posterior part of the body, where it is continued into the tail as the **caudal artery.**

There is some disagreement among comparative anatomists as to which aortic arches are represented in *Necturus.* The work of Figge (F. H. Figge, 1930, *J. Exptl. Zool.,* **56**:241) indicates that in this perennibranchiate amphibian, arches **3, 4,** and **5** are the ones which persist.

A small **vertebral artery** comes from each radix lateral to the vertebral column and passes forward to the brain. Another short vessel, the **carotid duct,** springs from the radix near its junction with the first efferent branchial artery. It is continued forward as the **internal carotid artery,** which courses medially and anteriorly to the roof of the mouth. The external carotid artery, previously noted, is connected only indirectly to the carotid duct via the gill bypass and base of the first afferent branchial artery. Just before the common trunk formed by the second and third efferent branchial arteries joins the radix, a large **pulmonary artery** is given off. It passes posteriorly along the dorsal surface of the lung. Since the blood in the pulmonary artery has, for the most part, been oxygenated in the gill region, the lungs are of use primarily as accessory or emergency organs of respiration. The vascular skin and gills normally secure adequate amounts of oxygen, but when oxygen is not available in sufficient quantity, the animal can, by gulping air, inflate the lung and thus secure enough oxygen through its pulmonary vessels to carry on its metabolic processes.

Dorsal Aorta and Its Branches

As the aorta courses posteriorly it gives off numerous paired and unpaired branches.

Paired vessels. A short distance beyond the point where the radices join to form the aorta, the latter gives off a pair of **subclavian arteries.** Each of these sends off a **cutaneous artery** which is distributed to the skin. The subclavian artery then continues out the arm as the **brachial artery.**

Parietal arteries come from the aorta at segmental intervals. They are distributed to the muscles of the body wall.

Genital arteries come from the aorta in the region of the gonads. In the male, in which they pass to the testes, they are called **spermatic arteries.** The genital arteries of the female supply both ovaries and oviducts.

Renal arteries are branches of the aorta coming off at the level of the opisthonephric kidneys which they supply.

At the level of the hind limbs is a pair of **iliac arteries.** Each iliac gives off an anterior **epigastric artery** to the body wall and a **hypogastric artery** to cloaca and bladder. It continues into the hind limb as the **femoral artery.** A small pair of **cloacal arteries,** supplying part of the cloacal region, comes off the dorsal aorta at the level of the cloaca.

Unpaired vessels. Not very far posterior to the point where the subclavian arteries arise, a large unpaired **gastric artery** comes off the aorta. In addition to supplying the stomach with dorsal and ventral branches, it is distributed to a portion of the spleen.

Some distance caudally, a **coeliacomesenteric artery** arises from the aorta. It is distributed to the duodenal region of the small intestine and to the pancreas, liver, and posterior end of the spleen.

Several unpaired **mesenteric arteries** come from the aorta at intervals posterior to the coeliacomesenteric. They supply the remainder of the intestine.

Venous System

Common cardinal veins and their tributaries. As was previously noted, a **common cardinal vein** enters the sinus venosus on each side from the dorsal part of the pericardial cavity. Each is joined posteriorly (Fig. 3.19) by a large **hepatic sinus** close to its opening into the sinus venosus. Laterad the pericardial cavity the common cardinal receives several vessels. These consist of (1) a **jugular vein** formed by **external** and **internal tributaries** from the head region, (2) a small **lingual vein** from the tongue, (3) a **subclavian vein** formed by the junction of the **brachial vein** from the arm and the **cutaneous vein** from the skin, (4) a **lateral vein** from the muscles of the body wall, and (5) a **postcardinal vein** draining the kidneys, dorsal body wall, and some adjacent structures.

Renal portal system of veins. A single median **caudal vein** drains blood from the tail. When it reaches the body wall it divides into two, each branch passing along the lateral border of the kidney, where it is called the **renal portal vein.** The renal portal sends numerous **afferent renal veins** into the kidney and receives small **parietal vessels** from the body wall. At the anterior end of the kidney the renal portal is continued as the **postcardinal vein** which, as described above, passes anteriorly to join the common cardinal vein. Near the posterior end of the kidney each renal portal receives an **iliac vein,** which is joined by a **femoral vein** coming from the hind limb. The common vessel thus formed is the **pelvic vein.** The two pelvic veins soon unite to form a single **ventral abdominal vein** which, after receiving some

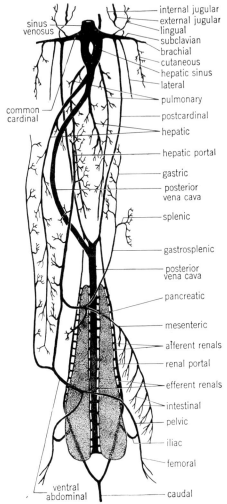

FIG. 3.19. Ventral view of venous system of *Necturus.*

vesicular branches from the bladder, and parietal veins from the body wall, forms connections with the hepatic portal vein (see below).

Posterior vena cava. A rather large vein, the **posterior vena cava,** lies between the kidneys along the dorsal side of the body cavity. The vessel gradually becomes larger as it courses anteriorly, receiving **efferent renal veins** from the kidneys and **genital veins** from the gonads.

Anterior to the kidneys the postcava forms connections with the **post-cardinal veins.** At a point a short distance posterior to this junction, the main part of the postcava passes ventrally and penetrates the dorsal aspect of the liver. It receives several **hepatic veins** from the liver. One of these is a comparatively large vessel coming from the ventral aspect of the liver. It joins the postcava near the point where it emerges from the anterior end of the liver. The postcava passes forward to the septum transversum and then divides into the two **hepatic sinuses,** which join the common cardinal before they enter the sinus venosus.

Hepatic portal system of veins. The hepatic portal vein drains the digestive tract and spleen. It breaks up into capillaries in the substance of the liver. The vein is formed by the confluence of several tributaries. A large **mesenteric vein,** originating in the intestine, courses forward along the intestinal wall. It is joined en route by a large number of small **intestinal veins.** At the level of the pancreas it is joined by a large **gastrosplenic vein** draining the stomach and spleen. The hepatic portal vein is formed by a joining together of the mesenteric, pancreatic, and gastrosplenic branches. It passes into the liver along the dorsal aspect of that organ.

The **ventral abdominal vein,** described in connection with the renal portal system, courses in the mesohepar and then sends branches to the liver. At the level of the hepatoduodenal omentum this vein forms a direct connection with the hepatic portal vein, thus effecting a connection between the two portal systems. The ventral abdominal vein of *Necturus* is homologous with the lateral veins of the shark.

Lymphatic System

The lymphatic system of *Necturus* does not lend itself to gross dissection. In caudate amphibians, in general, it consists of irregular vessels with thin walls. Two main portions are recognized. The first parallels the aorta and joins the two subclavian veins. The other courses beneath the skin and opens into the cutaneous and postcardinal veins.

Spleen

The **spleen** of *Necturus* is a dark, thin, elongated structure which lies to the left of the middle portion of the stomach. Like the digestive tract, it is drained by the hepatic portal vein.

NERVOUS SYSTEM

Since, in *Necturus,* the brain and spinal cord are surrounded by a bony protective covering, exposure of these structures for study is somewhat more difficult than in the shark with its cartilaginous skeleton. Exposure of the brain may be accomplished by slicing away thin layers of bone with a sharp scalpel. Chip away small bits of bone until you have a clear view of the brain and its connection with the spinal cord. Watch for delicate membranes surrounding the brain.

Central Nervous System

BRAIN

Two distinctly separated membranes surround the brain. The first of these, the **dura mater**, lies just inside the skull, from which it is separated by an **epidural space**. The second membrane, or **pia-arachnoid**, is a delicate vascular structure closely united with the brain. A **subdural space** filled with cerebrospinal fluid separates the dura from the pia-arachnoid.

The **brain** of *Necturus* (Fig. 3.20) is small, but its various components can nevertheless be clearly observed. The **cerebral hemispheres** (**telencephalon**) are elongated and separated from each other by a longitudinal fissure. An **olfactory nerve** joins the anterior end of each cerebral hemisphere. **Olfactory lobes** are not distinct structures in the mud puppy, being imperceptibly united with the cerebral hemispheres. The **diencephalon** lies immediately posterior to

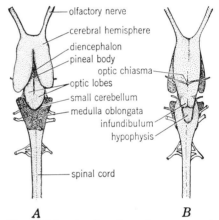

olfactory nerve
cerebral hemisphere
diencephalon
pineal body
optic chiasma
optic lobes
small cerebellum
medulla oblongata
infundibulum
hypophysis
spinal cord

A   *B*

Fig. 3.20. *A*, dorsal, and *B*, ventral views of brain of *Necturus*.

the cerebral hemispheres. Its membranous roof forms a **tela choroidea**. Projecting upward from the roof of the diencephalon is a small, flat, **pineal body**. The **optic lobes** forming the dorsal part of the **mesencephalon** lie posterior to the diencephalon. They are not very distinctly marked off from the latter. A small, transversely arranged **cerebellum** lies between the optic lobes and the **medulla oblongata** (**myelencephalon**). The cerebellum is poorly developed in *Necturus* in correlation with its sluggish habits. The medulla tapers posteriorly, where it is continuous with the **spinal cord**. A **tela choroidea** roofs over the medulla oblongata.

Before removing the brain in order to study its ventral surface, look for the cranial nerves, described below (page 112). Trace each of these as far as possible. After the cranial nerves have been identified, remove the brain. In order to do this, sever the spinal cord as well as the olfactory and other cranial nerves.   Place the brain ventral side up in a Syracuse watch glass filled with water and, if possible, examine it under a binocular dissecting microscope.   A few additional features will be noted.

On the ventral surface of the diencephalon is located the **optic chiasma**, formed by a crossing of the optic nerves.   Most of the remainder of the **hypothalamus** is composed of an **infundibulum**, which projects posteriorly and to which the **pituitary gland (hypophysis)** is attached.   An inconspicuous **saccus vasculosus** is present on the dorsal aspect of the infundibulum.

As in the dogfish, the cavities of the brain consist of **lateral, or first** and **second, ventricles** in the cerebral hemispheres which, through **interventricular foramina**, join the **third ventricle** in the diencephalon. This is connected by a narrow **cerebral aqueduct** to the **fourth ventricle** in the medulla oblongata.

SPINAL CORD

The posterior end of the medulla oblongata is continuous with the spinal cord.   The transition between the two is imperceptible.   The **spinal cord**, which lies within the neural canal, continues to the tip of the tail.   It is uniform in diameter except for a very slight enlargement in the sacral region.   Posterior to this point it gradually tapers down to a fine thread, the **filum terminale**.   A shallow, longitudinal groove, the **dorsal fissure**, or **dorsal longitudinal sulcus**, is present along the mid-dorsal line of the spinal cord.   On the ventral side is a prominent **longitudinal ventral fissure**.

Peripheral Nervous System

CRANIAL NERVES

Eleven cranial nerves are present in *Necturus*.   They are small and are dissected with difficulty.

Terminal nerve (O).   A small **terminal nerve** parallels the olfactory nerve and enters the forebrain at the ventral border of the cerebral hemisphere on each side.   It passes to the ventrolateral portion of the diencephalon.

Olfactory nerve (I).   The olfactory nerves are prominent bands which pass from the nasal mucosa to the anterior end of the cerebral hemisphere on each side.   As previously noted, the olfactory lobes of the brain are merged with the cerebral hemispheres.

Optic nerve (II).   The optic nerves are small in *Necturus*, in correlation with the poorly developed eyes.   They pass from the eyes to the ventral surface of the diencephalon, where their fibers cross, forming a typical optic chiasma.

Oculomotor nerve (III).   The third cranial nerves are very slender and apt to escape observation. They arise from the posterior part of the mesencephalon, passing to the superior rectus, inferior rectus, internal rectus, and inferior oblique eye muscles.

Trochlear nerve (IV). The exceedingly minute trochlear nerves arise from the dorsal part of the brain between the mesencephalon and the metencephalon. They innervate the superior oblique eye muscles.

Trigeminal nerve (V). The trigeminal nerve is the largest of the cranial nerves. It comes from the anterior lateral border of the medulla oblongata and passes forward in an oblique direction. Near its origin is the **Gasserian, or semilunar, ganglion.** Beyond the ganglion the nerve divides into three main trunks: **ophthalmic, maxillary,** and **mandibular.** The ophthalmic branch passes straight forward. The maxillary courses along the edge of the upper jaw. The mandibular passes to the angle of the mouth and then continues along the lower jaw. Ophthalmic and maxillary branches are sensory, but the mandibular contains both sensory and motor fibers.

Abducens nerve (VI). The sixth cranial nerve, like the fourth, is very fine and slender. Do not look for this until the ventral side of the brain is examined. It can be seen only with the aid of a dissecting microscope. The nerve arises rather far back on the ventral side of the medulla and passes to the external rectus and retractor bulbi muscles.

Facial and auditory nerves (VII and VIII). The seventh and eighth cranial nerves arise by a common trunk from the lateral border of the myelencephalon just posterior to the origin of the trigeminal. A branch of the facial joins the trigeminal at the Gasserian ganglion. Some of its fibers run together with the ophthalmic branch of nerve V, forming the **superficial ophthalmic** component of the facial nerve. Others, forming the **buccal branch** of the facial nerve, parallel the fibers of the maxillary branch of the trigeminal. These branches of the facial nerve are composed only of sensory fibers which innervate the lateral line organs of the head.

From the common trunk formed by the facial and auditory nerves, an anterior **hyomandibular branch,** composed of both sensory and motor fibers, is distributed to the hyomandibular region.

The auditory nerve proper is short and passes to the structures composing the inner ear.

Glossopharyngeal and vagus nerves (IX and X). The last two cranial nerves have a common origin from the medulla oblongata, arising by three distinct roots. The most anterior of these is the glossopharyngeal. The roots enter a common ganglion and then branch. The glossopharyngeal nerve passes laterally and then branches to the pharynx, tongue, and muscles of the gill region. It is a mixed nerve. The vagus gives off a **lateral branch** to the lateral line canal and sends other branches to the gills and viscera.

A **hypobranchial nerve** supplying the hypobranchial muscles is present in *Necturus*. It arises posterior to the vagus, but its exact components are somewhat uncertain. Apparently it contains fibers from the first and second spinal nerves.

SPINAL NERVES

The metamerically arranged **spinal nerves** are paired structures arising from the spinal cord by two **roots, dorsal** and **ventral.** The two roots join at the **intervertebral foramen** to emerge from the vertebral column as a spinal nerve. Just *outside* the intervertebral foramen is a swelling, the **spinal ganglion.** From it arise **dorsal** and **ventral rami.** A short distance beyond the ganglion the ventral ramus gives off a branch, the **visceral ramus,** or **ramus communicans,** which passes to a **sympathetic ganglion.**

In amphibians the dorsal roots of the spinal nerves carry some visceral efferent motor fibers as well as the usual somatic sensory and visceral sensory fibers. The ventral roots also carry visceral efferent fibers in addition to somatic motor elements.

In the regions of the limbs the ventral rami of certain spinal nerves form **plexuses** by sending intercommunicating branches to one another. In the region of the forelimbs the third, fourth, and fifth spinal nerves are involved, forming a **brachial plexus** on each side. The nerves then pass from the plexus to the forelimb. At the level of the hind limb is the **lumbosacral plexus.** Three or four spinal nerves enter into this plexus. The nerves which emerge pass to the hind limb.

Peripheral Autonomic Nervous System

The peripheral autonomic nervous system of *Necturus* is difficult to study. The **parasympathetic portion** apparently consists of fibers carried by the third, seventh, ninth, and tenth cranial nerves. Possibly the sacral spinal nerves may also be involved. The **sympathetic components** consist of two slender **sympathetic trunks,** running the length of the body on either side of the dorsal aorta from head to tail. They bear metamerically arranged **sympathetic ganglia,** with which the visceral rami of the spinal nerves form connections. Certain large nerve plexuses are located along the main arteries leaving the aorta. Arrangement of preganglionic and postganglionic fibers undoubtedly follows the pattern observed in higher forms.

SENSE ORGANS

The small size of *Necturus* precludes a detailed study of its sense organs. The following points, nevertheless, should be noted.

Lateral-line Organs

Necturus, in accord with its permanently aquatic mode of life, retains its **lateral-line organs** in the adult. They are similar in arrangement to those of fishes, consisting of a **lateral-line canal proper** on either side of the body and of various canals in the head region. Branches of the facial (VII), glossopharyngeal (IX), and vagus (X) nerves innervate these organs.

Olfactory Organs

Pass a probe into one of the external nares, cutting along the probe until it passes into the mouth through the internal naris. Examine the passage thus exposed. Lining the olfactory passage from external to internal nares are numerous folds which comprise the **olfactory epithelium**. Fibers of the olfactory nerve pass from the olfactory epithelium to the cerebral hemispheres (**olfactory lobes**), as previously noted. It should be recalled that in *Necturus* the nasal passages serve the dual functions of olfaction and respiration.

Eyes

The eyes of *Necturus* are poorly developed and probably of little use other than in discerning the direction of light. The red rod cells in the retina of *Necturus* are the largest known. There are no movable eyelids. The **cornea** is fused to the skin, and the eye is capable of little movement, despite the presence of the usual eye muscles. The **lens** is large in proportion to the other structures. Otherwise the various parts of the eye are similar to those of other vertebrates and require no separate description here.

Ears

In *Necturus* only the **inner ears** are present. Each consists of a **membranous labyrinth** surrounded by a **bony labyrinth**. There is no tympanic cavity as in salientian amphibians. The membranous labyrinth lies embedded within the **otic capsule**, from which it may be removed without too much difficulty after decalcification. It is composed of three **semicircular ducts** (anterior, posterior, and horizontal) as well as a saclike **vestibular region** with which the semicircular ducts communicate. Each semicircular duct has an enlargement, the **ampulla**, at its lower end. The vestibule is composed of an upper chamber, the **utriculus**, which lies over a lower chamber, the **sacculus**, from which it is indistinctly separated. The sacculus contains an **otolith** composed of crystalline granules. The ears of *Necturus* serve primarily as organs of equilibration.

CHAPTER 4

THE CAT (*Felis domestica*)

Classification:
  Phylum: Chordata
    Group: Vertebrata (Craniata)
      Subphylum: Gnathostomata
        Superclass: Tetrapoda
          Class: Mammalia
            Subclass: Theria
              Infraclass: Eutheria
                Order: Carnivora
                  Suborder: Fissipedia
                    Family: Felidae
                      Genus: *Felis*
                        species: *domestica*

NATURAL HISTORY

The domestic cat is familiar to most civilized peoples. It is believed that its origin goes back to the extinct saber-toothed tigers which lived in Eocene times. The common cat of today is descended from a cross between the European wildcat and the Egyptian race of the African wildcat. Manx cats, for which the Isle of Man in the Irish Sea is famous, are tailless, high-rumped forms. Ideally the tail is represented only by a tuft of hair. In this case the condition seems to have originated as a genetic mutation, and the exact mechanism of hereditary transmission is at present unknown. Tailless cats, found in many parts of Russia, are believed to have originated in the Orient. The royal Siamese cats, with their blue eyes, black or chocolate-brown head and feet, and light tan or cream-colored bodies, are domesticated descendants of the African jungle cat.

The average length of the domestic cat is about 2½ ft., the tail making up about one-third of this. Sexual dimorphism is exhibited primarily in size, full-grown males being larger than the females.

Cats have assimilated themselves well with our civilization yet seem to have retained many of their feral instincts. Those which have reverted to nature are destructive and seek birds, mammals, and even fish as their prey. They can apparently see well in dim light. Cats stalk their prey stealthily, catch them by surprise, and kill them with their sharply pointed teeth. The olfactory sense is poorly developed.

Cats are prolific animals, having from 3 to 12 young at a time. The kittens are born in a helpless condition with their eyelids fused together. The eyelids do not separate until the ninth day after birth. The body is covered with fur at the time the young are born. The mother cares for the young, but the male parent is lacking in parental instincts. The life span of the average cat is approximately 10 years.

Cats are of economic value as destroyers of rodent pests. Their fur is of poor quality and is known as **genet.**

EXTERNAL FEATURES

The external form of the cat is so familiar that a detailed description need not be given. The body is made up of four main regions: **head, neck, trunk,** and **tail.** The **eyes** have movable upper and lower **eyelids** as well as a **nictitating membrane.** This lies beneath the other eyelids and passes from the inner angle of the eye out over the surface of the eyeball. During life it is transparent. The **external ear** consists of a prominent **pinna** and an opening at its base which leads into the skull. This passage is the **external auditory meatus.**

The body is covered with **skin,** which is continuous with the mucous membranes lining the mouth, anus, and urogenital orifices. It varies in thickness in different parts of the body, being thickest in the ventral part of the neck region and on the pads of the feet. The skin is composed of an inner **dermis,** or **corium,** and an outer **epidermis.** The dermis is rather loosely bound to underlying structures by fibrous connective tissue. On the head and distal ends of the limbs, however, the skin is more firmly attached. **Hair,** a derivative of the epidermis, covers the entire body except the end of the nose and the foot pads. Special tactile hairs, the **vibrissae,** are to be found on either side of the nose, on the cheeks, and over the eyes. The **claws,** at the terminal ends of the digits, are also epidermal derivatives. Those of the cat family are *retractile,* being folded back into bony sheaths when not extended. There are five on the forefeet and four on the hind feet, in keeping with the number of digits. **Friction pads,** or **tori,** number seven on the forefeet and five on the hind feet.

Determine the sex of your specimen. The **anus** lies ventral to the base of the tail in the midline. In females the **urogenital opening** lies immediately anterior to the anus, which it rather closely resembles. The opening is bordered by the **outer lips,** or **labia majora,** the entire structure being referred to as the **vulva.** If your specimen is a female, look for the five pairs of **nipples** through which the ducts of the **mammary glands** open to the outside. They are located in two longitudinal rows on the ventral side of the body on either side of the midline.

In males, the **scrotum,** a saclike structure containing the testes, is located a short distance anterior to the anus. Immediately in front of this is a slight elevation consisting of the **prepuce, or foreskin.** The **penis,** or male copulatory organ, is retracted under normal circumstances and, therefore, is not visible externally. When protruded it passes through the opening in the center of the prepuce, which actually is not the true urogenital opening.

In both sexes the region in which both anus and urogenital organs lie is called the **perineum.**

SKELETAL SYSTEM

Mounted cat skeletons should be available in the laboratory for study. If feasible, each student will be provided with a box of bones containing a cat's skull, a sample of each type of vertebra, a rib, and specimens of those bones which make up the pectoral and pelvic girdles and limbs. It is well to have one or more disarticulated cat skulls on hand for study. Separate mounts of wrists and hands, ankles and feet, and the sternum will also aid in the study of these parts of the skeletal system.

The skeleton of the cat is completely bony except for the sternal ends of the ribs, which are cartilaginous and known as costal cartilages. Cartilage is also present at the articular surfaces of bones and in a few other places, such as in the external ear.

The skeleton is divided into axial and appendicular portions. The axial skeleton consists of the skull, vertebral column, ribs, and sternum. The appendicular skeleton is composed of the limbs and limb girdles.

Axial Skeleton

SKULL

The **skull** (Figs. 4.1 and 4.2) consists of three main parts: (1) the **cranium,** or bony case, which surrounds and protects the brain; (2) the **sense capsules,** which enclose the organs of special sense; and (3) the **visceral skeleton,** forming the jaws and hyoid apparatus and contributing to the formation of the larynx. Cranium, sensory capsules, and the part of the visceral skeleton forming the upper jaw are rigidly united. Several large spaces, at least partially surrounded by bone, are to be observed in the skull of the cat. The eye socket, or **orbit,** is prominent when viewed from the dorsal side. A gap usually occurs in the bones surrounding the posterior end of the orbit. Through this, the orbit is in communication with another large space, the **temporal fossa,** into which

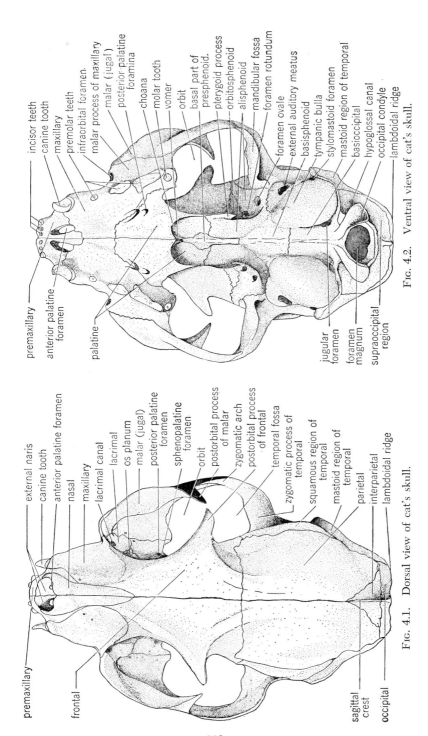

premaxillary

anterior palatine
foramen

palatine

incisor teeth
canine tooth
maxillary
premolar teeth
infraorbital foramen
malar process of maxillary
malar (jugal)
posterior-palatine
foramina
choana
molar tooth
vomer
orbit
basal part of
presphenoid.
pterygoid process
orbitosphenoid
alisphenoid
mandibular fossa
foramen rotundum
foramen ovale
external auditory meatus
basisphenoid
tympanic bulla
stylomastoid foramen
mastoid region of temporal
basioccipital
hypoglossal canal
occipital condyle
lambdoidal ridge

FIG. 4.2.   Ventral view of cat's skull.

jugular
foramen
foramen
magnum
supraoccipital
region

premaxillary

frontal

external naris
canine tooth
anterior palatine foramen
nasal
maxillary
lacrimal canal
lacrimal
os planum
malar (jugal)
posterior palatine
foramen
sphenopalatine
foramen
orbit
postorbital process
of malar
zygomatic arch
postorbital process
of frontal
temporal fossa
zygomatic process of
temporal
squamous region of
temporal
mastoid region of
temporal
parietal
interparietal
lambdoidal ridge

sagittal
crest
occipital

FIG. 4.1.   Dorsal view of cat's skull.

119

a projection, the **coronoid process** of the lower jaw, extends. A long, bony **zygomatic arch** lies ventral and lateral to both orbit and temporal fossa. A rather large opening at the posterior end of the skull is the **foramen magnum.** It lies completely within the **occipital bone.** A prominent transverse ridge above the foramen magnum is the **lambdoidal ridge.** Extending anteriorly from its central portion is a longitudinal ridge, the **sagittal crest.** Lambdoidal ridge and sagittal crest are absent in kittens but become more and more prominent with age. The external opening of the ear, the **external auditory meatus,** lies at the posterior end of the zygomatic arch. Ventral to this is a prominent swelling, the **tympanic bulla.** The **external,** or **anterior, nares** (nostrils) are located at the anterior end of the skull. On the roof of the mouth are the **choanae,** or posterior openings of the nasal passages. Other small openings to be observed on the skull are **foramina** for the passage of cranial nerves and blood vessels.

The **occipital bone,** as previously mentioned, surrounds the foramen magnum and forms most of the posterior face of the skull. In kittens this bone is composed of four separate elements, which in adults become inseparably fused. These are a single **basioccipital,** two **exoccipitals,** and one **supraoccipital.** The exoccipital portions bear the **occipital condyles,** rounded structures for articulation with the **atlas,** or first vertebra. The inner surface of the occipital bone has a roughened appearance, the depressions of which correspond to the convolutions of the cerebellar portion of the brain. The basioccipital extends anteriorly on the ventral side of the skull to meet the basal portion of the **sphenoid bone.** A small foramen perforates the occipital bone at the ventral anterior border of each occipital condyle. It is called the **hypoglossal canal,** since the hypoglossal cranial nerve (XII) passes through it. Inside the foramen magnum and dorsal to each condyle is a small **condyloid canal.** A vein from the transverse sinus inside the skull passes through the condyloid canal.

The large **parietal bones** lie anterior to the occipital on the dorsal surface. A prominent suture marks their point of union in the middorsal line. Each parietal extends rather far down on each side. On the inner surface is a prominent shelf, the **tentorium,** which in life lies between the cerebral and cerebellar portions of the brain. The tentorium really represents an ossification of the **dura mater** (page 204), which becomes secondarily united to the parietal bones. Each parietal articulates with the sphenoid bone by means of the tentorium. This is not obvious on casual examination.

A small, wedgelike, triangular **interparietal bone** lies between the occipital and posterior parts of the parietals. This bone is prominent in kittens but sooner or later fuses with the parietals.

Anterior to the parietals lie the paired **frontal bones** which form the remainder of the roof of the cranium as well as a large portion of the medial wall of each orbit. A **postorbital process** of the frontal on each side extends laterally and then ventrally toward a similar process projecting upward from the zygomatic arch. In some cats the two processes actually articulate with each other. Each frontal bone contains a cavity, the **frontal sinus.** This is in communication with the nasal passage.

A pair of **nasal bones** extends forward from the frontals to the external nares. A thin **nasoturbinate bone** passes inward from each nasal bone.

Paired **premaxillary bones** form the remainder of the boundary of the external nares. They also compose the anterior end of the upper jaw. Each bears three small **incisor teeth** set in sockets.

The **maxillaries** are large paired bones which form the rest of the jaw on each side as well as a large portion of the roof of the mouth, or **palate.** Each maxillary bears a single large **canine tooth,** three **premolars,** and a very small posterior **molar.** A large dorsal projection of the maxillary forms most of the lateral wall of the nasal passage. From this a thin **maxilloturbinate** extends into the nasal passage. The maxillaries articulate dorsally with nasals and frontals. A projection just above the premolar teeth is called the **malar process** of the maxillary, since it articulates with the **malar (jugal) bone.** A large **infraorbital foramen** pierces this portion of the maxillary bone. It serves for the passage of the infraorbital branch of the superior maxillary branch of the trigeminal (V) cranial nerve and for the infraorbital artery, which is part of the internal maxillary branch of the external carotid artery. On the ventral surface of the skull the two maxillaries join each other medially. Two large **anterior palatine foramina,** bounded by premaxillaries and maxillaries, lie on either side of the midline. Through these pass the nasal arteries and the nasopalatine branch of the maxillary portion of the trigeminal nerve.

The malar, or jugal, bones form the anterior part of the zygomatic arch. Each articulates with the malar process of the maxillary and is directed posteriorly. It sends a **postorbital process** dorsally toward the postorbital process of the frontal, with which it occasionally unites. The posterior extension of the malar is overlapped by a similar projection of the **temporal bone,** which forms the remainder of the zygomatic arch.

A small **lacrimal bone,** of irregular shape, forms part of the anterior medial wall of the orbit. It lies between maxillary and frontal. At its anterior border is the opening of the **lacrimal canal** which communicates with the nasal cavity.

Another small bone, the **os planum,** which is really part of the **ethmoid,** also forms part of the medial wall of the orbit between lacrimal and frontal.

The **temporal bone** on each side is a complex of four regions which become secondarily united. It forms most of the lateral wall of the cranium posterior to the orbit. The **squamous region** of the temporal is a thin portion which articulates dorsally with the parietal. From it a **zygomatic process** extends anteriorly to meet the similarly named process of the malar. At the base of this process on the ventral side is a depression, the **mandibular fossa**, with which the lower jaw articulates. Only in mammals does the lower jaw articulate in this manner. The **tympanic region** of the temporal consists of the **auditory, or tympanic, bulla,** previously mentioned. The cavity of the **middle ear** and the three ear bones, **malleus, incus,** and **stapes,** lie within the bulla. At its junction with the basioccipital lies the **jugular foramen.** It serves for the passage of the ninth, tenth, and eleventh cranial nerves and the inferior cerebral vein. The **mastoid region** is a heavy, thick portion posterior to the external auditory meatus, lying between squamous and tympanic regions. It bears a small **stylomastoid foramen** through which part of the seventh cranial nerve passes. The **petrous** (stony) **region** cannot be seen from the external surface. It is of dense structure and on the side of the bone toward the cranial cavity. The delicate **inner ear** is enclosed by the petrous region of the temporal bone. A fairly large opening, the **internal auditory meatus,** is to be seen on the medial side of the petrous region. Just within the bone the opening divides into dorsal and ventral portions. The dorsal part is the **facial canal,** through which the seventh cranial nerve passes. The main part of this nerve emerges through the stylomastoid foramen. The lower canal is for the passage of the eighth, or auditory, nerve.

Paired **palatine bones** are included among several other bones on the ventral side of the skull. They lie immediately posterior to the maxillaries, meeting in the midline to complete the **hard palate.** Their posterior borders form the margins of the choanae. A lateral, vertical projection of each palatine contributes to the medial wall of the orbit. Two foramina are located in each vertical plate. These are a small **posterior palatine foramen** and a larger, more dorsal **sphenopalatine foramen.** The former carries the greater palatine branch of the maxillary portion of the trigeminal nerve, which then emerges from the skull through two small foramina on that part of the palatine forming a portion of the roof of the mouth. The descending palatine artery also passes through this foramen. The sphenopalatine foramen carries the sphenopalatine nerve of the maxillary branch of the trigeminal, the sphenopalatine artery, and the posterior nasal nerve.

The **vomer** is a slender unpaired bone with a troughlike depression along its dorsal aspect. It lies in the floor of the nasal cavity, articulating anteriorly with the palatines and maxillaries, posteriorly with the presphenoid, and dorsally with the ethmoid. The vomer forms part of the **nasal septum.**

The unpaired **ethmoid,** which cannot be seen externally, is a complex structure consisting of three parts. Its posterior end is termed the **cribriform plate** because of the numerous **olfactory foramina** which it contains for passage of fibers of the olfactory nerve. The cribriform plate separates the nasal and cranial cavities. A thin median vertical plate of bone, the **lamina perpendicularis** of the ethmoid, extends anteriorly from the cribriform plate. It contributes to the nasal septum. Folded, scroll-like **ethmoturbinates** extend from the cribriform plate into the nasal cavity.

Immediately in back of the vomer and separating the posterior portions of the two palatine bones is the **basal portion** of the **presphenoid.** It is partially overlapped by the vomer, palatines, and wings of the sphenoid (see Fig. 4.2). On either side of the basal portion extends a wing of the presphenoid called the **orbitosphenoid.** These complete the medial walls of the orbits. Each orbitosphenoid bears an **optic foramen** which accommodates the optic nerve and ophthalmic artery.

The **sphenoid bone,** like the presphenoid, is composed of a basal portion, the **basisphenoid,** and two wings, the **alisphenoids.** The basisphenoid lies between the presphenoid and the basioccipital. Its *dorsal* face bears a depression, the **sella turcica,** in which the pituitary body lies. A slight bony projection forming the posterior border of the sella turcica is the **dorsum sellae.** The alisphenoids are thin projections which form articulations with the palatines, orbitosphenoids, frontals, parietals, and temporals. A small, curved **pterygoid process** projects forward from each wing. The alisphenoids partially overlap the basal portion of the presphenoid. Two foramina lie in each alisphenoid. These are an anterior **foramen rotundum** and a posterior **foramen ovale.** Both carry branches of the fifth cranial nerve. Another foramen, the **orbital fissure,** is formed at the junction of the orbitosphenoids and alisphenoids. Through it pass oculomotor, trochlear, and abducens nerves going to the eye muscles. Part of the trigeminal nerve, a vein, and a branch of the internal maxillary artery also pass through the orbital fissure. Anterior to the tympanic bulla and bounded by it and the alisphenoid is a **canal for the passage of the Eustachian tube.**

The lower jaw, or **mandible** (Fig. 4.3), consists of two halves united firmly at their anterior ends by the **mandibular symphysis.** Each bone bears several teeth along its alveolar surface. There are three small **incisors,** one large **canine,** two **premolars,** and one **molar.** A space, the **diastema,** separates the canine from the first premolar. A large depression, the **masseteric fossa,** on the lateral surface of the mandible marks the place of insertion of the masseter muscle. At the posterior ventral angle of the bone is an **angular process**, above which is an **inferior notch**. A **condyle** for articulation with the mandibular fossa of the temporal bone is dorsal to the inferior notch.   Above the condyle is the **superior notch** lying along the posterior border of the large **coronoid process** which projects into the temporal fossa.   On the medial face of the mandible near its posterior end is a large **mandibular foramen** through

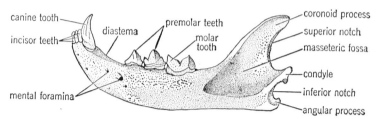

FIG. 4.3.   Lateral view of mandible of cat.

which the inferior alveolar nerve and blood vessels enter the lower jaw. They pass through the **mandibular canal** inside the bone, giving off branches to the teeth, and finally emerge on the lateral anterior face of the mandible as mental vessels and nerves through one or more **mental foramina** near the base of the canine tooth.

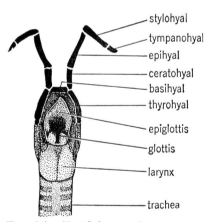

FIG. 4.4.   Hyoid bones of cat shown in relation to larynx and trachea, dorsal view.

The table on page 125 summarizes briefly the names of the various foramina of the cat's skull, their location, and the structures which pass through them.

The hyoid apparatus of the cat (Fig. 4.4) is derived from the second and third arches of the visceral skeleton. It serves to support the tongue and structures of the larynx. It consists on each side of a chain of bones extending from the tympanic bulla to the **thyroid cartilage** of the larynx. Named in order, these bones are **tympanohyal, stylohyal, epihyal, ceratohyal,** and **thyrohyal**. A crossbar, the **basihyal**, connects the two sides at the junction of ceratohyals and thyrohyals. The four bones between the tympanic bulla and the basihyal constitute the **anterior cornua**. The thyrohyals make up the **posterior cornua**. The former correspond to the lesser cornua of the human hyoid and the latter to the greater cornua.

FORAMINA OF THE SKULL OF THE CAT

Name	Location	Structures passing through
Olfactory...............	Cribriform plate of ethmoid	Fibers of olfactory nerve
Optic....................	Orbitosphenoid	Optic nerve and ophthalmic artery
Orbital fissure..............	Junction of orbitosphenoid and alisphenoid	Oculomotor, trochlear, abducens, ophthalmic branch of V, internal maxillary artery, vein from sinus cavernosus
Infraorbital...............	Malar process of maxillary	Infraorbital branch of maxillary of V, infraorbital artery
Anterior palatine...........	Between premaxillary and maxillary	Nasopalatine branch of V and nasal artery
Posterior palatine..........	Palatine	Greater palatine branch of V, descending palatine artery
Sphenopalatine.............	Vertical plate of palatine	Sphenopalatine branch of V, posterior nasal nerve, sphenopalatine artery
Rotundum...............	Alisphenoid	Maxillary branch of trigeminal
Ovale....................	Alisphenoid	Mandibular branch of trigeminal, internal maxillary artery
Mandibular...............	Inner face of mandible	Inferior alveolar nerve (V) and vessels
Mental...................	Lateral anterior face of mandible	Mental vessels and nerves (V)
Facial canal...............	Petrous region of temporal	Facial nerve (VII)
Stylomastoid..............	Mastoid region of temporal	Facial nerve (VII)
Internal auditory meatus....	Petrous region of temporal	Auditory nerve (VIII)
Jugular..................	Junction of temporal and basioccipital	Glossopharyngeal (IX), vagus (X), spinal accessory (XI), inferior cerebral vein
Hypoglossal..............	Occipital	Hypoglossal nerve (XII)
Condyloid canal...........	Occipital	Small vein
Magnum..................	Occipital	Spinal cord

Vertebral Column

The notochord, or precursor of the vertebral column, is present in the cat only during the early part of embryonic life. It is completely replaced by the bony centra of the vertebrae. The vertebral column is divided into five regions. There are **7 cervical, 13 thoracic, 7 lumbar, 3 sacral,** and from **4 to 26 caudal vertebrae.** Those in each region, although having several features in common, nevertheless possess certain distinguishing characteristics.

The following features are common to all the vertebrae with the exception of the first, or atlas, and most of those of the tail. Each consists of a **body,** or **centrum,** a solid, rounded portion which lies ventrad the spinal cord. The centra of adjacent vertebrae articulate with each other by means of cartilaginous **intervertebral discs** interposed between them. A thin bony plate, the **epiphysis,** is present at either end of the centrum. In kittens the epiphyses are easily separated from the remainder of the

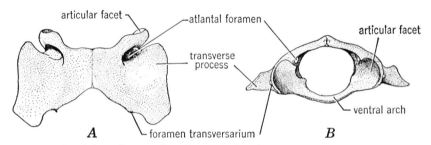

Fig. 4.5.   Atlas vertebra of cat: *A,* dorsal view; *B,* anterior view.

centrum, but in adults they are firmly united with it. Above the centrum and on either side a **neural process** extends dorsally. The two neural processes unite, forming a **neural arch** that encloses the spinal cord. A **neural spine,** or **spinous process,** projects dorsally from the top of the neural arch. **Transverse processes** are lateral projections from the centrum and sides of the neural arch. At the caudal border of each neural process is an **intervertebral notch** lying just above the centrum. A smaller notch of similar nature is present at the cranial border of each neural process. When two vertebrae are articulated, the two notches form an **intervertebral foramen** for the exit of a spinal nerve. On the cranial border of each neural process is a projection, the **cranial articular process,** or **prezygapophysis.** A smooth **articular facet** is located on its *dorsal* surface. On the caudal border at the base of the neural spine is a similar **caudal articular process,** or **postzygapophysis,** with an articular facet on its *ventral* surface. The prezygapophyses of one vertebra articulate with the postzygapophyses of the vertebra immediately in front of it by means of their articular facets.

Cervical vertebrae. The first two of the seven cervical vertebrae differ so markedly from the others that they are best described separately.

The **atlas**, or first cervical vertebra (Fig. 4.5), differs from all others in that it lacks a spinous process and a centrum. The centrum has been appropriated by the second cervical vertebra, as noted below. In place of the centrum there is a narrow **ventral arch**, at the caudal end of which is a slight median projection, the **tuberculum anterius.** The transverse processes are in the form of large winglike masses which extend laterally for some distance. A **foramen transversarium**, through which the vertebral artery and vein pass, is located at the base of each transverse process. The cranial border of the atlas is marked by a pair of deep depressions, the **articular facets,** which receive the occipital condyles of the

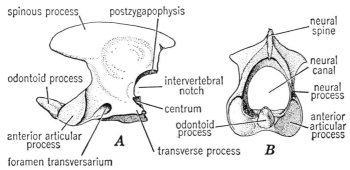

spinous process   postzygapophysis   neural
                                                             spine

                                                             neural
odontoid process   intervertebral   canal
                                         notch   neural
                                                             process
                             centrum
                             odontoid   anterior
                              process   articular
anterior articular   *A*   process
       process   transverse process   *B*
foramen transversarium

Fig. 4.6.   Axis vertebra of cat: *A,* lateral view; *B,* anterior view.

skull. Dorsal to them are located the **atlantal foramina,** through which the vertebral vessels are continued. At the caudal border of the bone are smaller articular processes, or depressions, for articulation with the second vertebra, the axis.

The **axis**, or **epistropheus** (Fig. 4.6), bears a marked projection, the **dens,** or **odontoid process,** at the anterior end of its centrum. This is really the centrum of the atlas which has formed a secondary union with the axis. On either side of the base of the odontoid process is a rounded **anterior articular process** for articulation with the atlas. A pair of small transverse processes extends ventrolaterally from the centrum and base of the neural process. Each is pierced by a foramen transversarium. The neural spine is long, flattened, and unusually prominent. The caudal end of the axis bears postzygapophyses with their characteristic ventral articular facets.

The remaining five cervical vertebrae are rather similar to one another. The spinous processes become progressively longer in passing posteriorly.

The distinguishing feature of the cervical vertebrae is the presence of foramina transversaria (Fig. 4.7), which are lacking only in the seventh, or last. The transverse processes arise by two roots, one from the neural process and one from the centrum. The foramen transversarium lies between the two on each side. Distally the transverse process divides into two projections, a dorsal **transverse process proper** and a ventral **costal process** that represents the remains of a cervical rib.

Thoracic vertebrae. The distinctive features of the thoracic vertebrae (Fig. 4.8) are those associated with rib articulation, for only these vertebrae bear ribs. Each transverse process, which is a lateral projection from the neural arch, has a smooth **tubercular facet** on the ventral side near the tip for articulation with the tuberculum of the rib. All except the first, eleventh, twelfth, and thirteenth bear **cranial** and **caudal costal**

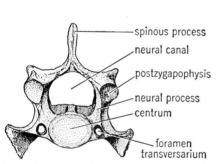
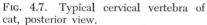
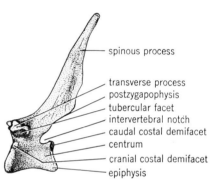

Fig. 4.7. Typical cervical vertebra of cat, posterior view.

Fig. 4.8. Thoracic vertebra of cat, lateral view.

demifacets. These are small, smooth areas at the dorsolateral angles of the cranial and caudal borders of the centrum. When in position, the caudal costal demifacet of one vertebra and the cranial costal demifacet of the next posterior vertebra together form a depression, or **costal facet,** for reception of the capitulum of a rib. Each rib, therefore, articulates with two vertebrae. The first thoracic vertebra bears an entire facet at its anterior end and a demifacet at its caudal end. Each of the eleventh, twelfth, and thirteenth thoracic vertebrae bears an entire facet on each side of the centrum. These three vertebrae lack tubercular facets. The neural spines of the anterior thoracic vertebrae are long and slope posteriorly, but, beginning with number 10, they become perceptibly shorter and change their direction so as to point anteriorly.

Lumbar vertebrae. The seven lumbar vertebrae are longer than those in the thoracic region. Their spinous processes project anteriorly (Fig. 4.9). The transverse processes, arising from the centra, are prominent and project in a ventrocranial direction. Smaller **accessory transverse processes,** coming from the neural arch above the intervertebral notch, are prominent. They are frequently lacking on the sixth and seventh lumbar vertebrae. The prezygapophyses bear articular facets on their medial surfaces and rather prominent **mammillary processes** on their dorsolateral surfaces.

Sacrum. Although the sacrum (Fig. 4.10) is considered to be a single bone, it is obviously formed by a union of three separate vertebrae. Two pairs of sacral foramina are present on both dorsal and ventral sides. These serve for the passage of the dorsal and ventral rami of the sacral spinal nerves. Three short spinous processes are present, lateral to which are two pairs of tubercles representing the points of union or fusion of prezygapophyses and postzygapophyses. The lateral surface of the anterior portion of the sacrum on each side consists of a large

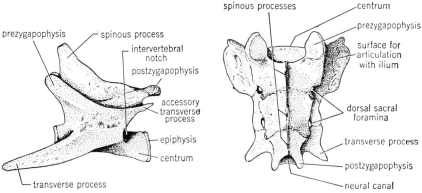

Fig. 4.9. Lumbar vertebra of cat, lateral view.

Fig. 4.10. Sacrum of cat, dorsal view.

roughened expanse, the **lateral mass,** which bears the surface for articulation with the ilium. It undoubtedly represents modified and expanded transverse processes to which sacral ribs have become indistinguishably fused. A pair of freely projecting transverse processes is present toward the caudal end of the bone. A pair of prezygapophyses serves for articulation with the seventh lumbar vertebra, and a pair of postzygapophyses for articulation with the first caudal vertebra.

Caudal vertebrae. The number of caudal vertebrae in the cat usually varies from 21 to 23, although as many as 26 have been observed. The caudal vertebrae decrease gradually in size from the sacrum to the tip of the tail. Only the first eight or nine caudal vertebrae are composed of the typical parts. Posterior to this they consist of little more than centra. On the eighth or ninth vertebra the neural canal is represented by a slight dorsal groovelike depression. Beginning with the third caudal vertebra a pair of rounded **hemal processes** is present on the ventral side. Small **chevron bones** articulate with these to form a hemal arch enclosing a hemal canal. These structures gradually diminish in size finally to disappear near the tip of the tail. Chevron bones are usually missing in prepared skeletons.

RIBS
(Fig. 4.11)

A typical rib, such as the fifth or sixth, consists first of a **head**, or **capitulum**, the end of which articulates with the centra of two adjacent vertebrae by means of their costal demifacets. Close to the capitulum

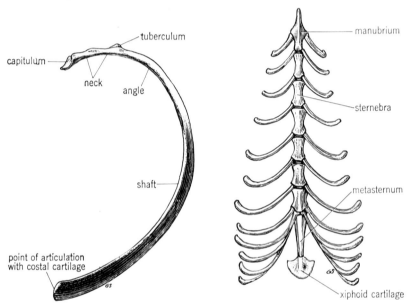

FIG. 4.11. Vertebral section of human rib. (*Drawn by G. Schwenk.*)

FIG. 4.12. Sternum of cat showing relation to costal cartilages. (*Drawn by G. Schwenk.*)

is the **tuberculum** (**tubercle**), which articulates with the tubercular facet on the ventral side of the transverse process. The portion between capitulum and tubercle is referred to as the **neck**. Distal to the tubercle is the long portion, or **shaft**, of the rib. The region where the shaft makes an abrupt turn, or bend, is the **angle**. The rib is bony. Its distal end is connected to the sternum by an intervening **costal cartilage**. There are 13 pairs of ribs in the cat. Only the first nine are considered to be **true ribs**, since they are the only ones to connect directly with the sternum. The remaining four are **false ribs**, of which the first three articulate with other ribs, the last ending freely and being called a **floating rib**. The length of the ribs of the cat increases from the first to the ninth. After the tenth they again become smaller. A decrease in thickness occurs from the fifth to the thirteenth. Not all the ribs are alike in structure. The first is flattened and has no perceptible angle. The last three lack tubercles.

The **breastbone** (Fig. 4.12) is composed of eight separate elements called **sternebrae.** The most anterior sternebra is the **presternum,** or **manubrium.** The costal cartilages of the first pair of ribs articulate with it near the central portion. The next six sternebrae, in their aggregate, make up the **mesosternum,** or **gladiolus.** The last piece is the **metasternum,** or **xiphoid process,** to the end of which is attached a flattened **xiphoid cartilage.** The second costal cartilage articulates at the junction of manubrium and gladiolus. The next five are attached at points of union of sternebrae. The eighth and ninth ribs join the seventh sternebra.

Appendicular Skeleton

PECTORAL GIRDLE

The **shoulder girdle** is composed of only two bones, the **scapula** and the **clavicle.** A third element, the coracoid, present in lower tetrapods but only in monotremes among mammals, is represented by the small **coracoid process** of the scapula.

The scapula, or shoulder blade (Fig. 4.13), is a large, flat bone, its shorter, more curved border being anterior. At its ventral end is a depression, the **glenoid fossa,** for articulation with the humerus. The coracoid process, mentioned above,

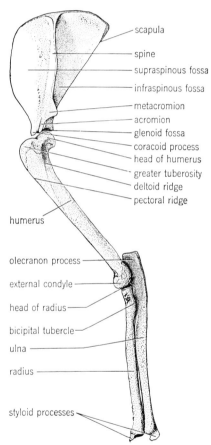

FIG. 4.13. Lateral view of left pectoral girdle and limb bones of cat.

is a medial projection at the anterior end of the glenoid fossa. A prominent keel, the **spine,** runs along the outer border of the scapula. It divides the surface into two large fossae, an anterior **supraspinous fossa** and a posterior **infraspinous fossa.** A projection at the end of the

spine near the glenoid fossa is the **acromion**.   Dorsal to this an angular
process of the spine, the **metacromion**, projects caudad.   The large,
shallow depression on the medial side of the scapula is the **subscapular
fossa**.

The clavicle of the cat is poorly developed.   It consists of a short,
slender rod of bone with no articulations.   It is merely embedded in
muscle tissue.   In some mammals, such as man, the clavicle is a well-
developed bone extending from scapula to sternum.

FORELIMB

The **upper arm** (Fig. 4.13) contains a single bone, the **humerus**.   A
rounded **head** on the medial side of the proximal end articulates with
the glenoid fossa.   The **greater tuberosity** is a prominent ridge extending
forward from the lateral border of the head.   A smaller ridge, the **lesser
tuberosity**, projects anteromedially from the head.   Between the tuberosities is a deep **bicipital groove** which receives the tendon of the biceps
muscle.   Two ridges extend distally from the greater tuberosity.   The
more anterior of the two is the **pectoral ridge**.   The **deltoid ridge** starts
at the posterior end of the greater tuberosity.   Not quite halfway down
the shaft of the humerus it meets the pectoral ridge.   The distal end of
the humerus is marked by two projections, the **external** and **internal
condyles**.   A large **supracondyloid foramen**, through which the brachial
artery and median nerve of the arm pass, is situated just above the inner
condyle.   The smooth area between the condyles is the surface for
articulation with radius and ulna.   On the caudal side of the bone between the two condyles is a deep depression, the **olecranon fossa**, into
which a projection of the olecranon process of the ulna fits.

Two bones, the **radius**, and the **ulna**, are located in the forearm.   The
ulna is the larger of the two.   The prominent notch at the proximal end,
for articulation with the humerus, is the **greater sigmoid cavity**.   The
part of the bone proximad this cavity is the **olecranon process**, or elbow.
Just distad the greater sigmoid cavity is a smaller depression arranged
in a transverse position.   This is the **lesser sigmoid cavity** with which
the head of the radius articulates.   A projection mediad the lesser
sigmoid cavity and distad the greater sigmoid cavity is the **coronoid
process**.   A **styloid process** projects from the distal end of the ulna.
The radius articulates by means of its head with the humerus and with
the lesser sigmoid cavity of the ulna.   Just distad the head is a **bicipital
tubercle** for insertion of the tendon of the biceps muscle.   The distal end
of the radius is larger than the head and, like the ulna, bears a **styloid
process.**

The **carpus, or wrist,** of the cat (Fig. 4.14) is composed of seven
bones arranged in two rows.   The three bones making up the proximal

row are the **scapholunar,** a large bone with which the radius articulates; the **cuneiform,** with which the ulna articulates; and the **pisiform,** somewhat smaller than the scapholunar and articulating with the styloid process of the ulna. In man the scapholunar is represented by two bones, the navicular and lunate. The cuneiform is referred to as the triangular. The pisiform is called by the same name in both. The distal row of carpal bones consists of four separate elements named in order, from medial to lateral sides, the **trapezium, trapezoid, magnum,** and **unciform.** In man these bones are called, respectively, the greater multangular, lesser multangular, capitate, and hamate. Several **sesamoid bones,** representing ossified areas in tendons, are present in addition to the bones mentioned.

The **metacarpus,** or **hand** (Fig. 4.14), is composed of five long **metacarpal bones.** They are numbered from 1 to 5 beginning on the medial side.

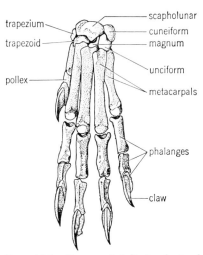

Fig. 4.14. Bones of left forefoot of cat as seen from above. The pisiform is not shown in this view.

The cat has five **digits,** or **fingers,** on the forefeet. Each except the first consists of three **phalanges.** The first, or most medial, digit, known as the **thumb,** or **pollex,** contains only two phalanges. The terminal phalanx in each case bears a depression, from the center of which projects a narrow bony plate. This gives support to the retractile claw. The second finger is known as the **index,** the third as the **medius,** the fourth as the **annularis,** and the fifth as the **minimus.**

PELVIC GIRDLE

The girdle supporting the hind limb is composed of two halves, the **innominate bones** (Fig. 4.15), joined together ventrally to form a **symphysis.** Near the center on the lateral side of each innominate bone is a depression, the **acetabulum,** which receives the head of the femur. The acetabulum marks the point of union of the three components of the innominate bone, namely the **ilium, ischium,** and **pubis.** Although easily recognizable as separate entities in kittens, these bones are rigidly fused together in adults. A fourth component, consisting of a small **acetabular,** or **cotyloid, bone** helps to form the acetabulum. It is wedged in between the others at their point of union. The ilium is the long portion of the innominate bone anterior to the acetabulum. It is joined to the vertebral column at the sacrum. The ischium lies posterodorsal to the acetabulum. It joins the symphysis ventrally. The pubis is the ventromedial projection. A large opening in each innominate bone between ischium and pubis is the **obturator foramen.**

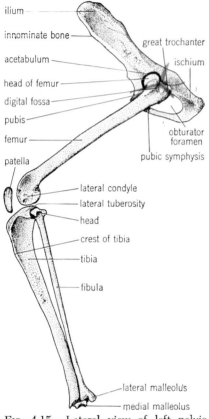

ilium

innominate bone

great trochanter

acetabulum

ischium

head of femur

digital fossa

pubis

obturator foramen

femur

pubic symphysis

patella

lateral condyle

lateral tuberosity

head

crest of tibia

tibia

fibula

lateral malleolus

medial malleolus

Fig. 4.15. Lateral view of left pelvic girdle and limb bones of cat.

HIND LIMB

The **femur,** or thigh, bone is the single large bone in the upper leg (Fig. 4.15). A large, rounded **head** articulates with the acetabulum. Lateral to the head is a constricted **neck,** anterolaterad of which is a prominent projection, the **greater trochanter.** A depression, the **digital,** or **trochanteric, fossa,** lies between the head and the greater trochanter on the posterior side of the bone. On the posteromedial side, a short distance below the head, is a small tubercle, the **lesser trochanter.** At the distal end of the shaft of the femur are lateral and medial **condyles** for articulation with the tibia. An **intercondyloid fossa** lies between them. In front of this is located the **patella,** or **kneecap,** a pear-shaped sesamoid bone within the tendon of the quadriceps femoris muscle. Three additional small sesamoid bones are usually found in the patellar region.

The **lower leg,** or **crus** (Fig. 4.15), is made up of two bones: a large stout **tibia** and a very slender **fibula.** The tibia of the cat is the longest bone in the body. At its proximal end are lateral and medial **tuberosities,** each with an articular facet for contact with the condyles of the femur. The anterior face of the proximal end of the shaft of the tibia is in the form of a narrow ridge, or **crest.** The distal end of the bone is longer on the medial side, the projection being spoken of as the **medial malleolus.** On the lateral side of the distal end is a facet for articulation with the end of the fibula. The fibula is situated along the lateral border of the tibia. Both ends of the fibula are expanded and form articulations with the tibia.   A projection at the distal end is the **lateral malleolus.**   It bears a facet at the point where it joins the tibia and another for articulation with the astragalus.

The **tarsus,** or **ankle,** of the cat (Fig. 4.16), like the carpus, is composed of seven bones arranged in two rows.   A prominent heel bone, or **calcaneum,** is the longest of all the tarsal bones.   Between it and the tibia is the **astragalus,** or **talus,** with which both tibia and fibula articulate.   Distad the astragalus is the **scaphoid,** or **navicular.** In human anatomy calcaneum, astragalus, and scaphoid are called calcaneus, talus, and navicular, respectively.   The distal row of four tarsal bones consists of a **cuboid,** at the end of the calcaneum, and **lateral, intermediate,** and **medial cuneiforms,** proceeding in order medially from the cuboid.   In man these are referred to as the cuboid and third, second, and first cuneiform bones.   The scaphoid lies between the astragalus and the three cuneiform bones.   The cuboid forms articulations with the fourth and fifth metatarsals, the lateral cuneiform with the third, the intermediate with the second, and the medial cuneiform with the very small, rudimentary first metatarsal.   In the cat the **big toe,** or **hallux,** is absent.   Each of the four remaining

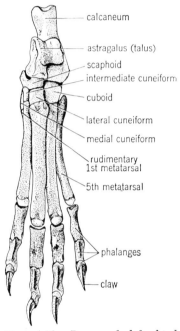

Fig. 4.16.   Bones of left hind foot of cat as seen from above.

digits is composed of three **phalanges,** the terminal one of which bears the claw.   Sesamoid bones are found near the joints in the hind feet.

Joints

Two general types of joints are recognized: (1) **synarthroses,** or **immovable joints;** (2) **diarthroses,** or **movable joints.**

Among synarthroses in the cat are the **sutures** located between the various bones of the skull.   The type of union exemplified by the roots of teeth fitting into sockets in the mandible, premaxillary, and maxillary bones is referred to as a **gomphosis.**   Another type of synarthrosis is called a **schindylesis.**   The articulation of the lamina perpendicularis of the ethmoid bone with the dorsal groove of the vomer is an example of a schindylesis.

In the diarthrosis, or type of joint permitting freedom of motion, the end of each bone is covered with cartilage. Between adjacent bones is a fluid-filled **synovial capsule,** composed of an outer, dense **fibrous layer** and an inner, very thin **synovial membrane** which is reflected over the cartilage at the end of the bone. About this complex are several ligaments which bind the bones together. Several types of diarthrosis are recognized. The **ball-and-socket joint,** or **enarthrosis,** is exemplified by such joints as are found at the shoulder and hip. The **hinge joint,** or **ginglymus,** is found at the elbow and knee. Gliding joints, or **arthrodia,** occur in the ankle and wrist. The **pivotal joint,** or **rotatorium,** is illustrated by the point of articulation of atlas and axis. In some diarthroses, **articular discs,** or **menisci,** may at least partially separate the joint cavity into two parts. Such are the **semilunar cartilages** in the knee joint, which add to its complexity.

MUSCULAR SYSTEM

The muscles of the body are of two types: involuntary and voluntary. **Involuntary,** or **smooth, muscles,** which are under control of the peripheral autonomic nervous system, occur in the form of continuous sheets. They are found in the walls of various parts of the alimentary canal, blood vessels, ureters, reproductive ducts, bronchial tubes, etc. The **cardiac muscle** of the heart is an involuntary muscle of a special type. Involuntary muscles do not lend themselves well to dissection. Special histological preparations are usually required for their study. We shall therefore disregard them in our consideration of the muscular system of the cat.

Voluntary muscles are responsible for all ordinary movements of various parts of the body. Since there are over 500 such muscles in the cat, it is not feasible to consider all of them in detail in a volume such as this. The student who is interested in a more comprehensive study of cat musculature is referred to the most recent edition of J. Reighard and H. S. Jennings, "The Anatomy of the Cat," Henry Holt and Company, Inc.

Voluntary muscles are innervated by branches of cranial and spinal nerves. They exist as separate masses which are easily isolated from one another in properly preserved specimens. The muscles of freshly killed animals are studied with much more difficulty than those of preserved specimens. Each muscle is surrounded by a sheet of connective tissue known as **fascia.** Fasciae also bind together groups of muscles. Dissection of muscles consists largely of tearing the fasciae between the separate elements so as to detach them.

Each end of a voluntary muscle is attached to some other structure. The structures to which they are attached are usually bones, but in some cases they join ligaments or tendons of other muscles. One end is generally attached to a part which is less movable than that to which the other end is joined. The former point of attachment is referred to as the **origin**; the latter as the **insertion**. Muscles may have one or more points of origin or insertion. Contraction of the muscle causes movement. The muscle must, therefore, pass over a joint in order to be effective in producing motion.

Muscles may have their origin or insertion in fasciae, but most frequently the attachment is accomplished by means of a **tendon**, a glistening white cord of regularly arranged, fibrous connective tissue. The term **aponeurosis** is applied to a broad flat tendon. Ossifications sometimes take place within tendons to form the sesamoid bones, referred to in connection with the skeletal system. The patella, or kneecap, is a good example of a sesamoid bone. Some muscles form ringlike bands around openings or cavities which are thus closed by muscular contraction. They are called **sphincter muscles**. Those sphincters closing the pylorus and anal openings are examples. Some muscles are attached to **raphes**. The term raphe is used to designate a furrow, or line, which marks the fusion of the two halves of certain sym-

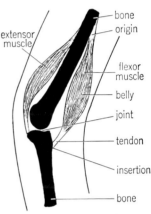

Fig. 4.17. Diagram showing method of origin and insertion of flexor and extensor muscles.

metrical parts. The midventral line in the abdominal region is marked by a raphe, the **linea alba,** which separates the ventral muscles of the two sides of the body. Other raphes are present in the ventral thoracic region and along the middorsal line.

Voluntary muscles are arranged, in most cases, in opposing groups or sets of two, one set acting in just the opposite manner from that of the other (Fig. 4.17). Such groups are named according to their action, thus:

Flexors tend to bend a limb or to bend one part of a limb against another.
Extensors tend to straighten a limb or one of its component parts.
Abductors draw a part away from a median line or from a neighboring part or limb. Abductors of a limb swing the limb in a direction away from the median longitudinal axis of the body; abductors of the digits move the digits in a direction away from the median longitudinal axis of the limb.
Adductors draw a part toward a median line or toward a neighboring part or limb. Adductors of a limb swing the limb in a direction toward the median longitudinal axis of the body; adductors of the digits move the digits in a direction toward the median longitudinal axis of the limb.

Rotators are muscles which revolve a part on its axis. Some rotators are called *pronators* when, as in the case of the arm, they turn the palm of the hand downward. Others, referred to as *supinators*, serve to turn the palm forward and upward.

Elevators, or *levators*, raise, or lift, parts, as in the case of closing the mouth by raising the lower jaw.

Depressors lower, or depress, a part, as when the lower jaw is depressed to open the mouth.

Constrictors draw parts together or contract a part. When constrictors surround an opening such as the mouth, anus, or pylorus, they are termed *sphincters*.

The cat supplied you is an embalmed specimen which has been either singly or doubly injected. Singly injected specimens are those in which the arterial system alone has been injected with colored latex. In doubly injected specimens the arterial system has been injected with latex of one color, and the venous system with that of another color. Sometimes triply injected specimens are available in which the hepatic portal system has been injected, in addition.

You will be asked to skin your own cat, following the directions given below. After the animal has been skinned it is important that the tissues be prevented from drying out and hardening. If this occurs, dissection may be impossible or, in any event, extremely difficult. Plastic bags are usually supplied by biological supply houses. When not working on the specimen, keep it in such a bag or other container to prevent drying.

Place the animal on its back and make a longitudinal midventral incision from the neck to the inguinal region, being careful not to cut too deeply. Next, cut through the skin on the underside of each limb from the midventral incision to wrist or ankle, as the case may be. Then make a circular cut around the neck, wrists, ankles, and base of the tail. We shall leave the skin on the head, feet, genital region, and tail for the time being, since these parts are more apt to dry than the others. The skin from these regions may then be removed at the appropriate point in your dissection.

Now, using the handle of your scalpel or your fingers, gradually loosen the skin from the body by tearing through the loose layer of connective tissue (superficial fascia) which binds the two together. Any exceptionally tough strands may be cut with the scalpel. Notice that there are certain muscles which have their insertion on the skin. Cut through these as near to the skin as possible. It will also be necessary to cut numerous small blood vessels passing to and from the skin. In female specimens, particularly if they are pregnant or lactating, care must be exercised so as not to remove the mammary tissue or the nipples. The skin around the base of each nipple may be cut so as to prevent this. Preferably the skin should be removed in one piece. It may then be used to wrap around the body when the specimen is put away. Surplus embalming fluid in the subcutaneous tissues will leak out within a few hours after skinning, and the underlying muscles will then have a fresh, clean appearance. If any difficulty is encountered, ask the instructor for help.

Dissection of muscles consists mostly in separating parts, not cutting them to pieces. As mentioned previously, this is done largely by tearing connective tissue. If time permits, most of the muscles of the cat should be studied. If time is limited, however, study of the muscles of the hind leg alone is often sufficient to give the student a fair comprehension of the manner in which muscles are arranged and how they function. Ask the instructor for aid in starting you on the work of dissection. Each muscle is to be identified separately, and its origin and insertion located.

In the following pages various muscles are grouped together according to certain regions of the body. A brief description of each, together with its origin, insertion, and action, is given in order that the student may locate the muscle without too much difficulty.

Cutaneous Muscles

Cutaneus maximus or panniculus carnosus. This dermal muscle consists of a thin layer of fibers on the undersurface of the skin over chest, shoulder, thoracic, and abdominal regions.

Origin. Linea alba, outer surface of latissimus dorsi (see page 146), muscles of the arm in the ventral axillary region.

Insertion. Dermis of the skin.

Action. To move or shake the skin.

Platysma. A thin layer of muscle fibers, the platysma, covers the sides of the neck and lower part of the face. It is divided into several parts which are separated with difficulty.

Origin. Fascia of middorsal line, side of neck near lower anterior border of scapula.

Insertion. Skin of face, neck, ears, eyelids, lips.

Action. Moves skin of neck and face.

Muscles of the Abdomen
(Fig. 4.18)

External oblique. On either side of the linea alba, in the abdominal region, lies the superficial external oblique muscle. It forms a broad, flat sheet, the fibers of which pass in an anterodorsal direction.

Origin. Fascia in dorsolumbar region, last 9 or 10 ribs.

Insertion. Midventral raphe of thoracic region, linea alba, cranial border of pubis.

Action. Constricts the abdominal region.

Internal oblique. Immediately beneath the external oblique lies a thin muscular sheet, the internal oblique muscle. Its fibers are arranged almost at right angles to those of the external oblique.

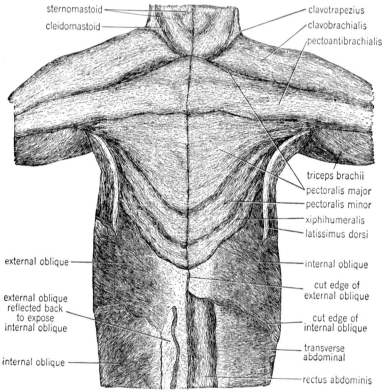

FIG. 4.18. Muscles of abdomen and chest of cat, ventral view. (*Drawn by Joanne Moore.*)

Origin. From the same dorsolumbar fascia where part of the external oblique originates; from the crest of the ilium.

Insertion. Linea alba by an aponeurosis.

Action. Compresses abdominal region.

Transverse abdominal. Another thin muscular sheet lies beneath the internal oblique. The fibers of this muscle course in a transverse direction over the entire abdominal region.

Origin. From costal cartilages of the false and floating ribs, transverse processes of lumbar vertebrae, ventral border of the ilium.

Insertion. Linea alba by a thin aponeurosis.

Action. Constricts the abdominal region.

Rectus abdominis. Consisting of two longitudinally directed halves separated by the linea alba, the rectus abdominis extends from the costal cartilage of the first rib to the pubis. This muscle lies within a sheath formed by the aponeuroses of the two oblique and the transverse abdominal muscles.

Origin. Pubis.

Insertion. Costal cartilages of first and second ribs, anterior end of sternum.

Action. Compresses abdominal region; draws ribs and sternum caudad.

Muscles of the Chest
(Fig. 4.18)

The thoracic muscles are arranged in superficial and deep layers. The superficial muscles are primarily associated with movements of the fore-limbs and pectoral girdle. On the ventral side lie the chest muscles, usually referred to as the **pectoralis group.** The four pairs of muscles of which this group is composed are not always easy to distinguish.

Pectoantibrachialis. The most superficial muscle in the pectoralis group is the pectoantibrachialis.

Origin. Manubrium of the sternum.

Insertion. Proximal part of ulna.

Action. Pulls arm toward chest.

Pectoralis major. The pectoralis major, which lies immediately above and caudad the pectoantibrachialis, is composed of superficial and deep portions.

Origin. SUPERFICIAL PORTION. Midventral thoracic raphe in region of manubrium.

Insertion. SUPERFICIAL PORTION. Pectoral ridge of humerus.

Origin. DEEP PORTION. Cephalic half of sternum and midventral raphe immediately anterior to the sternum.

Insertion. DEEP PORTION. Humerus along a line parallel to the deltoid ridge and continued on to lower pectoral ridge.

Action. PECTORALIS MAJOR. Draws arm inward and turns forefoot in a forward direction.

Pectoralis minor. The pectoralis minor lies just posterior to the pectoralis major, from which it is rather indistinctly separated.

Origin. From the six sternebrae making up the gladiolus of the sternum; in some cases from the xiphoid process as well.

Insertion. Humerus, along ventral border of bicipital groove and along pectoral ridge.

Action.   Pulls arm and shoulder toward chest.

Xiphihumeralis.   A narrow muscle, the xiphihumeralis, is situated just posterior to the pectoralis minor, of which it is sometimes considered to be a part.

Origin.   Midventral raphe in region of xiphoid process of sternum.

Insertion.   On ventral border of bicipital groove of humerus.

Action.   Aids pectoralis minor in pulling arm and shoulder toward chest.

Ventral and Lateral Muscles of the Neck and Head
(Fig. 4.19)

The large external jugular vein is easily observed on the ventrolateral side of the neck anterior to the muscles of the pectoralis group. It takes a rather superficial course. Lymph glands and the submaxillary salivary gland are also prominent in this region. They should be removed on one side so as to expose the underlying superficial muscles of the neck region for study.

Sternomastoid.   Immediately craniad the pectoantibrachialis and dorsal to the external jugular vein lies the sternomastoid muscle.

Origin.   Midventral raphe of thorax and manubrium of sternum.

Insertion.   Lambdoidal ridge, mastoid region of temporal bone.

Action.   Turns head; the two sides act together in pulling the head toward the neck.

Clavotrapezius.   Dorsolaterad the sternomastoid and pectoantibrachialis are two muscles which appear to be continuous. The more anterior of the two is the clavotrapezius. It is a wide muscle covering most of the lateral portion of the neck. The clavotrapezius is the most anterior of the three components of the trapezius muscle (see page 145).

Origin.   Lambdoidal ridge, middorsal raphe over axis vertebra.

Insertion.   Clavicle, raphe between clavotrapezius and clavobrachialis.

Action.   Pulls scapula forward and upward.

Clavobrachialis.   The posterior continuation of the clavotrapezius, mentioned above, is the clavobrachialis.

Origin.   Clavicle, raphe between clavotrapezius and clavobrachialis.

Insertion.   On brachialis muscle (see page 152) a short distance before the latter inserts on the medial side of the ulna near the greater sigmoid cavity.

Action.   Flexes the forearm.

Cleidomastoid.   When viewed from the ventral side, the cleidomastoid muscle is obscured by the sternomastoid and clavotrapezius, since it lies just above them. The latter muscles must be separated in order to observe the cleidomastoid.

Origin.   Mastoid region of temporal bone.

Insertion. Clavicle, raphe laterad the clavicle.

Action. Depends upon whether clavicle or head is in a fixed position. (1) Turns head, pulls head toward neck; (2) pulls clavicle forward.

Sternohyoid. Dorsal to the sternomastoid and coursing longitudinally on either side of the midventral line is the sternohyoid muscle. It is best to remove the sternomastoid in order to get a clear picture of the sternohyoid.

Origin. Anterior border of first costal cartilage.

Insertion. Basihyal bone.

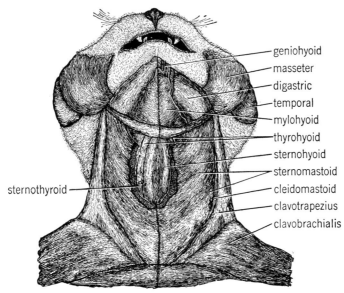

geniohyoid
masseter
digastric
temporal
mylohyoid
thyrohyoid
sternohyoid
sternomastoid
cleidomastoid
clavotrapezius
clavobrachialis

sternothyroid

FIG. 4.19. Ventral and lateral muscles of neck and head regions of cat, ventral view. (*Drawn by Joanne Moore.*)

Action. Depends upon whether hyoid or rib is in fixed position. (1) Pulls ribs and sternum forward and raises them; (2) draws hyoid posteriorly.

Sternothyroid. A small muscle with longitudinally directed fibers; lies dorsal to the sternohyoid on each side of the trachea. The latter muscle should be removed in order to expose the sternothyroid to view.

Origin. Costal cartilage of first rib.

Insertion. Thyroid cartilage of larynx.

Action. Draws larynx posteriorly.

Thyrohyoid. A short, narrow muscle, the thyrohyoid, is located on either side of the larynx anterior to the sternothyroid.

Origin. Thyroid cartilage of larynx.

Insertion. Thyrohyal bone.

Action. Elevates larynx.

Temporal. The temporal muscle can best be seen in a dorsolateral view of the head. It is a large muscle behind the eye and above the external ear.

Origin. Borders of the temporal fossa.

Insertion. Both inner and outer surfaces of the coronoid process of the mandible.

Action. Closes mouth by elevating lower jaw.

Masseter. At the angle of each jaw, posteroventrad the eye and below the temporal muscle, is the large, thick masseter muscle. It lies anterior to the submaxillary and parotid salivary glands. The masseter is the chief muscle used in mastication.

Origin. Zygomatic arch.

Insertion. Masseteric fossa and surrounding area of mandible.

Action. Closes mouth by elevating lower jaw.

Digastric. Just medial to the masseter on the ventral surface of the lower jaw is the digastric muscle.

Origin. Occipital bone a short distance laterad the condyle; mastoid region of temporal.

Insertion. Ventral side of mandible.

Action. Opens mouth by depressing lower jaw.

Mylohyoid. The thin superficial muscle, lying between the digastric and the midventral raphe on each side is the mylohyoid. Its fibers course in a transverse direction.

Origin. Posteromedial surface of mandible.

Insertion. Midventral raphe which extends from hyoid bone to symphysis of mandible.

Action. Pulls hyoid forward; elevates floor of mouth.

Geniohyoid. The geniohyoid muscle can be located by cutting the mylohyoids at their insertion and drawing back the cut edges. This will expose the geniohyoids.

Origin. Symphysis of mandible.

Insertion. Basihyal bone.

Action. Pulls hyoid apparatus forward.

Other Muscles of the Head

Several small muscles, which we shall not consider, are present in the deeper portions of the head and throat region. They are concerned primarily with movements of the tongue, pharynx, and hyoid apparatus and with the elevation of the lower jaw. Twenty or more superficial muscles have been identified on the head of the cat. They are the muscles of facial expression which are believed to be derived from specialized differentiation of various fibers of the platysma muscle (page 139). The separate elements are most difficult to identify.

Superficial Muscles of Dorsal Shoulder and Neck Regions
(Fig. 4.20)

Turning now to the dorsal and lateral side of the animal, several large superficial muscles can be observed in the shoulder and neck regions. The most anterior muscle mass to be observed is the **trapezius.** This muscle is actually composed of three parts, the most anterior of which, the clavotrapezius, has already been described.

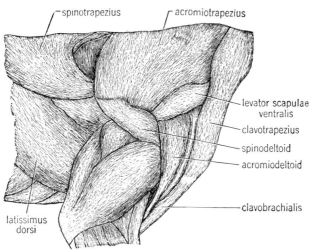

Fig. 4.20. Superficial muscles of right dorsal shoulder and neck regions of cat, lateral view. (*Drawn by Joanne Moore.*)

Acromiotrapezius. The acromiotrapezius, which is sometimes referred to as the superior trapezius, is a wide muscle which lies just posterior to the clavotrapezius.

Origin. Middorsal raphe from neural spine of axis vertebra to spinous processes of the first few thoracic vertebrae.

Insertion. On spine and metacromion of scapula.

Action. Pulls scapula upward; the two muscles aid in holding the scapulae together.

Spinotrapezius. The most posterior of the three trapezius muscles is the spinotrapezius. It is a flat, triangular muscle with a broad origin.

Origin. Tips of the neural spines of most of the thoracic vertebrae.

Insertion. Fascia of supraspinatus and infraspinatus muscles (to be considered later).

Action. Pulls scapula backward and upward.

Levator scapulae ventralis. On the lateral side of the anterior shoulder region the rather small levator scapulae ventralis can be observed lying between the clavotrapezius and acromiotrapezius muscles.

Origin. Transverse process of atlas vertebra; basioccipital bone near tympanic bulla.

Insertion. Ventral border of metacromion.

Action. Pulls scapula forward.

Acromiodeltoid. The acromiodeltoid is a flat muscle which lies ventrad the levator scapulae ventralis and posterior to the clavobrachialis.

Origin. Acromion of scapula.

Insertion. Fascia of spinodeltoid muscle which in turn inserts on the deltoid ridge of the humerus.

Action. Flexes humerus and rotates it in an outward direction.

Spinodeltoid. The spinodeltoid lies over the head of the humerus. It is ventrad the acromiotrapezius and between that muscle and the acromiodeltoid.

Origin. Lower portion of spine of scapula.

Insertion. Deltoid ridge of humerus.

Action. Flexes humerus and rotates it in an outward direction.

Latissimus dorsi. The most prominent of the superficial muscles of the shoulder region as well as the last is the latissimus dorsi. It may be readily identified as a large, flat muscle lying posterior to the trapezius muscles.

Origin. Neural spines of vertebrae from the fifth thoracic to the sixth lumbar.

Insertion. Medial surface of shaft of humerus near proximal end.

Action. Pulls arm backward and upward.

Deeper Muscles of Shoulder and Posterior Neck Region
(Figs. 4.21 and 4.22)

We shall not consider some of the small, deeper muscles of the neck which lie just ventral to the cervical vertebrae. In order to observe the deeper muscles of the shoulder and posterior neck region, it is best to cut across the three trapezius muscles as well as the levator scapulae ventralis, acromiodeltoid, and spinodeltoid. The underlying muscles, together with the borders of the scapula, will then be exposed.

Rhomboideus. The thick rhomboideus lies beneath the acromiotrapezius and spinotrapezius muscles. It connects the neural spines of the vertebrae in this region with the vertebral border of the scapula. The most anterior lateral portion of the rhomboideus may appear as a separate muscle to which the name **rhomboideus capitis** is sometimes applied.

Origin. Neural spines of the first four thoracic vertebrae and the interspinous ligaments in back of these spines.

Insertion. Vertebral border of scapula and its adjacent surfaces.

Action. Pulls scapula upward toward the vertebral column; the rhomboideus capitis portion helps to rotate the scapula by pulling it forward.

Splenius. Craniad the rhomboideus and under the trapezii is a large sheet of muscle which covers the dorsal and lateral sides of the neck. This is the splenius.

Origin. Middorsal line and adjacent fasciae.

Insertion. Lambdoidal ridge of occipital bone.

Action. The two acting together raise the head; each acting independently turns the head sideways.

Supraspinatus. The supraspinatus, which lies under the acromiotrapezius, covers most of the anterior, or supraspinous, fossa of the scapula.

Origin. Surface of supraspinous fossa of scapula.

Insertion. Greater tuberosity of humerus and the capsule covering the shoulder joint.

Action. Extends the humerus.

Infraspinatus. The infraspinatus is a smaller muscle than the supraspinatus. As its name implies, it occupies the greater part of the infraspinous fossa of the scapula. It is somewhat posterior in relation to the spinotrapezius muscle and

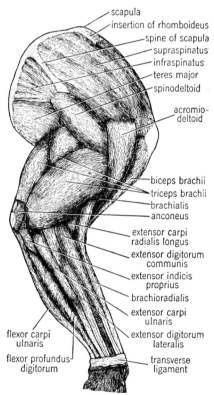

Fig. 4.21. Muscles of right forelimb of cat, lateral view. (*Drawn by Joanne Moore.*)

largely covered by the latissimus dorsi. The lower portion of the infraspinatus is covered by the spinodeltoid.

Origin. Surface of infraspinous fossa of scapula.

Insertion. Ventral portion of the greater tuberosity of humerus.

Action. Rotates the humerus.

Teres major. Covering the caudal border of the scapula is the teres major. It lies directly behind the infraspinatus.

Origin. Caudal border of vertebral portion of scapula and neighboring fasciae.

Insertion. With the tendon of the latissimus dorsi on the medial surface of the shaft of the humerus near its proximal end.

Action. Lowers and rotates the humerus.

Teres minor. The teres minor is a small muscle lying ventrad the infraspinatus and teres major. Its fibers run in a slightly different direction from that of the fibers of these other muscles.

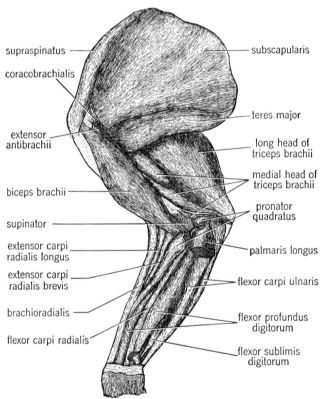

F<small>IG</small>. 4.22. Muscles of right forelimb of cat, medial view. (*Drawn by Joanne Moore.*)

Origin. Portion of caudal border of scapula near glenoid fossa.

Insertion. Greater tuberosity of humerus.

Action. Rotates the humerus.

Subscapularis. The large, triangular muscle on the under, or medial, surface of the scapula is the subscapularis.

Origin. Almost the entire surface of the scapular fossa.

Insertion. Lesser tuberosity of humerus.

Action. Draws humerus toward median line, thus serving as an adductor of the arm.

Serratus anterior. The serratus anterior lies underneath the scapula, between it and the body wall. This muscle is situated directly caudad the levator scapulae, with which it appears to be closely associated. Some authors refer to the levator scapulae as the anterior portion of the serratus anterior.

Origin. By several slips from the most anterior 9 or 10 ribs. The levator scapulae portion comes from the transverse processes of the last five cervical vertebrae.

Insertion. A small area on the medial surface of the scapula near its vertebral border.

Action. Pulls scapula toward wall of thorax in an anterior ventral direction.

Muscles of the Thoracic Wall
(Fig. 4.23)

A few muscles, not yet mentioned, are to be found in the thoracic wall. They are entirely dissociated from the limbs and limb girdles.

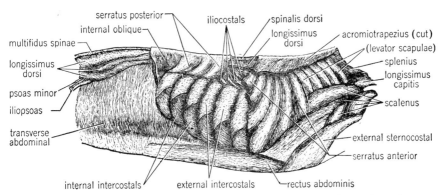

FIG. 4.23. Muscles of right thoracic and abdominal walls of cat, lateral view. (*Drawn by Joanne Moore.*)

Serratus posterior. Underneath the serratus anterior and continuing posteriorly is a thin muscular sheet, the serratus posterior. It covers the surface of the ribs in the upper part of the thorax and neck.

Origin. Middorsal raphe from axis to lumbar region.

Insertion. Outer surfaces of ribs.

Action. Pulls ribs forward.

Scalenus. The scalenus lies on the ventrolateral side of the neck and thorax. It is divided into several parts which are sometimes considered to be separate muscles.

Origin. From the ribs.

Insertion. Transverse processes of all the cervical vertebrae.

Action. Pulls ribs forward or bends neck, depending upon which structures are in a fixed position.

External intercostals. The external intercostal muscles lie in the outer part of the spaces between adjacent ribs. They are not present, however, between the costal cartilages of the first seven or eight ribs.

Origin. Ribs.

Insertion. Ribs.

Action. Pull ribs forward so as to raise them.

Internal intercostals. The small internal intercostal muscles lie directly beneath the external intercostals, from which they are separated with difficulty. The muscle fibers course in a direction almost at right angles to those of the external intercostals.

Origin. Ribs.

Insertion. Ribs.

Action. Pull ribs backward so as to lower them.

External sternocostal. The thin external sternocostal covers over part of the anterior end of the rectus abdominis.

Origin. Sternum between third and sixth ribs.

Insertion. First rib.

Action. Pulls sternum forward.

Internal sternocostal. The internal sternocostal is often referred to as the transverse thoracic muscle. It is really a continuation of the transverse abdominal muscle into the thoracic region and lies on the inner surface of the wall of the thorax.

Origin. Dorsolateral part of sternum from third to eighth ribs.

Insertion. Costal cartilages near their junction with ribs.

Action. Moves ribs.

Muscles of the Back
(Fig. 4.23)

Several muscles of the back, derived from the embryonic epaxial musculature, remain to be considered. Separation of the muscles into distinct masses is by no means so clear-cut as in the case of those which have already been discussed. We shall take up only a few of the more prominent muscles of the back.

Longissimus dorsi. The longissimus dorsi lies beneath the heavy fascia covering the lumbar region. It fills up most of the space between the neural spines and transverse processes of the caudal, sacral, lumbar, thoracic, and cervical vertebrae up to the atlas. The muscle appears to be divided into several parts.

Origin. Caudal, sacral, lumbar, thoracic, and cervical vertebrae; ilium.

Insertion. Parts of vertebrae all along vertebral column.

Action. Extends vertebral column.

Multifidus spinae. The multifidus spinae consists of large numbers of muscle fibers which pass from the transverse processes of one vertebra to the neural spine of another located some distance anterior to it. Anteriorly the multifidus spinae forms a long single muscle which is sometimes considered separately as the **semispinalis cervicis.**

Origin. Transverse processes of vertebrae.

Insertion. Neural spines.

Action. Extends back or bends it, depending upon the particular elements involved.

Iliocostal. Ventrolaterad the longissimus dorsi in the thoracic region lies the iliocostal muscle. It covers part of the dorsal aspect of the ribs and is composed of several separate bundles.

Origin. Ribs.

Insertion. Third or fourth rib craniad that from which it originates.

Action. Draws ribs toward each other.

Spinalis dorsi. Under the dorsal attachment of the serratus posterior lies the spinalis dorsi. It is mediad the anterior end of the longissimus dorsi.

Origin. Tips of neural spines of posterior thoracic vertebrae.

Insertion. Neural spines of anterior thoracic and most cervical vertebrae.

Action. Extends vertebral column.

Iliopsoas. The iliopsoas, which lies ventral to the vertebral column, is described in connection with the muscles of the hind leg (page 160).

Psoas minor. Also located ventral to the vertebral column is the psoas minor, which extends from the ilium to the more posterior thoracic vertebrae.

Origin. Centra of last one or two thoracic vertebrae and anterior lumbar vertebrae.

Insertion. Ilium anterior to acetabulum.

Action. Flexes lumbar region of back.

Quadratus lumborum. The flat quadratus lumborum lies ventral to the vertebral column in the lumbar region.

Origin. Last rib and posterior thoracic vertebrae.

Insertion. Transverse processes of lumbar vertebrae.

Action. Bends vertebral column laterally.

Many other muscles of epaxial origin, which we shall not take up in detail, are to be found in the back. They include the small **interspinal** and **intertransversarial** muscles which connect various parts of adjacent vertebrae. Portions of the longissimus dorsi in the neck region are often considered to be separate muscles. Extensor muscles in the tail are really caudal continuations of the mutifidus spinae or longissimus dorsi muscles. Several flexor and abductor muscles are also present in the tail.

Muscles of the Arm
(Figs. 4.21 and 4.22)

MUSCLES OF THE UPPER ARM, OR BRACHIUM

Triceps brachii. The largest and most conspicuous of the muscles of the upper arm of the cat is the triceps brachii. It is composed of three main parts, or heads, all of which insert by means of a common tendon. The long head is located along the posterior part of the upper arm, the lateral head being directly anterior to it on the lateral surface. The medial head lies under the other two and may, therefore, be observed only by spreading apart the long and lateral heads.

Origin. (1) Lateral head: proximal end of humerus on deltoid ridge; (2) long head: scapula along border of glenoid fossa; (3) medial head: proximal part of dorsal side of humerus.

Insertion. Olecranon process of ulna.

Action. Extends the forearm.

Biceps brachii. The biceps brachii is a thick muscle lying along the anterior portion of the upper arm. In man this muscle has two heads (hence the name) but in the cat there is only one.

Origin. By a tendon from the glenoid fossa of the scapula.

Insertion. Bicipital tubercle of radius.

Action. Flexes the forearm; aids in supination of forearm.

Coracobrachialis. A short muscle on the medial surface of the upper arm, the coracobrachialis covers the joint between humerus and scapula.

Origin. Coracoid process of scapula.

Insertion. Proximal end of humerus on medial surface.

Action. Adducts the humerus.

Extensor antibrachii. The extensor antibrachii, or **epitrochlearis,** is a flat muscle on the inner surface of the upper arm. It partially covers the long head of the triceps.

Origin. Lateral ventral surface of latissimus dorsi.

Insertion. Olecranon process of ulna.

Action. Extends lower arm.

Brachialis. Anterior to the lateral head of the triceps, a rather small muscle, the brachialis, passes along the anterior lateral surface of the upper arm.

Origin. Lateral surface of distal shaft of humerus.

Insertion. Ulna just below the greater sigmoid cavity.

Action. Flexes the forearm.

Anconeus. A small, short muscle, the anconeus, is found in the region of the elbow joint on the lateral side of the arm.

Origin. Dorsal side of distal end of humerus.

Insertion. Lateral side of proximal end of ulna.

Action. May cause a slight rotation of ulna.

MUSCLES OF THE LOWER ARM, OR ANTIBRACHIUM
(Figs. 4.21 and 4.22)

The muscles of the lower arm are chiefly concerned with movements of the hand and digits and with rotary movements required to place the lower arm in prone or supine positions, as the case may be.

Extensor muscles. The extensor muscles of the forearm consist of several long, narrow muscles more or less parallel to each other on the lateral or outer surface of the arm.

Extensor carpi radialis longus. The extensor carpi radialis longus is a long, thin muscle on the lateral side of the lower arm. It is the second muscle from the front of the arm, the first being the brachioradialis (see page 154). It crosses over to the radial or thumb side of the arm.

Origin. A short distance above the lateral condyle of the humerus.

Insertion. By a long, thin tendon on the base of the second metacarpal.

Action. Extends the hand.

Extensor carpi radialis brevis. A very slender muscle, the extensor carpi radialis brevis runs parallel and next to the extensor carpi radialis longus.

Origin. Above the lateral condyle of the humerus.

Insertion. Base of third metacarpal.

Action. Extends the hand.

Extensor digitorum communis. *Origin.* Above lateral condyle of humerus.

Insertion. The tendon of the muscle divides into four parts which insert on the dorsal surfaces of the phalanges of the second, third, fourth, and fifth digits, respectively.

Action. Extends the four digits on which it inserts.

Extensor digitorum lateralis. *Origin.* Above lateral condyle of humerus.

Insertion. The tendon of the muscle divides into three parts which insert on the dorsal surfaces of the phalanges of the third, fourth, and fifth digits.

Action. Extends digits 3, 4, and 5.

Extensor carpi ulnaris. *Origin.* Lateral condyle of humerus, above greater sigmoid cavity of ulna.

Insertion. Base of fifth metacarpal.

Action. Extends fifth digit and ulnar side of wrist.

Extensor indicis proprius. *Origin.* Ulna, distal to greater sigmoid cavity.

Insertion. The long, narrow tendon of the muscle divides into two or three parts which insert on the phalanges of digits 1, 2, and sometimes 3.

Action. Extends first two or three digits.

Extensor brevis pollicis. *Origin.* Shafts of ulna and radius.

Insertion. Base of first metacarpal.

Action. Extends and abducts the thumb, or pollex.

Flexor muscles. The flexor muscles of the forearm have a similar appearance to the extensors but are located on the medial, or inner, surface of the arm.

Flexor carpi radialis. *Origin.* Above medial condyle of humerus.

Insertion. Bases of second and third metacarpals.

Action. Flexes the hand.

Palmaris longus. *Origin.* Medial condyle of humerus.

Insertion. The tendon of the muscle divides into four or five parts which pass to the three-lobed pad on the palm of the hand to be inserted on the first phalanges of the digits.

Action. Flexes the digits.

Flexor carpi ulnaris. *Origin.* Medial condyle of humerus, lateral surface of olecranon process of ulna.

Insertion. Pisiform carpal bone.

Action. Flexes wrist.

Flexor profundus digitorum. *Origin.* Five heads: three from medial condyle of humerus, one from medial surface of shaft of ulna, one from shaft of radius.

Insertion. The tendon divides into five parts, each inserted on the terminal phalanx of a digit.

Action. Flexes the digits.

Flexor sublimis digitorum. *Origin.* From palmaris longus and flexor profundus digitorum.

Insertion. By four tendons passing to the second phalanx of the second, third, fourth, and fifth digits, respectively.

Action. Flexes digits 2, 3, 4, and 5.

Supinator muscles. Two muscles are used primarily in turning the lower arm and hand in a supine position.

Brachioradialis. The brachioradialis is a long, flat muscle lying along the lower lateral border of the upper arm and the anterolateral border of the forearm in front of the extensor carpi radialis longus.

Origin. Shaft of humerus.

Insertion. Styloid process of radius.

Action. Supinates the hand.

Supinator. *Origin.* Ligaments between humerus and proximal end of radius.

Insertion. By spirally arranged fibers on the proximal two-fifths of the shaft of the radius.

Action. Supinates the hand.

Pronator muscle. Only one pronator muscle, the pronator quadratus, is present in the forearm of the cat.

Pronator quadratus. *Origin.* Distal end of ulna.

Insertion. Distal end of radius.

Action. Pronates the lower arm and hand.

MUSCLES OF THE HAND

Several small muscles, which we shall not consider here, are responsible for the detailed and independent movement of the separate digits.

Muscles of the Leg
(Figs. 4.24 to 4.27)

MUSCLES OF THE UPPER LEG, OR THIGH, AND OF THE HIP

Biceps femoris. The largest muscle on the lateral side of the thigh is the biceps femoris. It covers the caudal two-thirds of this portion of the leg.

Origin. Posterior end of ischium.

Insertion. Patella and proximal third of tibia.

Action. Abducts thigh; flexes shank.

Tenuissimus. A very slender muscle, the tenuissimus, lies just beneath the biceps femoris and is closely adherent to it. This muscle is sometimes altogether lacking.

Origin. Transverse process of second caudal vertebra.

Insertion. Fascia of biceps femoris to tibia.

Action. Very slight aid to biceps femoris.

Caudofemoralis. The caudofemoralis lies just anterior to the proximal end of the biceps femoris and is largely covered by it. Just distad the greater trochanter the muscle passes into a very narrow tendon.

Origin. Transverse processes of second and third caudal vertebrae.

Insertion. By a thin tendon on lateral side of patella.

Action. Abducts thigh; aids in extending shank.

Gluteus maximus. A short muscle, the gluteus maximus, lies craniad the caudofemoralis which partly overlaps it.

Origin. Transverse processes of last sacral and first caudal vertebrae.

Insertion. Great trochanter of femur.

Action. Abducts the thigh.

Tensor fasciae latae. The tensor fasciae latae is a rather large muscle on the proximal cephalic face of the upper leg. It is difficult to separate the caudal border of the tensor fasciae latae from the cranial border of the gluteus medius.

Origin. Ventral border of ilium; fascia of underlying muscle, the gluteus medius.

Insertion. On the fascia lata, a wide, heavy, glistening white fascia

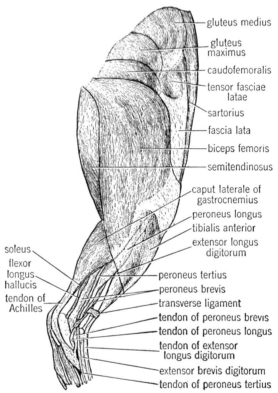

gluteus medius

gluteus maximus

caudofemoralis

tensor fasciae latae

sartorius

fascia lata

biceps femoris

semitendinosus

caput laterale of gastrocnemius

peroneus longus

tibialis anterior

extensor longus digitorum

soleus

flexor longus hallucis

tendon of Achilles

peroneus tertius

peroneus brevis

transverse ligament

tendon of peroneus brevis

tendon of peroneus longus

tendon of extensor longus digitorum

extensor brevis digitorum

tendon of peroneus tertius

Fig. 4.24.   Superficial muscles of right hind led of cat, lateral view. (*Drawn by Joanne Moore.*)

which covers most of the cephalic portion of the thigh. The fascia lata inserts on the patella.

Action. Pulls upon the fascia lata to help extend the shank.

Gluteus medius. Under the tensor fasciae latae and almost entirely covered by it is a short, thick, sturdy muscle, the gluteus medius.

Origin. Dorsal half of lateral surface of ilium, superficial fasciae, transverse processes of last sacral and first caudal vertebrae.

Insertion. Greater trochanter of femur.

Action. Abducts the thigh.

Gluteus minimus. Beneath the central part of the gluteus medius lies the small gluteus minimus.

Origin. Ventral portion of lateral side of ilium.

Insertion. Greater trochanter of femur.

Action. Rotates the thigh.

Pyriformis. The pyriformis lies underneath parts of both the gluteus medius and gluteus maximus, the insertions of which may be cut in order

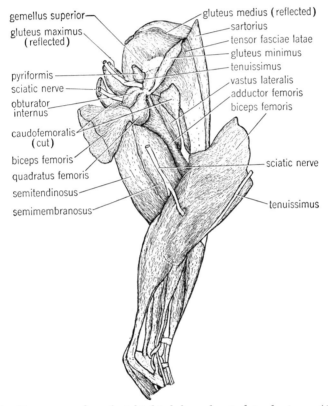

FIG. 4.25. Deeper muscles of right hind leg of cat, lateral view. (*Drawn by Joanne Moore.*)

to expose it. It lies directly over the proximal end of the large sciatic nerve of the upper leg.

Origin. Transverse processes of the last two sacral and first caudal vertebrae.

Insertion. Greater trochanter of femur.

Action. Abducts the thigh.

Gemellus superior. The gemellus superior is located directly beneath the pyriformis but is wider than the latter. Its cranial border is closely united with the caudal border of the gluteus minimus.

Origin.   Dorsal border of innominate bone in region of posterior ilium and anterior ischium.

Insertion.   Greater trochanter of femur.

Action.   Abducts femur and rotates it to some extent.

Capsularis.   A short, flat muscle, the capsularis, lies under the gluteus minimus and gemellus superior.

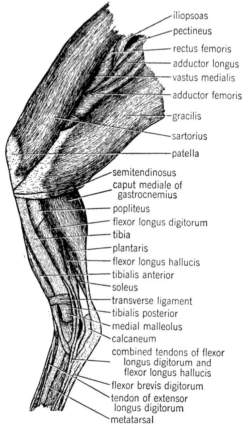

iliopsoas
pectineus
rectus femoris
adductor longus
vastus medialis
adductor femoris
gracilis
sartorius
patella
semitendinosus
caput mediale of gastrocnemius
popliteus
flexor longus digitorum
tibia
plantaris
flexor longus hallucis
tibialis anterior
soleus
transverse ligament
tibialis posterior
medial malleolus
calcaneum
combined tendons of flexor longus digitorum and flexor longus hallucis
flexor brevis digitorum
tendon of extensor longus digitorum
metatarsal

Fig. 4.26.   Superficial muscles of right hind leg of cat, medial view.   (*Drawn by Joanne Moore.*)

Origin.   Ilium in front of the acetabulum.

Insertion.   Femur, just distad the greater trochanter.

Action.   Rotates the thigh.

Obturator internus.   Just caudad the gemellus superior lies the obturator internus.

Origin.   Inner surface of ischium near the symphysis.

Insertion.   The muscle passes over the dorsal border of the ischium to insert in the digital fossa.

Action. Abducts the thigh.

Gemellus inferior. The gemellus inferior is a flat, triangular muscle entirely covered by the obturator internus. The latter muscle must be cut in order to expose it. The gemellus inferior lies adjacent to the gemellus superior.

Origin. Dorsal part of lateral surface of ischium.

Insertion. On the tendon of the obturator internus and thence to the trochanteric fossa.

Action. Abducts the thigh.

Quadratus femoris. The most caudal of the series of fan-shaped muscles which have just been described is the quadratus femoris. It lies posterior to the obturator internus and gemellus inferior.

Origin. Posterior end of ischium.

Insertion. Both greater and lesser trochanters of femur.

Action. Extends and rotates the thigh.

Sartorius. From a lateral view the sartorius appears as a thin band extending all along the cephalic border of the thigh. From a medial view, however, it is seen to be a broad, flat muscle covering almost half of the medial surface of the thigh.

Origin. Ventral border of ilium.

Insertion. Patella, proximal part of tibia, fasciae over knee joint.

Action. Adducts and rotates the femur; extends tibia.

Gracilis. The remainder of the medial surface of the thigh is covered by the gracilis, another broad, thin muscle like the sartorius. These two muscles diverge near the proximal part of the thigh, leaving between them a large, triangular area known as *Scarpa's triangle*. The large femoral artery and vein and the saphenous nerve are close to the surface in the region of Scarpa's triangle.

Origin. Caudal two-thirds of the puboischial symphysis.

Insertion. By a thin aponeurosis on the medial surface of the tibia. It is continuous with the fasciae of the lower leg.

Action. Adducts the leg and pulls it backward.

Semitendinosus. The caudal border of the thigh is formed by a long muscle, the semitendinosus.

Origin. Posterior end of ischium.

Insertion. Proximal part of tibia on medial side.

Action. Flexes the shank.

Semimembranosus. A thick muscle, the semimembranosus, usually separable into two large masses, lies in front of the semitendinosus and under the gracilis.

Origin. Posterior end of ischium.

Insertion. Distal end of femur and proximal end of tibia.

Action. Extends the thigh.

Adductor femoris.   The adductor femoris is a large muscle in front of the semimembranosus, lying between the latter muscle and the femur. It is also covered by the gracilis.

Origin.   Ventrolateral border of pubis and ischium, and from tendon of gracilis.

Insertion.   Shaft of femur.

Action.   Extends the thigh.

Adductor longus.   The adductor longus is a relatively small muscle overlapping the upper margin of the adductor femoris and running parallel to it.

Origin.   Anterior medial part of pubis.

Insertion.   Middle portion of shaft of femur.

Action.   Adducts the thigh.

Pectineus.   The fibers of the small pectineus ran parallel to those of the adductor longus along its upper border.   The two muscles are frequently united.

Origin.   Anterior border of pubis.

Insertion.   Proximal portion of shaft of femur.

Action.   Adducts the thigh.

Iliopsoas.   The iliopsoas has been referred to in connection with the muscles of the back.   Only its terminal portion can be observed in a dissection of the leg.   The capsularis, previously mentioned, lies anterior to the iliopsoas under the gluteus minimus.

Origin.   Ventral border of ilium, from centra and transverse processes of the lumbar and last thoracic vertebrae.

Insertion.   Lesser trochanter of femur.

Action.   Flexes the thigh and rotates it.

Obturator externus.   Underneath the adductor femoris lies a flat, triangular muscle, the obturator externus, which is not visible unless most of the thigh muscles are removed.

Origin.   Inner border of obturator foramen on pubis and ischium.

Insertion.   Trochanteric fossa of femur.

Action.   Rotates the thigh.

Quadriceps femoris.   The only muscle mass of the upper leg which remains to be considered is the large quadriceps femoris.   It occupies the entire front of the thigh.   Its lateral surface is covered by the fascia lata.   The quadriceps femoris is actually made up of four components with a common insertion on the patella and, by means of the patellar ligament, on the proximal end of the tibia.

Origin.   VASTUS LATERALIS.   This portion of the quadriceps femoris forms the entire lateral face of the muscle mass.   It originates from the greater trochanter and the shaft of the femur.

RECTUS FEMORIS.   A long, round muscle, visible only from a medial view, the rectus femoris lies next to the vastus lateralis and is partially covered by it. The muscle originates from the ilium just in front of the acetabulum.

VASTUS MEDIALIS. The vastus medialis lies entirely on the medial side of the leg next to the rectus femoris. It arises from along the shaft of the femur.

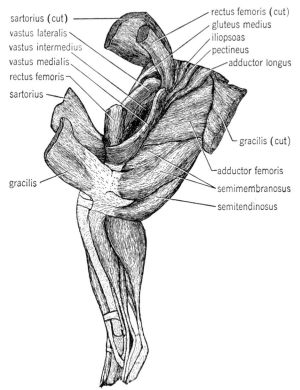

sartorius (cut)
vastus lateralis
vastus intermedius
vastus medialis
rectus femoris
sartorius
gracilis

rectus femoris (cut)
gluteus medius
iliopsoas
pectineus
adductor longus
gracilis (cut)
adductor femoris
semimembranosus
semitendinosus

FIG. 4.27. Deeper muscles of right hind leg of cat, medial view. (*Drawn by Joanne Moore.*)

VASTUS INTERMEDIUS. Since the vastus intermedius is entirely covered by the other three parts of the quadriceps femoris, it is not visible unless they are cut or removed. Cut through the rectus femoris and lift up the cut ends. The vastus intermedius, which lies beneath, is usually of a darker color than the other parts. It originates from almost the entire length of the shaft of the femur.

Insertion. Patella, by means of the patellar ligament on the proximal end of the tibia.

Action. Extends the shank.

MUSCLES OF THE LOWER LEG (SHANK OR CRUS) AND FOOT
(Figs. 4.24 to 4.27)

Gastrocnemius. The fleshy back part of the lower leg is commonly referred to as the calf. Toward the heel it narrows down into the heavy **tendon of Achilles.** The gastrocnemius muscle forms most of the muscle mass making up the calf. It arises from medial and lateral heads which have a common insertion.

Origin. CAPUT LATERALE. The lateral head of the gastrocnemius originates from four points: (1) a tendon from the lateral side of the patella; (2) a tendon from the sesamoid bone laterad the patella; (3) superficial fasciae of the shank; (4) an aponeurosis which covers the plantaris (see below).

CAPUT MEDIALE. The medial head of the gastrocnemius originates from the distal end of the femur and from a sesamoid bone mediad the patella.

Insertion. By means of the tendon of Achilles on the proximal end of the calcaneum.

Action. Extends the foot.

Plantaris. Between the two heads of the gastrocnemius lies the plantaris. Only a small portion of its proximal end is visible before dissection. It is rather difficult to separate from the caput laterale.

Origin. Lateral edge of patella, sesamoid bone laterad the patella.

Insertion. The inserting tendon of the plantaris forms the core of the tendon of Achilles. It passes to the ventral side of the calcaneum to form the origin of the flexor brevis digitorum (see page 164).

Action. Extends the foot.

Soleus. The fourth muscle forming the calf is the soleus.

Origin. Proximal part of fibula.

Insertion. Tendon of Achilles.

Action. Extends the foot.

Popliteus. The popliteus is a short muscle which runs obliquely under the knee joint.

Origin. Lateral side of distal end of femur.

Insertion. Medial side of proximal end of tibia.

Action. Rotates the leg so as to turn the toes inward to a slight extent.

Flexor longus digitorum. On the medial side of the shank just in back of the tibia is a long, slender muscle, the flexor longus digitorum. Its proximal portion is partially covered by the popliteus.

Origin. Head of fibula and proximal end of tibia.

Insertion. Joins tendon of flexor longus hallucis (see below) to form a wide tendon which divides into four parts, one for each toe. Each of the four tendons inserts on the base of the terminal phalanx of the digit.

Action. Flexes toes; may aid in extending foot.

Flexor longus hallucis. Directly lateral in position to the flexor longus digitorum, which partly covers its medial surface, is the flexor longus hallucis. It is a larger muscle than the flexor longus digitorum.

Origin. Head and shaft of fibula; shaft of tibia; fasciae.

Insertion. Its tendon joins that of the flexor longus digitorum as noted above.

Action. Flexes toes; may aid in extending foot.

Quadratus plantae. A very small muscle, the quadratus plantae, is located on the ventral side of the foot. It is closely related to the combined tendon of the flexor longus digitorum and flexor longus hallucis on which it inserts.

Origin. Lateral surface of calcaneum and cuboid.

Insertion. Tendon of flexor longus digitorum and flexor longus hallucis.

Action. Keeps the above tendon in position.

Tibialis posterior. Under the flexor longus digitorum and between it and the flexor longus hallucis is a slender muscle, the tibialis posterior, with a long, narrow tendon.

Origin. Head of fibula, proximal end of tibia near its head, adjacent aponeuroses.

Insertion. Scaphoid and medial cuneiform bones of tarsus.

Action. Helps to extend the foot.

Tibialis anterior. The anterolateral side of the tibia is covered by the fleshy tibialis anterior. As its tendon passes over the ankle, it goes beneath a transverse ligament.

Origin. Proximal end of shaft of tibia, head and shaft of fibula.

Insertion. First metatarsal.

Action. Flexes the foot.

Extensor longus digitorum. The extensor longus digitorum is closely related to the tibialis anterior which covers its proximal end.

Origin. Lateral surface of distal end of femur.

Insertion. Its tendon passes under the transverse ligament and then divides into four parts. Each inserts on the first and second phalanges of its respective digit.

Action. Extends the toes; may aid in flexing the foot.

Peroneus longus. Three peroneus muscles are all that remain on the lateral aspect of the lower leg. The largest and outermost of these is the peroneus longus.

Origin. Proximal half of shaft of fibula.

Insertion. Proximal ends of all the metatarsals.

Action. Flexes the foot.

Peroneus tertius. The peroneus tertius is the most slender muscle of the leg. It lies directly under the peroneus longus.

Origin. Lateral surface of shaft of fibula.

Insertion. Lateral side of fifth toe between first and second phalanges.

Action. Helps flex foot; extends and abducts the fifth toe.

Peroneus brevis. The peroneus brevis is a thick muscle surrounding most of the distal end of the fibula and lying under the other two peroneus muscles. It lies directly next to the flexor longus hallucis.

Origin. Distal half of shaft of fibula.

Insertion. Base of fifth metatarsal on lateral side.

Action. Extends the foot.

Extensor brevis digitorum. Confined entirely to the foot, the extensor brevis digitorum lies beneath the extensor longus digitorum.

Origin. From transverse ligament noted above; proximal ends of third, fourth, and fifth metatarsals.

Insertion. By three tendons which go to the spaces between the toes. Each tendon then splits into two parts which insert on the digits on either side of the interspace.

Action. Extends the toes.

Flexor brevis digitorum. The flexor brevis digitorum is located on the bottom, or plantar, surface of the foot.

Origin. The muscle is really a continuation of the tendon of the plantaris muscle; it also has attachments to the scaphoid and medial cuneiform.

Insertion. By four tendons, each passing finally to the base of the second phalanx of a toe.

Action. Flexes the toes.

Other Muscles of the Foot

Several small muscles, the description of which will be omitted, are to be found in the foot and ankle. They are concerned, for the most part, with detailed movements of the separate digits and phalanges.

COELOM AND COELOMIC VISCERA

After having completed the study of the muscular system, the body cavity, or coelom, should next be exposed, and the various internal organs identified. These will not, however, be studied in detail until after the circulatory system has been dissected.

In order to open the body cavity and expose the viscera, place the cat on its back. Make a transverse incision through the body wall about an inch anterior to the pubic symphysis. Extend this cut both to right and left, and then cut forward as far as the ribs. Now on the *left* side of the animal swing over toward the midline with your scalpel, and then go forward, cutting through the costal cartilages about ½ in. laterad the sternum. Continue forward into the neck region. Very few blood vessels of major importance will be severed if these directions are followed. Cut the diaphragm loose from the ventral and lateral body walls. Lift up the large flap now covering the ventral side of the body, and deflect it to the animal's right. All thoracic and abdominal viscera will now be exposed and should be identified.

The **body cavity**, or **coelom**, of the cat is divided into four separate compartments in which the viscera, or internal organs, lie. The **diaphragm** divides the coelom into anterior **thoracic** and posterior **abdominal regions**. It is composed largely of a dome-shaped sheet of muscle originating from the hypaxial region of certain cervical myotomes. It comes from the lower ribs, vertebrae, and sternum and inserts on a **central**, or **semilunar, tendon**. Part of it is homologous with the septum transversum of lower vertebrates. The **thoracic cavity** contains, among other structures, the heart and the great vessels which enter and leave the heart. It, in turn, is divided into three cavities, of which two, the **pleural cavities**, enclose the lungs; the other is the **pericardial cavity** containing the heart.

A sheet of serous membrane lines the coelom. A distinction is made between the serous membrane lining the body wall and that which is reflected over the viscera. They are called the parietal and visceral layers, respectively. The parietal serous membrane of the pleural cavities is the **parietal pleura;** the visceral portion, reflected over the lungs, is the **visceral pleura.** The medial walls of the two pleurae are in contact. Ventrally this forms a vertical partition, the **mediastinal septum,** which separates the two pleural cavities from one another. The two components of the mediastinal septum spread apart dorsally to form a large **mediastinal space.** All the thoracic viscera except the lungs lie in the mediastinal space. They include the heart, aorta, pulmonary trunk and arteries, venae cavae, azygos vein, esophagus, trachea, bronchi, thymus gland, and various nerves.

Strictly speaking, the heart does not lie in the mediastinal space, since it is surrounded by a sac, the **pericardium.** It is actually the pericardium which lies in the mediastinal space. The pericardium is comparable to the parietal layer of serous membrane in other parts of the coelom. Closely applied to the surface of the heart is the visceral pericardium, or **epicardium.**

Now turning to the abdominal cavity (Fig. 4.32), and with the aid of the instructor, identify the following: esophagus, stomach, pylorus, small intestine, caecum, large intestine, liver, gall bladder, bile duct, pancreas, kidneys, ureters, urinary bladder, urethra, and adrenal glands. If your cat is a female, find the ovaries, Fallopian tubes, and the uterus, composed of two horns, or cornua (see Fig. 4.36). If the specimen is a

male, look for the ductus deferens on each side. This is the only part
of the male reproductive system which can be seen in the abdominal
cavity. It leads from the testis, passing forward through the abdominal
wall and turning medially. It then passes between the urinary bladder
and ureter. After looping over the ureter it turns caudad, approaching
its partner from the other side. The two ducts then join the urethra on
its *dorsal* aspect a short distance below the neck of the bladder (Fig.
4.35).

The parietal layer of serous membrane lining the abdominal, or peritoneal, cavity is called the **parietal peritoneum;** that reflected over the
viscera is the **visceral peritoneum.** The viscera are thus actually outside
the body cavity. Mesenteries, ligaments, and omenta are double layers
of peritoneum which support the abdominal viscera. The term **mesentery** refers to the double layer of peritoneum which suspends the various
parts of the alimentary canal from the dorsal body wall (Fig. 2.17).
Ligaments suspend organs other than those of the alimentary canal from
the body wall. **Omenta** connect organs with other organs. The blood
vessels which supply the abdominal viscera course between the two
layers of mesenteries, ligaments, and omenta in order to reach their
destination.

Among the mesenteries supporting the alimentary canal are the
mesentery proper, suspending the small intestine, and the **mesocolon**
and **mesorectum,** supporting the large intestine. The **dorsal mesogastrium,** or peritoneal fold, which passes to the dorsal border or greater
curvature of the stomach, takes a rather indirect course. During development the stomach undergoes a change from its original position, so
that the greater curvature swings downward and to the left. In doing
so, the dorsal mesogastrium necessarily is pulled along. It later becomes
much elongated and forms a double fold which may extend posteriorly
as far as the pelvis. This fold, which comes to lie between the viscera
and ventral body wall, is called the **great omentum.** It really consists of
four sheets of serous membrane. The two layers of the descending
part of the great omentum enclose the left half of the pancreas and the
spleen. The portion of the great omentum between stomach and spleen
is spoken of as the **gastrosplenic omentum.** The great omentum is
usually a site for deposition of adipose tissue. Fat may accumulate
here in considerable quantity.

Between the two folds of the great omentum is a portion of the
peritoneal cavity called the **omental bursa** or **lesser peritoneal cavity.**
This is in communication with the rest of the peritoneal cavity through
an opening, the **foramen of Winslow,** or **epiploic foramen,** which lies
adjacent to the bile duct near the posterior end of the liver on the right
side.

The **lesser omentum** is a smaller sheet which connects the liver with the duodenum and the lesser curvature of the stomach. It is sometimes referred to as the **gastrohepatic omentum** or **duodenohepatic omentum,** depending upon the region concerned.

The liver is supported by several ligaments. A **falciform ligament** is attached to the ventral part of the diaphragm and ventral abdominal wall. A fibrous cord running from the umbilicus to the undersurface of the liver is the **round ligament, or ligamentum teres.** It represents the remnant of the left umbilical vein which functioned during embryonic life. The peritoneum is reflected over the ligamentum teres, which passes to the liver within the free margin of the falciform ligament. A single **coronary ligament** and two lateral **triangular ligaments,** from the dorsal and dorsolateral portions of the diaphragm, respectively, also support the liver.

At the posterior end of the body cavity the visceral peritoneum covers the urinary bladder. Along the midventral line it forms a connection between the linea alba and bladder to form the **suspensory ligament** of the bladder.

The peritoneal cavity in males is entirely closed to the outside. In females, however, an external connection exists via the Fallopian tubes, uterus, and vagina.

The circulatory system will be studied next. After this dissection has been completed the separate organ systems will be removed and studied in detail.

CIRCULATORY SYSTEM

Many variations are encountered in the arrangement of blood vessels, particularly in regard to their points of origin. This is especially true of the veins. The differences can be traced back to deviations which take place during embryonic development. So many variations are to be found that it is difficult to give an accurate description of them. In the following account, therefore, only the most usual arrangement is stressed. In identifying a blood vessel it is best to observe its course and distribution rather than its point of origin. Any marked differences from the description given here should be carefully noted.

The Heart and Its Vessels

External Features

The heart of the cat lies in the pericardial cavity which is enclosed by the pericardial sac, previously noted. This in turn lies in the mediastinal space ventromediad the lungs. The heart of the mammal is more compact than the hearts previously studied. Its cranial end is called the **base;** the caudal end, the **apex.** The apical region projects slightly toward the left side. It is in contact with the diaphragm. *The heart will not be cut open at this time.* Its internal structure is not to be studied until the entire circulatory system has been dissected (see page 181). Manipulate the walls of the heart with the fingers and determine which parts are the thickest. The mammalian heart is a four-chambered structure composed of two **atria** (**auricles**) and two **ventricles**. No sinus venosus is present. During development it becomes incorporated in the wall of the right atrium. The ventricles form the greater part of the heart and make up the posterior portion. The division between the right and left ventricles is marked externally by a slight groove which extends from the left of the base to the right of the apex. Note that the wall of the left ventricle is considerably thicker than that of the right.

The **atria** may be identified by their darker color and thinner walls. An external groove, the **sulcus coronarius,** marks the point of junction of atria and ventricles. From each atrium projects a pouchlike **auricula*** or **auricular appendage**, with irregular edges.

Two main vessels may be observed leaving the ventricular region. The most ventral is the **pulmonary trunk,** or **pulmonary aorta,** arising from the right ventricle. The portion of the right ventricle leading to the pulmonary aorta is frequently referred to as the **conus arteriosus.** The pulmonary aorta divides into right and left **pulmonary arteries** which supply the right and left lungs, respectively. Dorsal to the pulmonary aorta and coming from the left ventricle is the **systemic aorta,** often referred to simply as *the aorta.*

Gently lift the heart so that its *dorsal* surface may be observed. Two large veins may be seen entering the right atrium. The one entering on the posterior face is the **posterior vena cava,** or **postcaval vein,** often called the **inferior vena cava.** The vessel entering the anterior face is the **anterior vena cava,** or **precaval vein,** often referred to as the **superior vena cava.** Several **pulmonary veins** may be observed entering the left atrium.

A complex of vessels may be observed on the surface of the heart. These are the **coronary arteries** and **veins** which supply and drain the muscle of the heart itself.

Venous System
(Fig. 4.28)

If your specimen is doubly or triply injected there will be no difficulty in identifying the larger venous vessels. However, because of the pres-

---

* Some confusion exists in the terminology applied to this portion of the heart. The word atrium applies to the chamber under discussion, whereas the term auricle is applied to the auricular appendage alone. Many authors, however, use the term auricle to include both atrium and auricular appendage.

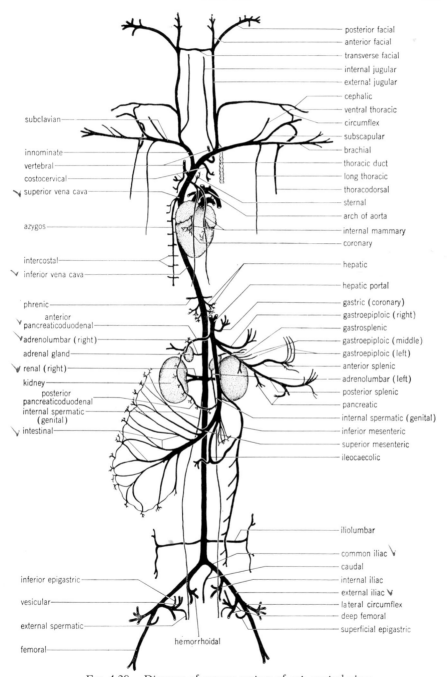

posterior facial
anterior facial
transverse facial
internal jugular
external jugular
cephalic
ventral thoracic
circumflex
subscapular
subclavian
brachial
innominate
thoracic duct
vertebral
long thoracic
costocervical
thoracodorsal
superior vena cava
sternal
arch of aorta
azygos
internal mammary
coronary
intercostal
hepatic
inferior vena cava
hepatic portal
phrenic
gastric (coronary)
anterior
pancreaticoduodenal
gastroepiploic (right)
adrenolumbar (right)
gastrosplenic
adrenal gland
gastroepiploic (middle)
gastroepiploic (left)
renal (right)
anterior splenic
kidney
adrenolumbar (left)
posterior
pancreaticoduodenal
posterior splenic
internal spermatic
(genital)
pancreatic
internal spermatic (genital)
intestinal
inferior mesenteric
superior mesenteric
ileocaecolic

iliolumbar
common iliac
caudal
inferior epigastric
internal iliac
external iliac
vesicular
lateral circumflex
deep femoral
external spermatic
superficial epigastric
femoral
hemorrhoidal

FIG. 4.28. Diagram of venous system of cat, ventral view.

ence of semilunar valves in many of the veins, the injected latex is sometimes prevented from entering them. They are then identified with difficulty. In specimens in which only the arterial system has been injected, the veins are not always easy to find. When the animal is killed, much of the blood is forced into the veins because of the contraction of the arteries with their thicker and more muscular walls. The veins may then appear as reddish-brown vessels because of the blood which they contain, or else, if no blood is present, as thin-walled, transparent structures.

A convenient starting point in the dissection of the venous system is the place where the azygos vein joins the anterior vena cava. To find this, place the fingers in the right pleural cavity and pull the lobes of the right lung forward. The azygos vein will be seen as a large, dark vessel lying against the ribs. Note that it is joined by numerous intercostal veins from the intercostal muscles which lie between the ribs.

After having become oriented, clean away the overlying connective tissue with a probe so as to expose the veins. At the same time most of the arteries will be exposed, since they usually run parallel to veins of similar name.

The venous system is composed of five main groups of veins. They include (1) the veins of the heart, (2) the superior vena cava and its tributaries, (3) the inferior vena cava and its branches, (4) the hepatic portal system of veins, and (5) the pulmonary veins.

Veins of the Heart

Numerous small veins which drain blood from the wall of the heart itself join together to form two main trunks, the right and left **coronary veins.** These in turn unite to enter the **coronary sinus** which opens into the right atrium, its opening being guarded by the **valve of Thebesius.** In addition, several small **cardiac veins** open independently into the right atrium. A few may even enter the ventricles.

Superior Vena Cava and Its Branches

The superior vena cava, previously identified, is a large vessel through which blood from the head, neck, forelimbs, and thoracic region is returned to the right atrium. It enters the anterior dorsolateral part of that chamber.

Azygos vein. A short distance anterior to the point of junction with the right atrium, the superior vena cava receives on its right side a large branch, the azygos vein, which has already been observed. This vessel drains the dorsal thoracic wall and dorsal part of the abdominal wall. The **intercostal veins** have already been identified. A few of the anterior intercostal veins usually enter the azygos by means of a common trunk. In addition, the azygos receives small **esophageal** and **bronchial veins** coming from the esophagus and bronchi, respectively.

Internal mammary veins. A pair of internal mammary veins, running along the lateral borders of the sternum, unites anteriorly to form a single vessel. The common trunk receives a small **sternal vein** and then enters the medial ventral side of the superior vena cava. The continuations of the internal mammary veins on the ventral abdominal wall are the **superior epigastric veins.**

Innominate veins. A short distance anterior to the entrance of the azygos and internal mammary veins, the superior vena cava is formed by a fusion of two large vessels, the right and left innominate, or **brachiocephalic, veins.** The branches of these vessels on the two sides are alike.

Vertebral veins. A large vertebral vein enters each innominate a short distance craniad their junction. Occasionally one or both vertebrals enter the superior vena cava directly. The vertebrals bring blood from the brain. They pass through the foramina transversaria of the cervical vertebrae, along with the corresponding arteries. The **costocervical vein** usually joins the vertebral near the innominate vein but may, in some cases, join the innominate vein directly. Beyond the vertebral vein each innominate is formed by the confluence of three main vessels.

Subclavian veins. A large subclavian vein on each side receives blood from the arm and shoulder region. Outside the body wall this vessel is called the **axillary vein.** The axillary receives the following vessels: (1) a small **ventral thoracic vein;** (2) a **subscapular vein** from the muscles of the dorsal shoulder region; (3) a **thoracodorsal vein** from the latissimus dorsi muscle; (4) a **long thoracic vein** which passes under the pectoralis muscles after it leaves the mammary region, where it is called the **external mammary vein;** (5) a **brachial vein** which drains the deeper portion of the arm. The last has numerous tributaries.

External jugular veins. A large external jugular vein drains the head and face on each side. The tributaries of the two external jugulars are much alike except that the left is joined at its base by the **thoracic duct** which is part of the lymphatic system (see page 184). Not far from its junction with the innominate, the external jugular receives the **transverse scapular vein,** which is a continuation of the **cephalic vein** returning blood from the superficial portion of the arm. Anteriorly the external jugular is formed by the junction of **anterior** and **posterior facial veins,** which in turn are formed by a large number of tributaries from all parts of the head and face. Certain vessels from the **sinus cavernosus** on the ventral side of the brain emerge through the orbital fissure to join the posterior facial. The anterior facial veins of the two sides are connected by a rather large **transverse facial vein.**

Internal jugular veins. The internal jugular vein is frequently quite small in diameter. It joins the external jugular at a point which varies greatly in different individuals. The internal jugular receives an **inferior cerebral vein,** which emerges from the cranial cavity through the jugular foramen.

INFERIOR VENA CAVA AND ITS BRANCHES

The inferior vena cava, or postcava, which drains blood from the posterior part of the body, passes through the caudate lobe of the liver and penetrates the diaphragm before entering the posterior part of the right atrium.

Phrenic veins. As the postcava passes through the diaphragm, it receives small phrenic veins which drain that structure.

Hepatic veins. Numerous small branched hepatic veins join the portion of the postcava which passes through the liver. These vessels collect the blood brought to the liver by the hepatic portal vein and hepatic artery and return it to the systemic circulation.

Other vessels. Posterior to the liver the postcava takes a rather straight course along the dorsomedial part of the abdominal cavity. In an occasional individual it may split into two separate vessels which run parallel to each other. An **adrenolumbar vein** on the right side, draining the dorsal body wall and adrenal gland, joins the postcava craniad the kidney. The corresponding vessel on the left side usually enters the renal vein on that side instead of making a direct connection with the postcava. The renal veins from the kidneys are large but short vessels. It is not uncommon to find two renal veins coming from a single kidney. Caudad the renal veins are the **genital veins** from the gonads: **ovarian veins** in the female, **internal spermatic** in the male. The right genital vein usually enters the postcava directly, whereas that on the left side most frequently joins the left renal vein. Occasionally the condition is just opposite to that described. A few small **lumbar veins** enter the dorsal side of the postcava. These drain the dorsal body wall. A pair of **iliolumbar veins** joins the postcava about midway between the kidneys and the pelvic girdle. Farther back, the postcava receives the large, paired **common iliac veins** and a small, median **caudal,** or **sacral, vein** from the tail. The latter often enters one of the common iliac veins. The common iliac on each side is formed by the junction of a large **external iliac** and a smaller, medial, **internal iliac** (**hypogastric**). Several vessels come together to form each external iliac. The arrangement of these vessels varies considerably in different specimens. They include the following: a deep **femoral vein** (see below) from the medial side of the thigh; a **femoral vein** proper, which forms the main tributary of the external iliac; a **lateral circumflex vein**, coming from the cranial portion of the thigh; and a small **superficial epigastric vein** which comes from the external abdominal wall where it anastomoses with the **external mammary vein**. The deep femoral vein on each side receives several small vessels which include (1) a **vesicular vein** from the urinary bladder; (2) an **external spermatic vein** (in the male) from the testis; (3) an **inferior epigastric vein** from the inner side of the abdominal wall where it forms anastomoses with the **superior epigastric vein**, which is a continuation of the **internal mammary**. The internal iliac vein is formed by the junction of several vessels from the gluteal region and a **hemorrhoidal** vein coming from the rectum and bladder region.

Hepatic Portal Vein

The large and important hepatic portal system of veins drains the organs of the digestive system that are situated in the abdominal cavity. In addition, it drains the spleen, a structure which is considered to belong to the circulatory system. The portal vein proper lies dorsal to the bile duct. Upon entering the liver, it breaks into branches supplying the various liver lobes. These divide and redivide within the liver, ultimately terminating in capillaries (sinusoids). The portal vein is formed by the confluence of several vessels.

Anterior pancreaticoduodenal vein. In the region of the pylorus the hepatic portal vein is joined by the anterior pancreaticoduodenal vein which drains the anterior part of the duodenum and that portion of the pancreas adjacent to it.

Coronary vein of stomach. From the lesser curvature of the stomach a coronary vein (**gastric vein**) emerges which may join the portal near the anterior pancreaticoduodenal. Frequently, however, it joins the gastrosplenic vein instead.

Gastrosplenic vein. A large gastrosplenic vein is another vessel which joins the portal. It receives small **pancreatic veins** from the lobe of the pancreas adjacent to the stomach, one or two **middle gastroepiploic veins** from the stomach and great omentum, a large **posterior splenic branch** from the caudal end of the spleen, and an **anterior splenic** from the cranial portion of the spleen. The latter receives several **left gastroepiploic veins** from the stomach and great omentum.

Right gastroepiploic. The pyloric region, greater curvature of the stomach, and part of the great omentum are drained by the right gastroepiploic vein which joins the portal near the point where the coronary and gastrosplenic veins enter.

Superior mesenteric vein. The largest tributary of the hepatic portal is the superior mesenteric vein. It is formed by a large number of radiating branches from the small intestine and part of the large intestine. These unite into a common vessel.

Posterior pancreaticoduodenal. From the posterior end of the duodenum and the adjacent region of the pancreas, a posterior pancreaticoduodenal vein arises which joins the superior mesenteric. Branches of posterior and anterior pancreaticoduodenal veins anastomose with one another. In tracing these vessels be careful not to confuse them with the pancreatic ducts which ramify through the pancreatic tissue.

Inferior mesenteric vein. A rather large vessel, the inferior mesenteric vein courses along the large intestine. Anteriorly it joins the superior mesenteric.

PULMONARY VEINS

Three groups of **pulmonary veins** enter the left atrium. Each group is composed of two or three vessels which enter into a slightly expanded portion of the atrium. Right, left, and dorsal expansions are present. The right one receives blood from the anterior and middle lobes of the right lung; the left expansion is joined by vessels from the anterior and middle lobes of the left lung. Blood from the caudal lobes of the two sides enters the dorsal expansion.

Arterial System
(Fig. 4.29)

SYSTEMIC AORTA

The **systemic aorta,** which leads from the left ventricle, distributes blood to the entire body. A short distance from its point of origin it bends sharply to the left and then turns in a posterodorsal direction, swinging over to the left side of the midline underneath the vertebral column. It passes through the diaphragm and continues to the posterior end of the abdominal cavity. The bend is referred to as the **arch of the aorta;** the portion between the arch and the diaphragm is called the **thoracic aorta;** the remainder, posterior to the diaphragm, is the **abdominal aorta.** Numerous branches come off the aorta along its course. Slight variations from the following description are frequently encountered.

BRANCHES OF THE THORACIC AORTA

Coronary arteries. Two **coronary arteries,** right and left, arise from the aorta near its base, just craniad the semilunar valves (Fig. 4.30). These vessels, as previously mentioned, supply blood to the wall of the heart itself.

Brachiocephalic artery. The next vessel coming off the aorta is a large artery which passes craniad from the arch. This is the **brachio-**

cephalic, or **innominate, artery**. It gives off a small **mediastinal artery** to the mediastinum and then branches into two **common carotid arteries**. A small **inferior thyroid artery** is frequently found coming off each common carotid artery. It courses craniad along the trachea up to the thyroid gland (see page 198), giving off small branches to the esophagus and trachea.

From the base of the right common carotid a large **right subclavian artery** is given off. This vessel passes to the arm. Before it goes through the body wall, it gives off several branches.

An **internal mammary artery** passes posteriorly from the subclavian, coursing along the lateral border of the sternum. Branches are distributed to the ventral side of the thorax, pericardium, mediastinum, and diaphragm. Posteriorly the internal mammary is continued as the **superior epigastric artery** in the ventral abdominal wall, supplying the rectus abdominis and other ventral muscles of the abdomen.

Close to the internal mammary and opposite the first rib, a **vertebral artery** arises from the right subclavian. It turns dorsad and craniad and enters the foramen transversarium of the sixth cervical vertebra. The vertebral continues forward through the foramina transversaria of the anterior cervical vertebrae. When it reaches the atlas, it passes through the atlantal foramen into the neural canal under the spinal cord. At the level of the foramen magnum the vertebral artery joins its fellow from the left side to form the **basilar artery**. The basilar continues craniad along the midventral line of the brain as far as the pituitary body, where it divides into two. These branches anastomose with branches of the internal carotid arteries to form the **circle of Willis,** which encircles the optic chiasma (Fig. 4.37*B*) and the pituitary body. Branches of the vertebral artery pass through the intervertebral foramina to the muscles of the neck. Other branches are distributed to the ventral surface of the spinal cord.

The **costocervical trunk** comes off the subclavian near the internal mammary and vertebral arteries. It quickly divides into two branches. The smaller branch is the **superior intercostal artery.** It passes caudad and is distributed to the most anterior intercostal muscles. The other branch of the costocervical trunk soon divides into lateral and dorsal branches. The lateral branch, or **transverse colli,** goes to the serratus anterior, levator scapulae, and rhomboideus muscles. The **dorsal, or deep, cervical branch** passes to the deep muscles of the neck.

The **thyrocervical trunk, or thyroid axis,** is another branch of the subclavian. It passes directly anteriorly, giving off numerous branches to various muscles of the shoulder.

The continuation of the subclavian outside the body wall is referred to as the **axillary artery.** Several branches arise from the axillary. These

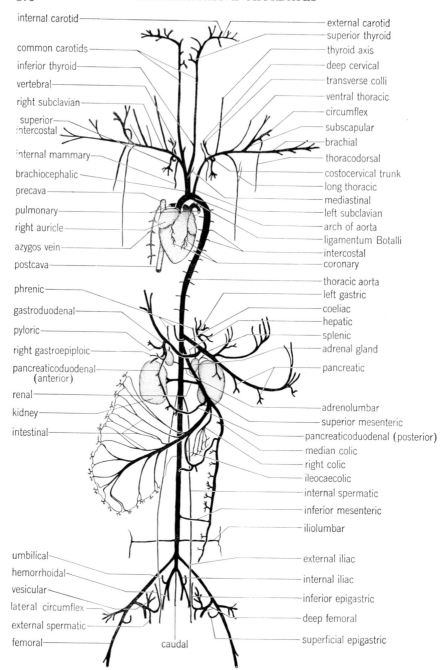

internal carotid

common carotids

inferior thyroid

vertebral

right subclavian

superior intercostal

internal mammary

brachiocephalic

precava

pulmonary

right auricle

azygos vein

postcava

phrenic

gastroduodenal

pyloric

right gastroepiploic

pancreaticoduodenal (anterior)

renal

kidney

intestinal

umbilical

hemorrhoidal

vesicular

lateral circumflex

external spermatic

femoral

caudal

external carotid

superior thyroid

thyroid axis

deep cervical

transverse colli

ventral thoracic

circumflex

subscapular

brachial

thoracodorsal

costocervical trunk

long thoracic

mediastinal

left subclavian

arch of aorta

ligamentum Botalli

intercostal

coronary

thoracic aorta

left gastric

coeliac

hepatic

splenic

adrenal gland

pancreatic

adrenolumbar

superior mesenteric

pancreaticoduodenal (posterior)

median colic

right colic

ileocaecolic

internal spermatic

inferior mesenteric

iliolumbar

external iliac

internal iliac

inferior epigastric

deep femoral

superficial epigastric

FIG. 4.29. Diagram of arterial system of cat, ventral view.

include a small **ventral thoracic artery** going to the pectoralis muscles; a **long thoracic artery**, which passes posteriorly on the abdominal wall as the **external mammary artery**; a **subscapular artery**, which gives off a number of branches distributed to the muscles of the scapular region. A main branch of the subscapular, called the **thoracodorsal artery**, supplies the latissimus dorsi and teres major muscles. Another branch, the **circumflex**, extends dorsally beside the head of the humerus.

The continuation of the axillary beyond the subscapular is called the **brachial artery**. It passes into the arm, where it gives off many branches. It is the brachial artery that passes through the supracondyloid foramen of the humerus.

After giving off the right subclavian artery, the right common carotid continues forward. At the level of the larynx a small **superior thyroid artery** branches off, supplying the thyroid gland, larynx, and sternohyoid muscles. Other branches of the common carotid are distributed to the dorsal neck muscles and those of the occipital region. The common carotid then divides into two branches, the **internal** and **external carotid arteries**.

The internal carotid is a small vessel which passes forward to the anterior end of the tympanic bulla, where, in company with the Eustachian tube, it enters the bulla. A small **foramen lacerum** in the cranial part of the petrous region of the temporal bone provides passage for the internal carotid artery into the cranial cavity, where it helps supply the brain. Branches of the internal carotids, together with those from the basilar artery, form the circle of Willis, as mentioned above.

The external carotid passes anteriorly along the side of the face, where numerous branches are distributed to the tongue, larynx, and facial muscles. Branches of the **internal maxillary branch of the external carotid** enter the skull through the orbital fissure and foramen ovale. These are distributed to the dura mater and brain.

The left common carotid artery, unlike that on the right side, does not serve as the point of origin of the subclavian artery on that side. Otherwise the branches on the two sides correspond.

Left subclavian artery. The left subclavian artery arises independently from the aorta on the arch a short distance beyond the point of origin of the brachiocephalic artery. Its branches correspond to those of the right subclavian.

Intercostal arteries. From the arch of the aorta to the diaphragm, the thoracic aorta gives off paired **intercostal arteries** from its dorsal side. These vessels are distributed to all except the first two intercostal spaces, which, it will be recalled, are supplied by the superior intercostal arteries. Branches of the intercostal arteries pass to the muscles between the ribs, to the deep muscles of the back, and via the intervertebral foramina to the spinal cord, its membranes, and the vertebrae.

Bronchial arteries. A pair of **bronchial arteries,** arising directly from the aorta or from the fourth pair of intercostal arteries, passes to the lungs along the bronchi. These vessels supply the tissues of the lungs themselves with blood.

Esophageal arteries. Small **esophageal branches** of the thoracic aorta pass directly to the esophagus, which is in very close proximity to the aorta.

Branches of the Abdominal Aorta

Three kinds of vessels arise from the abdominal aorta: (1) paired parietal vessels pass to the body wall; (2) visceral branches supply the visceral organs, three of these being unpaired; (3) paired terminal branches supply the hind limbs.

Parietal Vessels

Adrenolumbar arteries. A pair of adrenolumbar arteries arises from the aorta 3 or 4 cm. from the diaphragm. Each passes to the dorsal body wall, giving off a small branch to the adrenal gland en route.

Phrenic arteries. The arteries which supply the diaphragm show considerable variation in origin, but their size is not of any great magnitude. They may arise independently from the aorta or else as branches of the adrenolumbar arteries to supply the diaphragm. Sometimes a phrenic branch arises from the unpaired coelic artery.

Iliolumbar arteries. A rather prominent pair of iliolumbar arteries arises from the abdominal aorta near its caudal end. Each divides into cranial and caudal branches which supply adjacent muscles.

Lumbar arteries. Paired lumbar arteries, corresponding to the intercostal arteries of the thoracic aorta, arise from the abdominal aorta and pass directly between the centra of the lumbar vertebrae and adjacent muscles to the dorsal body musculature in this region. Branches enter the neural canal through the intervertebral foramina.

Visceral Vessels

Paired Arteries

Adrenolumbar arteries. Although the adrenolumbars were included among the parietal vessels, they might just as well be included among the visceral vessels, since they supply the adrenal glands in addition to the dorsal body wall.

Renal arteries. The large renal arteries arise from the aorta just caudad the adrenolumbars. Each usually divides just before entering the kidney.

Genital arteries. The genital arteries in the male are called the **internal spermatics;** in the female they are known as the **ovarian arteries.**

The internal spermatics are small in diameter, come off the aorta posterior to the renals, and pass posteriorly to the inguinal region, running parallel to the ductus deferens and to the corresponding vein to the testis and epididymis.

The ovarian artery is shorter but of greater diameter than the internal spermatic. It passes laterally to the ovary and ovarian end of the uterus.

Unpaired Arteries

Coeliac artery. The most anterior of the three unpaired visceral vessels is the coeliac artery. It arises from the ventral side of the abdominal aorta a short distance from the diaphragm and divides into **hepatic, left gastric,** and **splenic branches.** The **phrenic artery,** as noted above, may come off the proximal part of the coeliac.

The hepatic artery passes anteriorly to the liver and gall bladder, in company with the hepatic portal vein and bile duct. Just before the artery enters the liver a **gastroduodenal branch** is given off. This in turn divides into **pyloric, anterior pancreaticoduodenal,** and **right gastroepiploic branches.** The pyloric branch passes to the pylorus and continues along the lesser curvature of the stomach, where it breaks up into numerous vessels. The anterior pancreaticoduodenal supplies the duodenum and duodenal portion of the pancreas. The right gastroepiploic artery is distributed to the greater curvature of the stomach and part of the great omentum.

The left gastric branch of the coeliac goes to the lesser curvature of the stomach, where it anastomoses with the pyloric artery.

The splenic artery is the largest branch of the coeliac. It passes to the spleen, giving off branches to the pancreas, greater omentum, and stomach.

Superior mesenteric artery. The large superior mesenteric artery arises from the aorta a short distance caudad the coeliac. It is the vessel which supplies the greater part of the intestine. The **posterior pancreaticoduodenal** is a branch of the superior mesenteric, supplying the caudal end of the duodenum and the adjacent pancreatic tissue. Watch carefully for the pancreatic ducts so as not to destroy them. An **ileocaecolic branch** passes to the region of the ileocaecolic valve. A large **median colic branch** goes to the transverse and descending colon to anastomose with the inferior mesenteric artery. Another branch, the **right colic,** carries blood to the ascending colon and first part of the transverse colon. The main part of the superior mesenteric artery is represented by a large number of radiating branches which are distributed to all parts of the small intestine.

Inferior mesenteric artery. Posterior to the genital arteries the inferior mesenteric artery comes off the aorta. When it reaches the large intestine, it divides into anterior and posterior branches. The **anterior branch** goes forward to anastomose with the median colic branch of the superior mesenteric. The **posterior branch** supplies the rest of the colon and rectum.

Terminal Vessels

External iliac arteries. The external iliac arteries consist of a pair of large vessels arising from the aorta near the anterior end of the pelvic girdle. Just before each vessel leaves the abdominal cavity, it gives off, on its medial side, a **deep femoral** branch which courses caudad. About ½ in. from its origin this vessel in turn gives off three branches: (1) a **vesicular artery** to the urinary bladder; (2) an **external spermatic artery** (in the male), which passes along the spermatic cord to the testis; (3) an **inferior epigastric artery**, which passes along the peritoneal side of the rectus abdominis muscle and courses anteriorly to anastomose with the **superior epigastric**, which is a continuation of the **internal mammary artery.** The deep femoral artery proper is distributed to the deep muscles of the thigh.

After the external iliac artery emerges from the body cavity it is called the **femoral artery.** At Scarpa's triangle (page 159) it lies close to the medial surface of the thigh. Just external to the body wall a small **superficial epigastric artery** is given off. This courses anteriorly in superficial fascia outside the body wall to anastomose with the **external mammary artery.** About ½ in. from the point of emergence of the femoral artery from the body cavity a **lateral circumflex artery** is given off. It is distributed to muscles making up the cranial portion of the thigh. Numerous branches of the femoral artery are distributed to the remainder of the leg and foot; these need not be traced.

Internal iliac arteries. The internal iliac, or **hypogastric, arteries** arise from the aorta a short distance caudad the point of origin of the external iliacs. Almost immediately each gives off an **umbilical artery** which passes to the bladder, where **vesicular branches** are distributed to both bladder and urethra. Farther on, the internal iliac sends branches to the pelvic wall, gluteal muscles, rectum, and reproductive organs.

PULMONARY ARTERIES

A short distance after leaving the conus arteriosus, the pulmonary aorta divides into **right** and **left pulmonary arteries.** The **ligamentum Botalli,** or **ligamentum arteriosum,** connects the systemic and pulmonary aortae at a point just proximad the division. This is the remnant of a shunt between the two vessels which functioned during embryonic and fetal life. Branches of the pulmonary arteries pass to the various lobes of the lung. The cranial lobe of the right lung is said to be *eparterial*, since it lies anterior to the point where the pulmonary artery enters the lung. All the other lobes are *hyparterial*, lying caudad the pulmonary artery.

The Structure of the Heart

INTERNAL FEATURES

After the study of the veins and arteries is completed, the heart may be removed from the body in order to study its internal structure. Cut the blood vessels which enter and leave the heart, leaving at least a small stump attached to the heart in each case. There may be some difficulty in distinguishing the pulmonary vessels from the bronchi which lead from the trachea to the lungs. DO NOT CUT THE BRONCHI BY MISTAKE. Ask the instructor for aid.

Again note the following structures previously observed: ventricles, conus arteriosus, pulmonary aorta, systemic aorta, atrium, auricular appendages, inferior vena cava, superior vena cava, coronary vessels, and pulmonary veins. The pulmonary veins which bring blood from the lungs to the left atrium are arranged in three groups called the right, left, and dorsal groups.

Now dissect the heart according to the following directions. There may be some difficulty in finding various structures if the chambers of the heart contain latex. Ask for help if the instructions do not seem clear to you.

1. Remove the dorsal wall of the right atrium and of its appendage, except that portion to which the venae cavae are attached.
2. Remove the ventral wall of the right ventricle, taking care not to injure its internal surface and structures any more than is absolutely necessary.
3. From the left cephalic region of the right ventricle insert a probe into the pulmonary aorta. Slit the latter open along the probe.
4. Remove the dorsal wall of the left atrium and its appendage, except for that portion receiving the pulmonary veins.
5. With even greater care remove the ventral wall of the left ventricle, being careful not to injure internal structures more than is necessary.
6. From the right cephalic region of the left ventricle insert a probe into the systemic aorta. Cut along this probe *toward* the heart.

Now examine the internal structures of the heart, and with the aid of the diagram shown in Fig. 4.30 identify as many features as possible.

The wall of the heart is made up of three layers. Covering the surface is a thin layer of cells, the **epicardium.** It corresponds to the visceral layer of peritoneum and pleura covering the abdominal viscera and lungs, respectively. Next comes the muscular layer, or **myocardium.** The membrane lining the cavity of the heart is the **endocardium.**

The separation of the heart into chambers was not very clearly indicated when the organ was viewed externally. It is separated into right and left halves by a dorsoventral partition. Each half in turn consists of an anterior atrium and a posterior ventricle, separated by valves. The **tricuspid valve** lies between the right atrium and ventricle; the **bicuspid valve** guards the opening between the two chambers on the left side.

The inferior and superior venae cavae bring blood to the right atrium from the posterior and anterior parts of the body, respectively. The

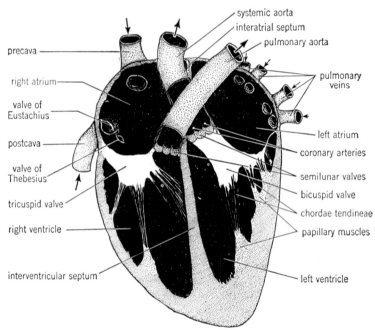

Fig. 4.30. Diagram showing internal structure of four-chambered mammalian heart, ventral view.

blood then passes into the right ventricle. From here it goes to the conus arteriosus and pulmonary aorta. This divides into right and left branches going to the lungs. The tricuspid valve prevents the blood in the right ventricle from being regurgitated into the right atrium. After the blood has been oxygenated in the lungs, it again returns to the heart. This time it passes through the pulmonary veins which enter the left atrium. It then goes past the bicuspid valve into the left ventricle. The systemic aorta carries blood away from the left ventricle. Branches of the systemic aorta distribute blood to all parts of the body. **Semilunar valves** at the base of both the pulmonary and systemic aortae prevent blood in these vessels from returning to the ventricles.

A complex of vessels can be observed on the surface of the heart itself. These are the **coronary arteries** and **veins.** The coronary arteries arise from the systemic aorta just craniad the semilunar valves. They supply the walls of the heart itself with blood. The coronary veins collect this blood from the walls of the heart and empty it into the right atrium through a common opening, the **coronary sinus.** Three vessels, therefore, bring blood to the right atrium.

Atria. The atria are relatively thin-walled sacs at the basal end of the heart. Each consists of two parts: a **principal cavity** and an **auricula,** or **auricular appendage.** The latter is a pouchlike projection with irregular edges. It overlaps the roots of the pulmonary and systematic aortae. Parallel muscular ridges, the **musculi pectinati,** line the internal surface of the auricular appendages, but the walls of the principal chambers are smooth. The **interatrial septum** which separates the two atria bears an oval depression, the **fossa ovalis.** It marks the location of the **foramen ovale,** an opening between the two atria normally present only before birth.

The right atrium is larger than the left, but its walls are thinner. The superior vena cava opens into the anterior dorsal part. There is no valve at the opening. The inferior vena cava enters the posterior dorsal side. Its opening is partially guarded by a small **Eustachian valve.** The coronary sinus, guarded by the **valve of Thebesius,** opens into the atrium between the opening of the inferior vena cava and the atrioventricular aperture.

The left atrium receives the pulmonary veins which enter in three groups, as already described.

Ventricles. The walls of the ventricles are much thicker than those of the atria, in correlation with the muscular force required to propel the blood to points at some distance from the heart. The walls of the left ventricle are two or three times as thick as those of the right. The internal surfaces of the ventricles are marked by numerous irregular muscular columns, the **trabeculae carneae,** or **columnae carneae.** They are fewer in number in the region of the interventricular septum and are not present in the wall of the conus arteriosus.

The tricuspid valve between the right atrium and right ventricle consists of three thin, semicircular membranous flaps, the bases of which are attached to the walls of the heart. One is dorsal, another ventral, and the third is on the interventricular septum. Several thin but tough nonelastic bands, the **chordae tendineae,** connect the free edge and ventricular surface of each flap to the walls of the ventricle. The chordae tendineae of the dorsal and ventral flaps unite near the ventricular wall, where they are attached to muscular columns, the **papillary muscles.** The chordae tendineae restrict the movement of the tricuspid valve, thus preventing regurgitation of blood into the atrium when the ventricle contracts.

The biscuspid valve between the left atrium and left ventricle consists of two flaps. The base of one is attached to the interventricular septum; the other to the lateral wall. Chordae tendineae serve to attach their free edges to the ventricular wall. Trabeculae carneae are less numerous in the left ventricle than in the right.

Lymphatic System

Dissection of the delicate vessels making up the greater part of the lymphatic system is impracticable and will not be attempted. However, a description of the lymphatic system is given here for the sake of completeness.

The lymphatic system is that part of the circulatory system which is concerned with collecting lymph from all parts of the body and carrying it to the external jugular veins. The system originates in a fine meshwork of delicate vessels called **lymph capillaries** which drain lymph from the tissue spaces. The small lymphatic vessels in the villi of the small intestine are known as **lacteals**. Small vessels unite to form larger vessels, which in turn join to form still larger vessels. Gradually the vessels increase in size, ultimately forming **lymphatic ducts**. Two lymphatic ducts drain the anterior portion of the body, and a single **thoracic duct** drains lymph from the posterior region.

Lymph, which is a colorless fluid, flows slowly through the lymphatic vessels, finally entering the venous system via the external jugular veins near their junction with the subclavians. Valves are present in the larger lymphatic vessels. This gives them a moniliform, or beaded, appearance. **Lymph glands**, or **lymph nodes**, interrupt the passage of the larger lymphatic vessels at various points. They serve as filters through which the lymph slowly passes. **Lymphocytes** are contributed to the lymph by the lymph nodes. Other structures considered to belong to the lymphatic system include the **thymus gland, spleen, tonsils, and bone marrow.** No special pumping organ is present in the cat to propel the lymph. Movements of the muscles in various parts of the body are largely responsible for the passage of lymph along the lymphatic vessels.

Since detailed features of the lymphatic system are difficult to observe in ordinary dissections, only a few of the more obvious structures will be treated here.

Superficial and deep lymphatic vessels of the head, neck, and forelimb of the cat, interrupted by lymph glands, finally unite on each side to form a single vessel. That on the left usually joins the thoracic duct, which drains lymph from the posterior regions, the two having a common opening into the left external jugular vein. On the right side the lymphatic duct enters the external jugular vein directly.

The largest vessel of the lymphatic system is the thoracic duct (Fig. 4.28). It is most clearly observed in the dorsal part of the body cavity along the left side of the vertebral column anterior to the kidneys. In the region of the kidneys it is somewhat enlarged to form the **cisterna chyli.** All the lymph from the thoracic and abdominal viscera, hind legs, pelvic wall, abdominal wall, and most of the thoracic wall ultimately enters the thoracic duct. Many lymph glands are present in these areas. In the mesentery of the small intestine the lymph glands are united into one large mass often referred to as the **pancreas aselli.** This is the largest lymph gland in the body.

Spleen

The spleen is generally considered to be a lymphatic organ. Small areas of lymphoidal tissue called **Malpighian corpuscles** are scattered throughout the spleen. They manufacture lymphocytes. In addition, the spleen serves for the storage of blood and plays a part in the final destruction of blood cells. It is a large, curved, flattened organ of a dark-red color. It lies close to the greater curvature of the stomach on the left side of the body. The spleen is actually enclosed within the descending limb of the greater omentum. It is the only structure not belonging to the digestive system that is drained by the hepatic portal vein.

DIGESTIVE SYSTEM

The digestive system of the cat consists of the **alimentary canal** and its associated organs. The alimentary canal is divided into several regions. Listing them in order from anterior to posterior ends, they are mouth, pharynx, esophagus, stomach, small intestine (duodenum, jejunum, ileum), and large intestine (colon, rectum, anal canal). The associated structures include the salivary glands, liver, pancreas, and their ducts.

Mouth. The **oral cavity,** or **mouth,** is the region between the lips and pharynx. It is divided into two parts: a **vestibule,** which is the portion between the lips and the teeth; and an **oral cavity proper,** which makes up the remainder. The portion of the vestibule bounded by the cheeks is referred to as the **buccal cavity.**

The **lips** are folds of skin covered with hair on the outside and with mucous membrane on the inner surface. Each is fastened to the jaw in the median line by a fold of tissue, the **labial frenum.**

Remove any skin that remains on the head of your specimen, being careful not to destroy the main mass of the parotid salivary gland which lies just in front of the ear and adheres closely to the skin. It is best at this point to locate the salivary glands and to trace their ducts to the mouth. Do not confuse some of the large lymph glands in this region with the salivary glands.

The cat has five pairs of salivary glands, the ducts of which open into the mouth. The largest of these is the **parotid gland.** It lies just anteroventrad the external auditory meatus and covers part of the masseter muscle. The duct of the parotid gland is called **Stensen's duct.** It courses over the surface of the masseter muscle in fascia to a point near the angle of the mouth, where it passes through the cheek to open on the inside opposite the last premolar tooth of the upper jaw. The second largest of the salivary glands is the **submaxillary.** It lies ventrad the parotid gland in back of the angular process of the lower jaw. Its duct, which is known as **Wharton's duct,** passes under the masseter, mylohyoid, and digastric muscles parallel to the mandible to open on a papilla located just in back of the incisor teeth. The **sublingual gland** is small. Its base is closely applied to the anterior border of the submaxillary gland. Its duct, the **sublingual duct,** runs parallel to Wharton's duct and opens on the same papilla. A very small **molar gland** is also present in the cat. It lies ventrad Stensen's duct near the angle of the mouth. The gland has several ducts, not easily seen, which penetrate the cheek to open on its inner surface. The last of the salivary glands is the **infraorbital,** or **zygomatic, gland.** It lies in the floor of the orbit near the lateral side. Do not look for this gland now. It will be studied when the eye is removed from the orbit later on (page 210). From the ventral portion of the gland a duct leads to the roof of the mouth caudad the small molar tooth.

Study of the mouth and the structures in the mouth is difficult because of the restricted size of the mouth opening and the rigidity of the muscles in preserved specimens. In order to expose the mouth cavity, proceed as follows: With your scalpel cut through the muscles attached to the *inner* surface of the mandible on each side. Be sure that the incision goes all the way through into the mouth cavity. With your fingers force the tip of the tongue through the opening between the two halves of the mandible. Pull the tongue downward as far as possible without tearing the surrounding tissues. Next, cut the muscles on either side of the base of the tongue as well as the hyoid apparatus, continuing to exert gentle traction on the tongue until a pale, pointed structure, the epiglottis, appears in the back of the throat. The various portions of mouth and pharynx should now be clearly visible.

First examine the **tongue,** which normally occupies the floor of the mouth. It is a mobile, fleshy organ, the surface of which is covered with small projections, or **papillae,** of four different types. **Conical,** or **filiform, papillae** are horny projections pointing caudad. They are concentrated in the middle portion of the free part of the tongue. No taste buds are associated with the filiform papillae. **Fungiform papillae** are small mushroom-shaped structures scattered over the surface of the tongue, most of them lying posterior to the main mass of filiform papillae. The fungiform papillae bear taste buds. **Vallate,** or **circumvallate, papillae** are few in number. They are arranged in two oblique rows of two or three each. The two rows meet in the form of a V, the apex of the V pointing caudad. The small depression at the apex is the **foramen caecum.** It represents the point of origin of the thyroid gland during embryonic development. Each circumvallate papilla is surrounded by a trenchlike depression, along both sides of which taste buds are located. **Foliate,** or **flat, papillae** are numerous in the region of the root of the tongue and along the sides near the base (Fig. 4.31). Taste buds are present on the borders of the foliate papillae. A thin vertical fold of mucous membrane, the **frenum linguae,** attaches the anterior ventral part of the tongue to the floor of the mouth.

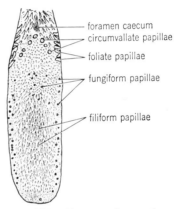

FIG. 4.31. Tongue of cat, showing arrangement of papillae.

The **teeth** of the cat were studied in connection with the skull. They are **thecodont** (set in sockets), **heterodont** (of various shapes), **diphyodont** (only two sets, temporary and permanent), and **secodont** (cheek teeth adapted for cutting). The number of teeth on the two jaws differs. On each half of the lower jaw, or mandible, beginning at the anterior end, are three small, poorly developed **incisors;** one large, strong, pointed **canine;** two well-developed **premolars;** and a single large posterior **molar.** Molars are distinguished from premolars chiefly by the fact that they have no predecessors in the temporary set of teeth. A large gap, or space, between the canine and first premolar is called the **diastema.** The teeth of the upper jaw, on each side, consist of three small incisors attached to the premaxillary bone; a single large canine; three premolars; and a single very small molar at the posterior end, all set in sockets in the maxillary bone. There is no diastema in the upper jaw.

The **roof of the mouth** is composed of an anterior **hard palate** and a posterior **soft palate.** The hard palate is supported by premaxillary, maxillary, and palatine bones. Its mucous membrane is thrown into a number of prominent transverse ridges, or **rugae.** The soft palate has no bony support. At its ventral end on either side is a small swelling, the **palatine tonsil,** partially embedded in a shallow pocket.

Pharynx. The pharyngeal region, which lies in back of the soft palate, is common to both the digestive and respiratory systems. Its upper portion is called the **nasopharynx.** During the act of swallowing, the soft palate is pushed against the roof of the pharynx, temporarily blocking the opening between the nasopharynx and pharynx. The nasopharynx communicates anteriorly with the nasal passages through the **choanae,** or **internal nares.** At about the center of the nasopharynx

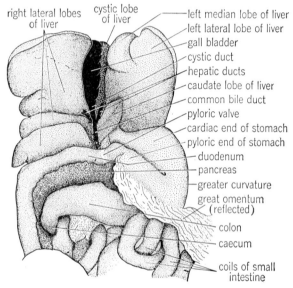

right lateral lobes of liver — cystic lobe of liver — left median lobe of liver — left lateral lobe of liver — gall bladder — cystic duct — hepatic ducts — caudate lobe of liver — common bile duct — pyloric valve — cardiac end of stomach — pyloric end of stomach — duodenum — pancreas — greater curvature — great omentum (reflected) — colon — caecum — coils of small intestine

FIG. 4.32. Ventral view of a portion of the abdominal viscera of cat. The liver and great omentum have been deflected to expose the structures covered by them.

is a pair of dorsolateral slits. These are the openings of the **Eustachian tubes.** It may be necessary to cut through the soft palate before these can be discerned.

The **glottis** is located on the floor of the pharynx. It is a longitudinal slit which marks the opening leading to the larynx, trachea, bronchi, and lungs. A flaplike projection, the **epiglottis,** previously observed, lies craniad the glottis, which it guards. Posteriorly the pharynx narrows down to join the esophagus.

Esophagus. The narrow tube of uniform diameter, connecting pharynx and stomach, is the esophagus. It passes through the thoracic cavity, its ventral surface being closely applied to the trachea. It finally penetrates the diaphragm to join the cardiac end of the stomach.

Stomach. The shape of the stomach (Fig. 4.32) is somewhat like that of a pear, with its broad end to the left. This is the **cardiac end** to which the esophagus is attached. The narrow end, which lies to the right, is the **pyloric end** of the stomach. It joins the duodenum, or first part of the small intestine. At the junction of the two is a thick sphincter muscle, the **pyloric valve.** The convex, longer outer border of the stomach is the **greater curvature.** It is here that the greater omentum is attached. The smaller, concave side of the stomach is the **lesser curvature.**

Small intestine. The small intestine begins at the pyloric valve and terminates at its junction with the large intestine. It is very much coiled, and its length is $2\frac{1}{2}$ to 3 times the length of the entire cat. The division of the small intestine into duodenum, jejunum, and ileum is not too clear-cut. The **duodenum,** or first part of the small intestine, is from 12 to 15 cm. long. It bends rather sharply at the pylorus and runs backward for a short distance on the right side. Farther on it forms another sharp bend, this time to the left and craniad. Still farther on it joins the **jejunum,** the next bend generally being considered its termination. The beginning and end of the jejunum cannot be determined with exactitude. It is about 25 cm. long. The **ileum** is the longest part of the small intestine, making up about two-thirds of it. At its junction with the large intestine another valve-like sphincter is to be found. This is the **ileocolic,** or **ileocaecolic, valve** (Fig. 4.33).

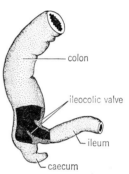

colon

ileocolic valve

ileum

caecum

FIG. 4.33. Junction of ileum and colon of cat, showing caecum and ileocolic valve.

Large intestine. The first part of the large intestine is the **colon.** It begins on the right side of the body where the ileum joins it. Posterior to the point of union the colon forms a small pouch, the **caecum.** The tip of the caecum ends in a slight projection which is, to a mild degree, comparable to the vermiform appendix of man. The regions of the colon are named according to their position. **Ascending, transverse,** and **descending portions** are recognized. The **rectum** is the terminal part of the large intestine. It begins where the colon reaches the median line and terminates at the **anus,** which is surrounded by sphincter muscles. On either side of the anus is a scent gland, the **anal gland,** the duct of which opens into the anus a short distance from the outside.

Liver. The largest gland of the body is the liver, which occupies the anterior part of the abdominal cavity. It lies against the diaphragm. The liver is divided into right and left lobes, each of which is subdivided. Each half bears a small **median** and a large **lateral lobe.** The median lobe on the right side is often called the **cystic lobe,** since the gall bladder lies against it. The right lateral lobe is deeply cleft. A small projection of the right lateral lobe is the **caudate lobe.** It lies in the omental bursa and partially closes the foramen of Winslow.

The **gall bladder** is a green pear-shaped organ situated on the right side of the body and partly surrounded by the cystic lobe of the liver. The narrow end of the gall bladder opens into a **cystic duct.** This is joined about 2 or 3 cm. from the gall bladder by two **hepatic ducts,** one from each side of the liver. Additional hepatic ducts are frequently encountered. The **common bile duct,** or **ductus choledochus,** empties into the duodenum about 3 cm. from the pyloric sphincter. Just before entering the duodenum, it is joined by the duct of Wirsung of the pancreas. A dilatation of the common duct at the entrance of the duodenum is called the **ampulla of Vater.** Its opening is regulated by a sphincter muscle, the **sphincter of Oddi.**

Pancreas. The second largest gland in the body is the pancreas. It is a flattened, irregular, elongated structure, sharply bent in the center to form two lobes. One lobe lies within the curve of the duodenum. The other is located within the descending portion of the greater omentum, opposite the greater curvature of the stomach and close to the spleen. The pancreas basically has two ducts: a **ventral duct (of Wirsung)** and a **dorsal duct (of Santorini).** The duct of Wirsung is the chief duct of the gland. It receives branches from both lobes of the pancreas and joins the bile duct just before the latter opens into the duodenum. The duct of Santorini in the cat is usually found with difficulty or is missing entirely. It is by far the smaller of the two, its opening into the duodenum being located about 2 cm. beyond the ampulla of Vater. In order to locate these ducts, gently tease away the pancreatic tissue with a probe. They may be readily identified unless they were destroyed when the circulatory system in this region was studied.

It should be recalled that the pancreas is both an exocrine and an endocrine gland. The endocrine activity is brought about by the hormone **insulin,** secreted by the cells of the **islands of Langerhans.** Special histological preparations are necessary to demonstrate their presence.

After identifying the various parts of the digestive tract, slit the entire tract longitudinally and examine the inner surface. Wash out any food material that it may contain. Do not slit the last 10 cm. of the rectum, however, until the urogenital system has been studied. Look particularly for the pyloric valve, the openings of bile and pancreatic ducts, and the ileocolic valve.

RESPIRATORY SYSTEM

The structures making up the respiratory system include the nasal passages, nasopharynx, pharynx, glottis, larynx, trachea, bronchi, and lungs.

Nasal passages, nasopharynx, pharynx, and glottis. The external nares lead to the nasal passages. These are situated above the hard palate and are surrounded by the anterior bones of the face (page 119). Turbinate projections of nasal, maxillary, and ethmoid bones fill the greater portion of the nasal passages with their scroll-like folds. A septum, supported by the lamina perpendicularis of the ethmoid bone, separates the two sides. Mucous membrane covers all parts of the nasal passages. These passages open into the nasopharynx through the internal nares, or choanae. Nasopharynx, pharynx, and glottis have been discussed in connection with the digestive system.

In order to study the remainder of the respiratory system it is best to remove it from the body. Pull the tongue forward and cut the remaining muscles around its base. Also cut through the dorsal and lateral walls of the pharynx, dissecting away connective tissues until the entire base of the tongue, pharynx, and esophagus are free. Continue to pull forward gently, and the entire respiratory system should be liberated from surrounding tissues. Sever the esophagus somewhat anterior to the point where it penetrates the diaphragm. Now strip the esophagus free from the trachea, and note the groove marking its former location. Dissect the anterior end of the esophagus free from the larynx and discard it.

Larynx. The first part of the respiratory tube leading from glottis to lungs is the **larynx**, or **voice box** (Fig. 4.34). It is supported by cartilages derived chiefly from the visceral skeleton. In addition to the cartilage supporting the epiglottis, a pair of **arytenoid cartilages** and unpaired **thyroid** and **cricoid cartilages** are the skeletal structures involved. The thyrohyal bones of the hyoid apparatus are attached to the thyroid cartilage. The single basihyal is fastened to the cranial end of the ventral border of the larynx (Fig. 4.4).

Make a longitudinal incision through the middorsal part of the glottis down to the second or third tracheal cartilage. Spread the cut edges apart and examine the internal surface.

On either side of the base of the epiglottis is a fold of mucous membrane. These make up the **false vocal cords**. A short distance behind the false vocal cords is another pair of membranous folds, the **true vocal cords**. The space in front of them is called the **vestibule**. The cavity of the larynx extends from the glottis to the first cartilaginous ring of the trachea.

Trachea. The long tube extending posteriorly from the larynx is the **trachea.** Immediately above it lies the esophagus. The walls of the trachea are supported by about 45 incomplete cartilaginous rings which are open on the dorsal side. The gap, which is filled with connective tissue and muscle, forms a place for the reception of the ventral surface of the esophagus. The trachea divides at its caudal end to form two **bronchi** which almost immediately enter the lungs, where they divide

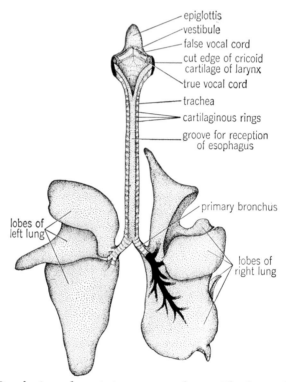

FIG. 4.34. Dorsal view of respiratory organs of cat. The larynx has been split open to show the vocal cords.

and redivide. The bronchi, like the trachea, are supported by cartilaginous rings which prevent their walls from collapsing. The terminal branches of the bronchi are termed **bronchioles.** They lead into small sacs, the **infundibula,** which are lined with **alveoli.**

Lungs. The lungs are divided into several lobes. In the cat there are three lobes on the left and four on the right. As previously noted, the lungs are invested by the visceral pleura. The pleural cavities of the two sides are not confluent but are separated dorsally by the mediastinal space and ventrally by the mediastinal septum.

Cut through one of the bronchi and trace it to its finer ramifications in the lobes of the lung.

EXCRETORY SYSTEM

The structures making up the excretory system of the cat are paired kidneys and ureters and an unpaired urinary bladder and urethra. In the male, as will be pointed out, there is a close relationship between the excretory and reproductive systems. This is less marked in the case of the female.

Kidneys. The cat possesses the **metanephric type** of kidney. The kidneys are located along the dorsal part of the abdomen on either side of the vertebral column in the region of the fourth lumbar vertebra. The right one is usually slightly more anterior in position than the left. The peritoneum does not surround the kidneys as it does the other abdominal viscera but covers only the ventral side. The kidneys are therefore said to be **retroperitoneal.**

Each kidney (Fig. 4.35) is bean-shaped, with a notch, the **hilum,** along the medial border. Carefully dissect away the fatty tissue in the vicinity of the kidney so as to expose it clearly to view. It is at the hilum that the renal vessels enter or leave the kidney and the **ureter** emerges on its way to the bladder. The latter appears as a narrow, whitish thread. Remove one of the kidneys, and split it with a sharp scalpel into dorsal and ventral halves. It will be noted that a rather loose, fibrous **capsule** surrounds the kidney. Beneath the capsule is a dark layer of tissue, the **cortex,** surrounding a lighter-colored central **medulla.** A cavity, the **pelvis,** adjacent to the hilum, empties into the ureter. A projection of the medulla extends into the pelvis in the form of a cone-shaped **papilla.** Excretory products from the kidney pass into the pelvis and thence to the ureter.

Ureters. The duct of the kidney on each side is called the ureter. It is a slender tube which begins at the pelvis and passes posteriorly to the level of the caudal end of the bladder, where it turns in a ventro-craniad direction to enter the dorsal side of that organ near its narrow neck. The ureters are invested by a fold of peritoneum in which considerable fat may be deposited. Clean this away carefully. If your specimen is a male, note carefully how the ductus deferens on each side loops over the ureter close to the junction of the ureter with the bladder.

Urinary bladder. The pear-shaped **urinary bladder** is a large sac in the ventral posterior part of the abdominal cavity. It lies just craniad the pubic symphysis below the rectum. Visceral peritoneum is reflected over it. A fibromuscular cord of tissue, the **middle umbilical ligament,** connects the apex of the bladder with the umbilicus on the inner body wall.   It represents the remnant of the embryonic **urachus,** or **allantoic stalk.**   A peritoneal fold, the **suspensory ligament,** joins the bladder to the linea alba.   In addition, the bladder is supported dorsally by a pair of **lateral ligaments.**   The caudal portion of the bladder, into which the ureters open, is the **neck.**   It joins a narrow tube, the **urethra,** the course of which differs depending upon the sex.   Do not trace the urethra at this time.   It will be studied in detail when the reproductive system is dissected.   In the male the urethra passes through the penis to open near its tip on the ventral side; in the female it joins the vagina to form the urogenital sinus, which in turn opens to the outside.

REPRODUCTIVE SYSTEM

In studying the reproductive system, work with a partner who has a specimen of the opposite sex.   Each student will be held responsible for knowledge of both male and female reproductive systems.

Carefully remove any skin that remains in the genital region.   In males be particularly heedful not to remove the scrotum and the testes which lie within the scrotum.   In both sexes it is necessary to cut through the pubic symphysis with a sharp scalpel in order to get a complete picture of the urogenital system.   This is usually easily done if the cut is made directly in the median line.   In young animals the union of the pubic bones is cartilaginous.   In older specimens, however, the union is bony, and it may be necessary to use a bone forceps in order to cut through the symphysis.   After having made the cut, grasp the thighs with your hands and spread the edges of the symphysis apart.   The lower part of the urogenital system will then be exposed so that it may readily be dissected free of surrounding tissues.

The Male
(Fig. 4.35)

The **primary reproductive organs** of the male are the **testes.**   In addition to producing spermatozoa, the testes are endocrine glands.   The hormone **testosterone,** produced by the **cells of Leydig,** or **interstitial cells** of the testes, controls the development and function of the **accessory sex organs** as well as the **secondary sex characters.**

Scrotum.   The testes are located in an external pouch, the **scrotum,** which is covered with skin.   The scrotum is divided by a septum into two halves, each of which contains a testis.   A diverticulum of the abdominal cavity, lined with peritoneum, extends into each half of the scrotum.   It does not completely surround the testis.

Testes.   The peritoneum reflected over part of the surface of the testes forms the **tunica vaginalis propria.**   Beneath this is a tough membrane, the **tunica albuginea**, which invests the testis closely. Each testis measures approximately 1½ cm. in length and 1 cm. in thickness.

Epididymis. On the dorsal surface of the testis lies a flattened structure, the **epididymis.** Its enlarged cranial end is the **caput epididymidis.** This narrows down to form the body, or **corpus epididymidis,** which in turn joins the expanded caudal portion, or **cauda epididymidis.** Actually the entire structure consists of a long, coiled, very compactly arranged tube. A few **efferent ductules** connect the caput epididymidis with the **seminiferous tubules** of the testis, in which spermatozoa are produced.

Ductus deferens. The coiled tube just mentioned leaves the cauda epididymidis as the **ductus deferens,** which courses craniad. The first part of the ductus deferens is highly convoluted, but it then gradually straightens out. It runs forward parallel with the spermatic artery and vein. All three are contained within a mesentery-like fold of tissue, the **spermatic cord,** which also contains nerves and lymphatic vessels. After penetrating the abdominal wall at the **inguinal ring,** the ductus deferens leaves the spermatic cord and turns medially and craniad the neck of the bladder, passing between the bladder and ureter, as previously noted. After looping over the

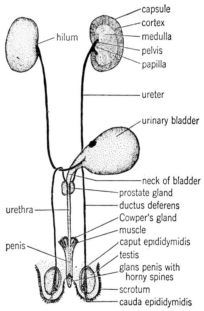

Fig. 4.35. Male urogenital system of cat, ventral view (semidiagrammatic).

ureter, it turns caudad and approaches its fellow from the other side. The two ducts enter the *dorsal* side of the urethra at a point about 2 or 3 cm. from the bladder.

Prostate gland. An enlargement on the urethra at the point where the two deferent ducts enter marks the location of the **prostate gland.** It is composed of many small tubules which pour their secretion into the urethra. The prostatic secretion serves as a vehicle for transport of spermatozoa to the outside. In many mammals a prominent seminal vesicle comes off the ductus deferens near its junction with the urethra. The cat lacks seminal vesicles.

Urethra. The urethra is made up of three portions. The first, or **prostatic urethra,** is the region surrounded by the prostate gland. Next comes the **membranous urethra,** which extends to the base of the penis. The last, or **spongy, portion** passes along the underside of the penis. The walls of this portion are composed of erectile tissue forming the **corpus spongiosum** of the penis. The opening of the urethra at the ventral side of the tip of the penis is called the **meatus.**

Penis. The cylindrical **penis** projects caudad. When relaxed, it measures about 3 cm. in length. It is covered with skin which forms a sheath, the **prepuce,** over its free end. The end of the penis, or **glans,** is covered with **horny spines.** On its underside the glans is connected to the prepuce by a fold of tissue, the **frenum** of the prepuce.

Cowper's glands. At the base of the penis a pair of **Cowper's glands** is to be found. Each opens by means of a duct into the urethra.

The Female
(Fig. 4.36)

The reproductive organs of the female consist of a pair of ovaries, and oviducts, or tubes, which transport ova and in which the young develop.

Ovaries. The gonads of the female lie in the dorsolateral part of the body cavity just caudad the kidneys. They are narrow, oval bodies measuring about 1 cm. in length. Each ovary lies in a shallow pocket in a fold of peritoneum, the **broad ligament,** which in this region suspends the ovary from the body wall. The part of the broad ligament attached to the ovary is referred to as the **mesovarium.** In addition to producing eggs, or ova, the ovaries have an endocrine function. Small, light-colored vesicles projecting from the surface of the ovaries are **Graafian follicles,** each of which contains a microscopic ovum. The ovarian hormone **estradiol** is believed to be secreted by the cells of the Graafian follicle.

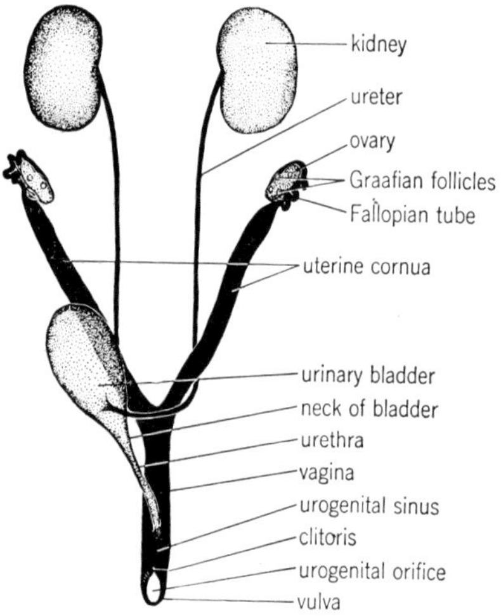

FIG. 4.36. Female urogenital system of cat, ventral view (semidiagrammatic).

Other dark, solid elevations, called **corpora lutea,** may also be present on the surface of the ovaries. A second ovarian hormone, **progesterone,** is secreted by the cells of the corpora lutea.

Fallopian tubes. From each ovary a narrow, twisted **Fallopian tube** extends in a caudal direction. At its ovarian end the Fallopian tube widens out into a funnel-shaped structure which receives ova after their discharge from the ovary. The opening into the Fallopian tube is called the **ostium tubae.** Each tube curves around the ovary and then extends a short distance caudad, where it joins the uterus.

Uterus. The uterus of the cat is of the **bipartite type.** It consists of two expanded **cornua,** or **horns,** which are united caudally to form the **body** of the uterus. The body, which is approximately 4 cm. long, lies between the bladder and the rectum, its caudal end being located near the anterior border of the pubic symphysis. At this point the uterus joins the vagina. The caudal end of the uterus projects into the vagina for a short distance, this portion being referred to as the **cervix** of the uterus. A small opening in the cervix, the **os uteri,** connects the cavities of uterus and vagina. Ovaries, Fallopian tubes, and uterus are supported by a fold of peritoneum, the broad ligament referred to above. A **round ligament** on each side also aids in supporting the uterus. It is connected to the broad ligament and extends from about the middle of the uterine horn to the posterior body wall at a point which corresponds to the inguinal ring of the male.

Vagina. From the os uteri the vagina passes caudally to a point about opposite the posterior end of the ischial symphysis, where it is joined on the ventral side by the urethra. The terminal tube common to urethra and vagina is the **urogenital sinus,** or **vestibule.** Its external portion is called the **vulva.** At the ventral side of the urogenital sinus near its orifice is a small elevation no larger than the head of a pin. This structure, the **clitoris,** is homologous with the penis of the male. Slit the wall of the urogenital sinus and vagina, and look for the urethral opening and cervix of the uterus.

Mammary glands. Although the mammary glands are integumentary derivatives, they are best considered in connection with the reproductive system. They are undeveloped or rudimentary in the male. In the female their size varies according to whether the animal is pregnant or not pregnant, lactating or nonlactating. The mammary tissue, in the form of a pair of longitudinal bands of tissue, lies beneath the skin on the ventral side of the body, extending forward from the posterior end of the abdomen to about the level of the fourth rib. The ducts of the various parts of the mammary glands converge at five distinct places on each side. Here are located the elevated **nipples** through which the mammary ducts open to the outside.

ENDOCRINE SYSTEM

Some of the glands making up the endocrine system have already been discussed (pancreas, testes, ovaries) and require no further treatment here. Others include the thyroid, parathyroids, adrenals, and pituitary gland. The thymus gland and pineal body, although no longer classified as endocrine glands by most authorities, are also mentioned.

Thyroid gland. On either side of the trachea just caudad the larynx is a dark-colored glandular structure. These are the **lateral lobes** of the thyroid gland. The two lobes are connected across the ventral side of the trachea by a narrow strip, the **isthmus,** composed of the same kind of tissue. The isthmus may be so thin as to escape ordinary notice. The hormone of the thyroid gland, **thyroxin,** is important in controlling the metabolic activity of the entire body.

Parathyroid glands. The parathyroid glands of the cat, usually four in number, are exceedingly minute structures embedded, at least partially, in thyroid tissue. They are not noticeable in an ordinary dissection. **Parathormone,** the hormone of the parathyroid glands, is important in regulating the calcium and phosphorus metabolism of the body. The parathyroid glands are essential for life.

Adrenal glands. The adrenal glands are often referred to as the **suprarenal bodies.** They are two oval-shaped solid structures, scarcely 1 cm. long, lying a short distance craniad the kidneys on the dorsal side of the abdominal cavity near the median line. Each is composed of an outer layer, the **cortex,** and an inner **medulla.** Although so closely related anatomically, the two portions are functionally independent. The hormones secreted by the cortex are concerned with maintaining the sodium level of the blood and regulating blood volume. They also have some relation to the carbohydrate metabolism of the body. **Adrenalin,** or **epinephrine,** the secretion of the medulla, is effective in raising the blood pressure.

Pituitary body. The pituitary body, or gland, will not be identified until the brain has been removed (page 203). It is a small glandular structure attached to the ventral part of the brain in the region of the diencephalon. It lies in the sella turcica on the cranial side of the basisphenoid bone. The pituitary body is made up of **anterior, intermediate,** and **posterior lobes,** each of which secretes one or more hormones.

Thymus gland. The thymus gland is large in young animals but degenerates after puberty, so that in adults only vestiges remain. It lies in the mediastinal space between the sternum and lungs and extends forward from the heart into the neck region. The thymus is a flattened, irregular-shaped glandular structure which is often incompletely divided into lobes. It seems to have some relation to sexual development, but there is considerable doubt as to whether the thymus is an endocrine gland. Most evidence points to its being part of the lymphatic system.

Pineal body. Lying on the dorsal side of the brain, the small **pineal body,** or **epiphysis,** is practically hidden by surrounding parts. It will be identified later (page 202). It is located between the anterior, or superior, colliculi. Although the pineal body is considered by some authorities to be part of the endocrine system, the present consensus regards it as being merely an interesting vestigial structure related to the median pineal eye found in certain lower vertebrates.

NERVOUS SYSTEM

The nervous system of the cat is studied with some difficulty because of the hard consistency of the bony cranium and vertebral column, which enclose the brain and spinal cord, respectively. Other portions of the nervous system may have been removed or damaged during the dissection of some of the other organ systems. A complete study of the nervous system would require a new specimen. Enough remains in your specimen, however, to make a successful study of the more salient features of the nervous system as described below.

With a bone forceps make a hole in the top of the skull. Beginning at this point carefully chip away small bits of bone until the dorsal surface of the skull has been completely removed and the brain, with its surrounding membranes (meninges), exposed. Particular care must be exercised in removing the tentorium, which, it will be recalled, extends inward from the parietal bones and lies between the cerebral hemispheres and cerebellum. Chip away the dorsal portions of the atlas, axis, and remaining cervical vertebrae, and continue posteriorly until the spinal cord has been exposed. Make as many observations as possible before removing the brain and cord. When you are ready to remove these structures, place a blunt instrument between the brain and skull, working gradually around the entire brain so as to loosen it. Watch carefully for cranial nerves and sever them as near as possible to the foramina through which they emerge. The cranial nerves of the cat are much smaller than those of the dogfish and may be rather difficult to identify. Also watch for the pituitary body on the ventral side of the brain, and make every attempt to keep its attachment intact.

As in the case of other vertebrates, the nervous system of the cat is made up of three main divisions: the central, peripheral, and peripheral autonomic nervous systems. The three parts are intricately interconnected functionally and structurally.

Central Nervous System

The spinal cord and brain belong to the **central nervous system.** They are well protected by surrounding bony structures: vertebrae enclose and protect the spinal cord; the cranial portion of the skull surrounds and protects the brain.

Spinal cord (**myelon**). The spinal cord is continuous with the brain at the foramen magnum in the occipital bone. It lies wholly within the neural canal of the vertebral column. The cord is a long tubular structure, slightly flattened in a dorsoventral direction. The cavity within the spinal cord, the **central canal**, is very small in diameter. In the sacral region the cord narrows down to terminate in a slender **filum terminale** in the tail region. Two swellings, or enlargements, are to be observed in the spinal cord of the cat and other mammals: an anterior **cervical enlargement** and a posterior **lumbar enlargement**. These mark the sites of origin of the nerves passing to the arms and legs, respectively.

Several external longitudinal grooves, or fissures, are to be observed on the spinal cord. These include a **posterior median sulcus** along the mid-dorsal line, and an anterior median fissure along the midventral line. **Anterior and posterior lateral sulci** along the sides are less prominent. Spinal nerves, belonging to the peripheral nervous system, form metamerically arranged connections with the spinal cord.

Meninges of the cord. Surrounding the spinal cord are several membranes which, in their aggregate, are spoken of as **meninges.**

PIA MATER. Closely investing the cord is a delicate membrane, the **pia mater.** It closely follows the configurations of the cord and is well supplied with blood vessels.

ARACHNOID MEMBRANE. Surrounding the pia mater is a delicate **arachnoid membrane.** It does not dip into the fissures and sulci as does the pia mater. The arachnoid is separated from the pia by a **subarachnoid space,** which is filled with **cerebrospinal fluid.**

DURA MATER SPINALIS. A loose sheath, the **dura mater spinalis,** or **spinal dura,** lies outside the arachnoid membrane, separated from the latter by a **subdural space** containing cerebrospinal fluid. An **epidural space** outside the dura mater separates this membrane from the periosteum lining the neural canal of the vertebral column.

Brain. The brain (Figs. 4.37 and 4.38), lying wholly within the cranial cavity, is continuous at the foramen magnum with the spinal cord. Like the latter, it is essentially a tubular structure. The cavities, or **ventricles,** within the brain are enlarged and subdivided. They are continuous posteriorly with the central canal of the cord. The mammalian brain differs from the brains of lower forms chiefly in the great development of the cerebral hemispheres.

Medulla oblongata (*myelencephalon*). The most posterior part of the brain is the **medulla oblongata.** It appears as an expanded continuation of the anterior end of the spinal cord. The place where the anterior pair of spinal nerves connects with the central nervous system is arbitrarily chosen as the point of demarcation between brain and spinal cord. The anterior part of the medulla is overhung by another portion of the brain, the cerebellum. The expanded cavity within the medulla oblongata is called the **fourth ventricle.** Its roof is composed of a thin membrane fused to the pia mater, which in this region is very vascular. The two together are known as a **tela choroidea.** Tufts of this vascular tissue, extending into the fourth ventricle form the **posterior choroid plexus.** Cranial nerves V through XII arise from the medulla oblongata.

Metencephalon. The medulla oblongata together with the metencephalon make up the hindbrain, or rhombencephalon. The dorsal part

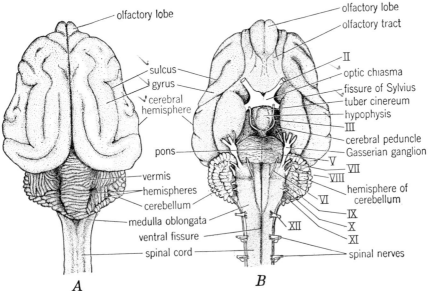

FIG. 4.37. Brain of cat from *A*, dorsal, and *B*, ventral, aspects.

of the metencephalon, the **cerebellum,** lies above and overhangs the anterior part of the medulla oblongata. The surface of the cerebellum is thrown into numerous folds (**gyri**) and depressions (**sulci**). The entire mass is subdivided into a central portion, the **vermis,** and two lateral areas, the **hemispheres.**

The ventral portion of the metencephalon is called the **pons.** It consists of a mass of transversely arranged fibers on either side of the median line. The pons lies just anterior to the medulla oblongata.

Cerebral hemispheres (telencephalon). The two symmetrical **cerebral hemispheres** make up the greater portion of the brain of the cat. The hemispheres lie on either side just anterior to the cerebellum. Like the latter structure, their surfaces are thrown into elevated gyri separated by sulci. At about the middle of the lateral surface is a short, deep fissure called the **lateral fissure, or fissure of Sylvius.** It serves as a landmark in dividing the hemisphere into **frontal** and **temporal lobes.** The cavities within the cerebral hemispheres are the **lateral, or first** and **second, ventricles.** If the two hemispheres are gently separated, a broad white mass will be observed connecting them ventrally. This is the **corpus callosum,** which consists of masses of nerve fibers connecting the two cerebral hemispheres.

Olfactory lobes (rhinencephalon). At the anterior end of each cerebral hemisphere is a small projection, the **olfactory lobe,** which appears to be an extension of the hemisphere. The olfactory cranial nerve (I) forms connections with the olfactory lobe on each side.

Midbrain (mesencephalon). The **midbrain** is not visible from a dorsal view of the brain, being concealed by the cerebral hemispheres and cerebellum. From a ventral view, two **cerebral peduncles,** small areas just anterior to the pons, are all of the midbrain that is visible. If the covering structures are removed, the roof of the midbrain is seen to consist of two pairs of rounded elevations, the **corpora quadrigemina, or colliculi.** A small epiphysis, or pineal body, lies between the two anterior (superior) colliculi. This structure is actually a derivative of the diencephalon. The cavity of the midbrain is a narrow canal called the **cerebral aqueduct, or aqueduct of Sylvius.** It connects the third ventricle of the diencephalon with the fourth ventricle in the medulla oblongata.

'Tween brain (diencephalon). The portion of the brain between the cerebral hemispheres and the midbrain is the **'tween brain.** Like the midbrain, the **diencephalon** is covered over by the cerebral hemispheres, so that it is not visible from the dorsal side unless the latter structures are removed. Telencephalon and diencephalon together make up the **prosencephalon, or forebrain.** The olfactory lobes, or rhinencephalon, are considered to be part of the telencephalon.

The anterior end of the diencephalon, the **lamina terminalis,** lies in the median line in the deep fissure between the two cerebral hemispheres. This is considered to be the primitive cranial end of the brain. The roof of the diencephalon is very thin and fused to the pia mater, forming a tela choroidea. The cavity in this portion of the brain is referred to as the **third ventricle.** Vascular folds of the roof form the **anterior choroid plexus.** Similar folds also extend into the lateral ventricles. The **pineal body** is a dorsal projection of the caudal end of the roof of the diencephalon.

The lateral walls of the diencephalon are called the **thalami.** They are integrating and relay centers for nerve tracts which connect the cerebral hemispheres with the more posterior parts of the brain. Several important nuclei of gray matter are located in the thalami.

The ventral portion of the diencephalon, which is the only part visible externally, is called the **hypothalamus.** At its anterior end is located the **optic chiasma,** where fibers of the optic nerve cross. Posterior to the chiasma is an area, the **tuber cinereum,** which is attached ventrally by a narrow stalk to the infundibulum. A portion of the latter forms part of the **pituitary body.** The pituitary body, it will be recalled, lies in the sella turcica, a depression in the cranial aspect of the basisphenoid bone. A diverticulum of the third ventricle extends into the infundibular stalk.

Before cutting the brain find as many of the cranial nerves as possible, following the description given below (page 204). Then carefully split the brain into right and left halves, and study the surfaces thus exposed, noting as many of the above-mentioned features as possible. Take one

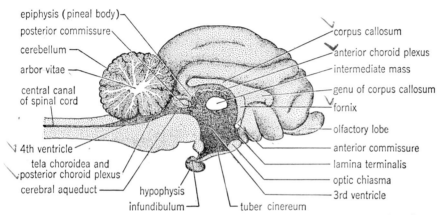

epiphysis (pineal body)
posterior commissure
cerebellum
arbor vitae
central canal of spinal cord
4th ventricle
tela choroidea and posterior choroid plexus
cerebral aqueduct
hypophysis
infundibulum
tuber cinereum

corpus callosum
anterior choroid plexus
intermediate mass
genu of corpus callosum
fornix
olfactory lobe
anterior commissure
lamina terminalis
optic chiasma
3rd ventricle

FIG. 4.38. Diagram of sagittal section of brain of cat. (*After Reighard and Jennings, "Anatomy of the Cat," Henry Holt and Company, Inc. By permission.*)

of these lateral halves of the brain and carefully remove the dorsal portion of the cerebrum. This is best accomplished by making a series of slices through the cerebrum in the frontal plane, using a sharp scalpel. Make observations on structures not visible prior to this.

Sagittal section of the brain (Fig. 4.38). A sagittal section of the brain exposes a few important structures not seen otherwise. A complexly branched central mass of white matter in the cerebellum, the **arbor vitae,** is conspicuous. The continuity of the third ventricle, cerebral aqueduct, fourth ventricle, and central canal of the spinal cord is best observed in a sagittal section. The relation of anterior and posterior choroid plexuses to the third and fourth ventricles is also more clearly brought out in such a section. The **corpus callosum,** through which fibers pass between the two cerebral hemispheres, appears as a broad band of white matter above the diencephalon. A similar band, the

fornix, is located ventrad the corpus callosum. Two transverse bands of white fibers, the **anterior** and **posterior commissures,** connect the two sides of the diencephalon. The anterior commissure lies at the ventral end of the fornix; the posterior one is located at the base of the pineal body. The two halves of the diencephalon meet across the middle of the third ventricle, forming an **intermediate mass** which shows prominently in a sagittal section.

Meninges of the brain. The brain, like the spinal cord, is surrounded by meningeal membranes, of which there are three.

PIA MATER AND ARACHNOID. The pia mater and arachnoid membrane surrounding the brain bear the same relation to the brain as the similarly named structures bear to the cord.

DURA MATER CRANIALIS (CRANIAL DURA). The cranial dura mater, unlike the spinal dura, serves as the internal periosteum of the cranial bones as well as a membrane protecting the brain. It will be recalled that these two membranes are separate over the spinal cord. The cranial dura is continuous with the spinal dura at the foramen magnum.

A prominent fold, the **falx cerebri,** extends into the fissure between the two cerebral hemispheres. Another fold, the **tentorium,** is transverse in position, lying between the cerebral hemispheres and the cerebellum. It is ossified in the cat and attached to the parietal bones.

The **diaphragma sellae** is the portion of the cranial dura which roofs over the sella turcica in which the pituitary body lies. It bears a small opening for the passage of the infundibular stalk.

Peripheral Nervous System

The cranial and spinal nerves arising, respectively, from the brain and from the spinal cord, make up the peripheral nervous system.

Cranial nerves. Twelve cranial nerves (Fig. 4.37) are present in the cat in addition to the inconspicuous *terminal nerve* (0).

Olfactory nerve (I). The purely sensory olfactory nerve for the sense of smell consists of a large number of branches which pass from the mucous membrane of the nose through the olfactory foramina in the cribriform plate of the ethmoid bone to form connections with the olfactory lobe. The cell bodies of the olfactory nerve are derived from the olfactory epithelium.

Optic nerve (II). The fibers of the purely sensory optic nerve arise in the retina of the eye. The nerve leaves the eyeball and passes through the optic foramen in the orbitosphenoid bone to the ventral side of the diencephalon, where the nerves from the two sides form the optic chiasma. The fibers of the optic nerves, after leaving the chiasma, form two **optic tracts** which terminate in the midbrain.

Oculomotor nerve (III). The third cranial nerve is a motor nerve which arises from the cerebral peduncle on the ventral side of the mid-brain. It passes through the orbital fissure and sends branches to four of the six eye muscles: the superior, inferior, and internal rectus, and the inferior oblique. Small branches also pass to the retractor oculi muscle, to the levator palpebrae muscle of the upper eyelid (page 210), and to the ciliary apparatus of the eyeball itself.

Trochlear nerve (IV). The small, purely motor trochlear nerve comes from the dorsolateral portion of the posterior end of the midbrain. It passes through the orbital fissure on its way to the superior oblique eye muscle.

Trigeminal nerve (V). The fifth cranial nerve is a large structure with a wide distribution. It bears both sensory and motor fibers which arise from two roots from the posterolateral border of the pons. The dorsal root bears a large **Gasserian, or semilunar, ganglion.** The nerve gives off three main branches: **ophthalmic, maxillary,** and **mandibular.**

OPHTHALMIC BRANCH. After leaving the Gasserian ganglion, the ophthalmic branch of the fifth nerve emerges from the cranial cavity through the orbital fissure, in company with the third, fourth, and sixth cranial nerves. It gives off numerous branches to the skin of the upper eyelid, skin and mucous membrane of the nose, and to the eyeball.

MAXILLARY BRANCH. The maxillary branch of the trigeminal leaves the cranium through the foramen rotundum in the alisphenoid bone. It is a sensory branch which sends fibers to the palate, upper lip, teeth of upper jaw, forehead, and cheek.

MANDIBULAR BRANCH. The mandibular branch contains both sensory and motor fibers. It passes through the foramen ovale in the alisphenoid bone. Some of its fibers join those of the facial nerve. The mandibular branch is distributed to the skin of the ear, skin and muscles of the temporal region, chewing muscles, tongue, teeth of lower jaw, lower lip, mucosa and muscles of the lower jaw, pharynx, submaxillary and sublingual salivary glands.

Abducens nerve (VI). The sixth cranial nerve arises from the medulla oblongata on its ventral aspect, passes through the orbital fissure to the external (lateral) rectus eye muscle and to the nictitating membrane. It is a small motor nerve.

Facial nerve (VII). The seventh cranial nerve also has its origin in the medulla oblongata near the posterior border of the pons. From the brain it passes through the internal auditory meatus and facial canal. An enlargement in the facial canal is the **geniculate ganglion** of the facial nerve. The main part of the nerve emerges through the stylomastoid foramen of the temporal bone. Three branches are given off by the facial nerve within the facial canal. One goes to the small stapedius muscle. Another, the **chorda tympani,** passes across the tympanic cavity to emerge through a small opening between the tympanic bulla and the squamous region of the temporal bone. It receives fibers from the taste buds in the anterior part of the tongue and sends motor fibers to the submaxillary and sublingual salivary glands. A third branch, the **superficial petrosal,** joins a similarly named branch of the fifth nerve. The main part of the seventh nerve, after leaving the stylomastoid foramen, is widely distributed over the surface of the face and to the muscles of facial expression.

Auditory nerve (VIII). The purely sensory auditory nerve, which bears an **acoustic ganglion,** arises from the medulla oblongata near the floor of the fourth ventricle. It passes into the internal auditory meatus, where it divides into cochlear and vestibular branches which supply the auditory and equilibratory portions of the inner ear, respectively.

Glossopharyngeal nerve (IX). The ninth nerve also arises from the medulla oblongata along its lateral border. It is a mixed nerve which bears two ganglia. The first, or **superior, ganglion** is smaller than the second. The nerve emerges through the jugular foramen. The second, or **petrosal, ganglion** of the glossopharyngeal nerve lies just outside the jugular foramen. The nerve supplies the pharyngeal muscles and mucosa as well as the taste buds of the posterior portion of the tongue.

Vagus nerve (X). The vagus, or pneumogastric, nerve is of great importance in controlling such vital functions as respiration, heartbeat, and digestion. It is a mixed nerve arising by numerous roots from the ventrolateral part of the medulla oblongata. Like the ninth nerve, it bears two ganglia. The proximal one is called the **jugular;** the other, the **ganglion nodosum.** The latter lies just outside the jugular foramen through which the nerve emerges. The vagus is distributed to the external ear and to the muscles of the pharynx, larynx, esophagus, lungs, heart, and most of the visceral organs in the abdominal cavity.

Spinal accessory nerve (XI). The eleventh cranial nerve is rather small. It is a motor nerve and lacks a ganglion. It arises over a considerable distance along the side of the medulla oblongata by a number of roots, leaving the jugular foramen in company with the ninth and tenth cranial nerves to supply certain muscles of the neck and shoulder.

Hypoglossal nerve (XII). The twelfth, or last, cranial nerve comes from the ventral side of the medulla and emerges from the cranial cavity through the hypoglossal canal. It is a motor nerve going to the muscles of the tongue and neck region.

Spinal nerves. The spinal nerves are paired metameric structures. In the cat there are usually 38 or 39 pairs. Of this number 8 are **cervical, 13 thoracic, 7 lumbar, 3 sacral,** and **7** or **8 caudal.** The number corresponds to the number of vertebrae in each region with the following exceptions: The first cervical nerve emerges through the atlantal foramen of the atlas vertebra. The last cervical passes through the intervertebral foramen between the seventh cervical and first thoracic vertebrae. The other spinal nerves take their names from the vertebra which lies just anterior to the point of exit. Since the posterior caudal vertebrae consist of little more than centra and the spinal cord extends only a short distance into the tail, no spinal nerves are associated with them.

Each spinal nerve arises from the cord by two roots: dorsal and ventral. The **dorsal, or sensory, roots** bear ganglia. The cell bodies of the **ventral, or motor, roots** are located within the cord. Dorsal and ventral roots unite within the neural canal to form the spinal nerves, which emerge through the intervertebral foramina. Except in the case of the first two spinal nerves, the dorsal root ganglia are located *within* the neural canal or in the intervertebral foramina. The ganglia of the first two nerves are situated *outside* the vertebral column and lie embedded among muscles in the vicinity of the intervertebral foramina.

Only the more anterior spinal nerves leave the vertebral column at a point directly opposite their point of origin. Others course in a posterolateral direction within the neural canal before emerging. This arrangement becomes more and more accentuated toward the posterior end, where the nerves run parallel to the cord for some distance before they pass through their respective intervertebral foramina. The region where the last sacral and the caudal spinal nerves run parallel to the filum terminale has a brushlike appearance and is referred to as the **cauda equina** (horse's tail).

After the spinal nerve leaves the vertebral column, it characteristically divides into two branches, the **dorsal** and **ventral rami,** each of which bears both sensory and motor fibers. The dorsal ramus is small and is distributed to the skin and muscles of the back. Just past its origin the ventral ramus gives off a **visceral ramus** (**white ramus, ramus communicans**). The ventral ramus then continues in a ventral direction to supply the skin and muscles of the ventral side of the body. In the pectoral and pelvic regions the ventral rami are also distributed to the limbs. It will be recalled that in these regions the spinal cord is of greater diameter than elsewhere and forms the cervical and lumbar enlargements. The visceral rami are short. They pass in a ventromedial direction to join the **sympathetic ganglia** of the peripheral autonomic nervous system. Visceral rami carry both sensory and motor fibers, the latter often being referred to as **preganglionic fibers.**

In the regions of the limbs the ventral rami of several spinal nerves give off branches which anastomose with one another in such a manner as to produce a complex **plexus** of nerves, which then continue into the limb. In the region of the forelimb, cervical nerves 5, 6, 7, and 8 and the first thoracic nerve are concerned in the formation of the **brachial plexus** (Fig. 4.39). A **phrenic nerve**, which supplies the diaphragm, is formed from branches of the fifth and sixth cervical nerves. It accompanies the vagus nerve on its way to the diaphragm. The **lumbosacral**

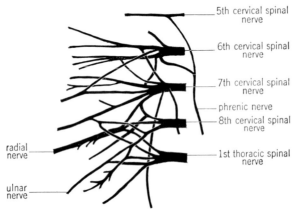

FIG. 4.39. Diagram of right brachial plexus of cat, ventral view. (*After Reighard and Jennings, "Anatomy of the Cat," Henry Holt and Company, Inc. By permission.*)

plexus is composed of intercommunicating branches of lumbar nerves 4, 5, 6, and 7, and the three sacral spinal nerves.

Peripheral Autonomic Nervous System

The portion of the nervous system which controls all involuntary functions of the body is the **peripheral autonomic nervous system.** It is composed of two divisions which bring about opposite effects.

Not a great deal of the structure of the peripheral autonomic nervous system can be learned from gross dissection, particularly in a specimen in which the other organ systems have already been removed or dissected. Histological and physiological studies, however, have brought to light many of the intricate interrelations between the peripheral autonomic, peripheral, and central nervous systems. These will be omitted from the following description.

Sympathetic nervous system. The sympathetic system is sometimes referred to as the **thoracolumbar outflow.** This is because preganglionic nerve fibers pass through the visceral rami of the thoracic and first four lumbar spinal nerves to connect with outlying ganglia of the sympathetic system. These ganglia include those in the sympathetic trunks and those which lie among the viscera.

The **sympathetic trunk** is a long nerve cord extending the length of the body cavity on either side under the centra of the vertebrae. Each trunk continues forward in close association with the vagus nerve, common carotid artery, and internal jugular vein, terminating just posterior to the tympanic bulla. Here it is enlarged and forms the **superior cervical ganglion.** The sympathetic trunk consists of a chain of ganglia united by nerve cords. The visceral rami of the thoracic and first four lumbar spinal nerves join these ganglia. Other collateral ganglia, lying along the abdominal aorta and its main branches, are the **coeliac, superior mesenteric,** and **inferior mesenteric ganglia.** Some preganglionic fibers of the thoracolumbar outflow continue through the chain ganglia of the sympathetic trunk to terminate in the collateral ganglia. **Postganglionic fibers** from the various sympathetic ganglia are distributed to all parts of the body. They are gray in color, since their fibers lack myelin sheaths. So-called **gray visceral rami,** which parallel the white visceral rami, are composed of postganglionic fibers which follow the spinal nerves, ultimately to be distributed to the skin. All spinal nerves possess gray rami.

Parasympathetic nervous system. The anatomical relations of the nerves making up the parasympathetic nervous system are, for the most part, not so distinctly marked as those of the sympathetic system. The parasympathetic system is also referred to as the **craniosacral outflow,** since preganglionic fibers of certain cranial and sacral nerves are chiefly involved. Fibers in the **oculomotor, facial, glossopharyngeal,** and **vagus nerves** form connections with ganglia which lie close to, or within the walls of, the structures which they supply. From these ganglia short postganglionic fibers pass to the actual tissues which this portion of the nervous system affects. In the cat the **visceral rami of the second and third sacral nerves** carry preganglionic fibers which pass directly to ganglia in the pelvic viscera, from which short postganglionic fibers pass in turn to the tissues.

SENSE ORGANS

Basically the organs of special sense are specialized endings of sensory nerves. They have been so modified in each case that the nerve cells with which they are supplied are normally capable of receiving only one kind of stimulus.

Cutaneous sense organs. The integument is richly supplied with nerve endings which do not lend themselves to dissection and will not be discussed here. Stimuli for **touch, pressure, warmth, cold,** and **pain** are received by these widely distributed nerve endings.

Olfactory sense. The cells in the moist **olfactory mucous membrane,** or **Schneiderian membrane,** in the nasal passage carry impulses set up by olfactory stimuli via the olfactory nerve to the olfactory lobe of the brain. Substances must be in solution before they can stimulate the olfactory receptors.

Sense of taste. **Taste buds,** associated with the papillae of the tongue as well as those on the soft palate and region about the epiglottis, are special structures for reception of gustatory stimuli. Sensory branches of the seventh and ninth cranial nerves are responsible for conveying impulses from the taste buds to the brain. As in the case of the sense of smell, substances must be in solution before they can stimulate the gustatory nerve endings.

Sense of sight. The eye of the cat is well protected by the incomplete bony orbit in which it lies.

Accessory structures. The external surface of the eye is guarded by the upper and lower **eyelids,** which are extensions of the integument. Beginning at its border, each eyelid is lined by a thin layer of mucous membrane, the **conjunctiva,** which is also reflected over the exposed surface of the eyeball. A sphincter muscle, the **orbicularis oculi,** located on the margins of the eyelids is used in closing the eye. Another muscle, the **levator palpebrae,** arising near the optic foramen, is inserted on the border of the upper eyelid. It serves to raise the upper lid.

The angle at either end of the slit, or **palpebral fissure,** between the eyelids is called the **canthus.** At the medial, or nasal, canthus are two small openings, the **lacrimal puncta,** which enter small canals. These unite to form the **nasolacrimal duct,** which passes through the **lacrimal canal,** bounded by lacrimal and maxillary bones, to open into the nasal passage. A prominent fold, the **nictitating membrane,** is present at the inner canthus. This is well developed in the cat in which it may cover the entire surface of the eye when expanded. A cartilage supports the nictitating membrane. On its undersurface is the **Harderian gland.**

The **lacrimal gland** lies on the surface of the eyeball in the dorsolateral region. Its ducts open on the undersurface of the upper lid.

Cut away the eyelids and any skin which remains in this area. Next cut away the zygomatic arch and mandible on one side, using bone forceps to break the bones concerned. Gently push the eyeball downward and observe the strong sheet of fibrous tissue which connects the eyeball with the wall of the orbit. This will be found actually to consist of two bands of tissue which form a sort of pulley, over which one of the eye muscles, the superior oblique, passes on its way to insert on the eyeball. Clean away any connective and fatty tissue that may be present. Look for the **infraorbital salivary gland** on the floor of the orbit (see page 186).

The usual six muscles controlling movements of the eyeball are present in the cat. They include the four **rectus muscles: superior,** inserted on the dorsal side; **inferior,** on the ventral side; **internal,** on the medial side;

external, on the lateral aspect. The four rectus muscles originate from the bone surrounding the optic foramen in the orbitosphenoid portion of the sphenoid bone. The **superior oblique** muscle arises from the cranial border of the optic foramen and passes forward and dorsally to form a narrow tendon. This in turn passes through the pulleylike ring of connective tissue mentioned above, then expands and turns caudo-laterad to insert on the eyeball beneath the superior rectus. The **inferior oblique** comes from the maxillary bone near its junction with the lacrimal and crosses over the ventral side of the eyeball to insert between the external and inferior rectus muscles. Another muscle, the **retractor oculi,** arises near the optic foramen and is inserted on the eyeball near the equatorial region by means of four separate heads. The four parts alternate with the four rectus muscles. They are rather inconspicuous, being hidden by the latter muscles which partially cover them. Remove the eye from the orbit.

Eyeball. The eyeball of the cat is approximately spherical in shape. Its outer coat is called the **fibrous tunic.** This, in turn, is composed of an anterior, exposed, transparent portion, the **cornea,** and a larger, opaque, posterior section, the **sclerotic coat** (**sclera**). The large optic nerve leaves the eyeball, piercing the sclerotic coat near its center.

Clean away all accessory structures from the eyeball, but leave a short stump of the optic nerve attached. With a sharp, fine pair of scissors make a cut from the optic nerve to the center of the cornea. Make a similar cut some distance to the right so that when the tissue is removed, about one-quarter of the covering of the eyeball will be lifted off. Examine the part of the wall of the eye that has been dissected away. Then study the internal structure of the remainder of the eyeball.

Beneath the sclerotic coat is the black vascular **choroid coat.** The choroid does not line the inner surface of the cornea, but at the junction of cornea and sclera it becomes thickened to form the **ciliary ring.** It is then continued as the outer portion of the disclike **iris** which projects into the eyeball, forming a curtainlike structure some distance behind the cornea. An opening, the **pupil,** is present in the center of the iris. The pupil varies in shape, depending upon the amount of light striking the iris. It is circular when dilated in poor light, but forms a vertical slit when contracted in strong light. Action of muscles in the iris is responsible for changes in the shape of the pupil. Part of the choroid is lined with a layer, the **tapetum lucidum,** which contains light-reflecting crystals. These are responsible for the metallic luster with which the eyes of the cat "shine" at night.

The inner coat of the eye is the sensitive **retina** containing **rod and cone cells,** which are the actual light receptors. At the ciliary ring the retina appears to form a free border, the **ora serrata.** Actually, however it is continued onto the iris as a very thin layer, the **iridial portion of the retina.** The point where the optic nerve leaves the retina is called the **blind spot,** since rods and cones are lacking there. In the direct line of the optical axis a small yellowish area is present on the retina. This is the **macula lutea,** or **area centralis.** A small depression in the macula, called the **fovea centralis,** marks the area of most acute vision.

The **crystalline lens** of the eye lies directly behind the iris. It is elastic and compressible during life. A thin **capsule** surrounds the lens. To this are attached numerous radiating fibers of the **suspensory ligament** which, in turn, are attached to the **ciliary body. Ciliary muscles,** which, at their other end, are anchored to the ciliary ring, insert on the walls of the ciliary body.

The lens and ciliary apparatus divide the cavity of the eyeball into two parts. The cavity between the lens and cornea is in turn partially separated by the iris into **anterior** and **posterior chambers,** which are continuous only through the pupil. These chambers are filled with a watery fluid, the **aqueous humor.** The large cavity behind the lens and ciliary apparatus is the **chamber of the vitreous humor.** It is bordered by the retina. The chamber contains a transparent, jellylike substance, the **vitreous humor.**

Senses of hearing and equilibrium. The auditory organ of the cat is made up of three main parts: the external, middle, and internal ears. The internal ear is the actual organ of hearing and equilibration, the other structures all serving to transmit sound waves to the sensory receptors.

External ear. The **pinna** is the visible portion of the external ear. It is covered with skin, is supported by cartilage, and can be moved in various directions by muscles. Within the external ear are several prominent **ridges.** A deep depression, the **concha,** leads to the **external auditory meatus.** This terminates at the **tympanic membrane** stretched across the opening of the tympanic bulla.

Middle ear. The cavity within the tympanic bulla is called the **middle ear,** or **tympanic cavity.** Clean the area around the tympanic bulla so as to expose it clearly. Carefully chip away the bone making up the ventral wall of the bulla. It will be noted that a bony plate partially separates the tympanic cavity into lateral and medial chambers. Open up the lateral chamber and note that it contains a chain of three small bones, the **auditory ossicles.** These are the **malleus, incus,** and **stapes.** The **malleus** is attached to the inner surface of the tympanic membrane on one side and to the incus on the other. The **incus,** in turn, articulates with the **stapes.** The base of the stapes serves as a plug, completely filling a small opening in the petrous region of the temporal bone, the **fenestra ovalis.** The ossicles are held in position by small muscles and ligaments. The tympanic cavity connects with the pharynx by means of the **Eustachian tube.**

Internal ear. The **membranous labyrinth,** which serves as an organ of both equilibrium and hearing, lies wholly within the dense petrous region of the temporal bone. Since it does not lend itself to gross dissection, the inner ear is studied with difficulty. The interested student may find it feasible to decalcify the petrous region of the temporal bone in 10 per cent nitric acid. Then by carefully dissecting away surrounding tissue, the membranous labyrinth can be exposed. For further information on the internal ear the reader is urged to consult textbooks on physiology and histology in which details of structure are described.

INDEX

215